A Gift *for* Healing

How to Use Therapeutic Touch

DEBORAH COWENS, M.S.N., R.N., A.N.P.

with TOM MONTE

PIATKUS

First published in 1996 by Crown Trade Paperbacks, New York

This UK edition published in 1996 by
Judy Piatkus (Publishers) Ltd of
5 Windmill Street, London, W1P 1HF

The moral right of the author has been asserted

A catalogue record for this book is available from the British Library

ISBN 0 7499 1698 2

Design by June Bennett-Tantillo

Printed and bound in the United States of America

*This book is dedicated to all the students
of energy work and to all our patients
who teach us.*

Author's Note

It is my hope that you, the reader, will be able to raise your inherent gift for healing by using the techniques put forth in this book. Remember, your learning and growth are a journey that is not completed in one reading. Take time to do each of the exercises. Provide the space and time to allow yourself to grow with the process. As you are patient with your clients, be patient with yourself in your learning.

This book is intended to complement, and not replace or substitute for, the medical advice of physicians. Before commencing any healing touch therapy, the patient should have a thorough physical by a doctor.

The case histories are real and are presented as accurately as possible. All names and identifying characteristics of people and places have been changed to assure their anonymity.

Contents

Acknowledgments

I wish to acknowledge with love all my family, especially David, Meghan, and Samantha, for all their support for me through this process.

In addition, I would like to thank Joyce, Doris, Linda, Phyllis, Sandy, and Connie, without whose advice, encouragement, and typing I would have faltered.

A special thanks to Clark Godfrey, Betty Taylor Godfrey, and Emily Osman for their artistic input.

Illustrations

'Tis the human touch in this world that counts,
The touch of your hand and mine

FROM *THE HUMAN TOUCH*
BY SPENCER MICHAEL FREE

Introduction

Therapeutic touch is perhaps the first form of health care ever utilized. Every parent since Adam and Eve has used this practice instinctively when he or she has placed a loving hand on a child to reduce discomfort, help heal a wound, or alleviate a fever. Therapeutic touch is the most human of all forms of healing, using the hands to reach out in service to another person in a gesture of peace, balance, and love.

This book is meant to teach you how to help yourself and others—your family, friends, and loved ones—overcome disorders of the body, mind, or spirit. You do not have to have any special knowledge or expertise to learn or utilize this practice effectively. All you need is provided in the pages that follow. People who practice therapeutic touch regularly will find its power to heal remarkable, and sometimes even miraculous. My intention for this book is that it help people directly and also that it serves as a bridge between two worlds of healing: the modern and the alternative forms of medicine. I would like doctors and other health professionals to understand therapeutic touch so that they can begin to utilize it in hospitals and medical practices. By providing you, the reader, and, perhaps, the patient with information that will give you a real understanding and confidence in the efficacy of therapeutic touch, I hope to help you begin to take part in your own healing and take charge of your own health. By educating yourself in this healing art and seeing its effectiveness, you will be part of a grass-roots influencing of the medical profession. For these reasons, I have deliberately tried to keep this book practical and simple, without oversimplifying or doing an injustice to the traditional and ancient philosophies that underlie the practice.

I do not intend for this book to replace or substitute for medical advice or intervention. Healing touch should be used in conjunction with conventional medical therapies. Because healing touch relaxes the body and triggers the body's self-healing energies, it increases the effectiveness of medicines and other treatments.

I became a practitioner of healing touch after traveling a long, circuitous path that led me into both orthodox medicine and alternative healing. I have bachelor's and master's degrees in nursing, an advanced degree in nutrition, and I'm a certified nurse practitioner, which means that I am licensed to prescribe medication and to treat patients independently while under the supervision of a medical doctor. On the other hand, I am a certified herbalist and have a formal training in therapeutic touch. Also, I have studied a wide range of holistic or traditional healing practices, such as Chinese medicine. This dual path in conventional and traditional medicine unfolded in a series of decisions that seemed at the time to be motivated chiefly by my immediate needs and desires. But looking back over the past twenty years at the myriad subjects I studied and the very different teachers with whom I studied, all seem so orderly now, as if my education was designed to get me precisely to the place I now find myself: a practitioner of modern and ancient medicine.

Getting Here from There

I was born and raised in Verona, New York, and ever since I was twelve or thirteen years old, I knew that I wanted to go into medicine. At first, I thought I would be a doctor, but my father dissuaded me. Medicine isn't really a good profession for women, he advised me. You're better off going into nursing or teaching, he said. This was the 1950s, and the world was different then, with both sexes locked into a worldview that seems archaic to most of us today. My father was looking out for me, and advised me according to how he saw things. I didn't realize it at the time, but he was actually helping me make the right choice, though he might have been influenced, at least in part, by some rather dated reasons. In any case, I have been thanking him for years for guiding me correctly.

My parents were conscious of the importance of eating healthful, good-quality food. We ate organic vegetables that my father grew in his garden and organic chicken and beef raised on my grandmother's farm. Healthy food and attitudes were an important part of my and my three siblings' upbringing.

While very traditional in some ways, my parents also possessed unique and special talents. My mother seemed to have a sixth sense about people. She had insight into their behavior and motives; she could perceive people's feelings that existed below the surface, sometimes even before they could articulate such feelings themselves. This ability was apparent to people, and many of my mother's friends and family came regularly to ask her advice.

My mother was also a wonderful dressmaker. She could take a pattern into a fabric store, look at five bolts of material, and visualize how the dress would look when made from those five different cloths. This visual ability extended to other areas of life, such as how a room would look if it were redecorated. I realized later that my mother had a highly developed ability to visualize, or mentally "see," three-dimensionally. My father had a similar trait. He was an industrial arts teacher and a carpenter and could make just about anything out of wood. Often, he would work without a schematic and produce the most beautiful furniture, cabinets, and other wood objects. These abilities were inherited by all four of their children—my brother, two sisters, and me. All of us talked about feelings—our own and others'—and could hold an image in our minds and discuss it at length without any sense that we were doing anything extraordinary.

After graduation from high school, I studied nursing at Niagara University, where, among other things, I was trained to be a keen observer. One of my teachers in medical-surgical nursing would bring us into the waiting room of our hospital and train us to observe and understand patients. She would insist that we ask ourselves specific questions that would open and expand our perceptions of people and situations. "What did you feel about the person you talked to?" she would ask. "What could you tell about the people you observed?" "What was the patient going through?" "What symptoms of disease did she or he exhibit?" And so forth.

During one of my early classes, which was held in the hospital wards, I witnessed how intuitive my instructor was about people. She asked us to list the things we observed about the patients we encountered as we followed her on her rounds that morning. We went into a patient's room with her and observed as she held the patient's hand, said "Good morning," and asked three questions: "How are you today?" "How did you sleep?" "How is your pain?" Everyone wrote down three or four sentences about what they had observed. When our teacher revealed what she had observed, it amounted to two pages of writing. Even more remarkable, she had gotten all of that information merely by holding the person's hand. I was amazed. I knew right then that I wanted to be able to touch like that—to feel a human being so deeply that I could discern his or her inner state merely by holding his or her hand.

During my senior year, I worked at Roswell Park, the cancer institute in Buffalo. The instructor and the nurses on the floor were wonderful in their teaching and guidance. In this place my ability to touch people on many levels began to develop. One patient, an elderly woman, had been hospitalized for a gynecological cancer that had spread to her bones. She was in great pain and was about to undergo gynecological surgery. Her doctors did not hold out much hope for her recovery, however. In those days, nurses still prepared patients for surgery by removing the hair from their abdomen with a razor, and I had to do this for this woman. After about five minutes, she began crying, both because of the pain the shaving caused and because of her fear of dying. I stopped shaving her and instinctively put my hands on the place where she had the most pain. Meanwhile, I said a prayer that the pain would be relieved. After a few minutes, she told me that she felt better and we could continue the shaving. Periodically, she asked me to stop, and I would have to put my hand on her stomach to relieve the pain. At this point, I had no awareness of therapeutic touch. I touched her instinctively and with the singular intention of relieving her discomfort.

During my senior year, I rotated into psychiatric practice, where I encountered Bertha, a woman in her sixties who went around the ward using her finger as an imaginary gun and shooting at make-believe beings. I asked my instructor for advice on how to deal with Bertha. "Mimic her in order to understand better what she may be feeling," my teacher advised. From that point on, I started to mimic Bertha's behavior. Once, while doing just that, I nearly knocked over a lamp, and as I righted it, I confessed to Bertha that I felt silly shooting at imaginary people. Bertha looked me straight in the eye and with utter lucidity said, "Well, you look silly." The other patients who were standing nearby all looked at me and nodded their agreement and then smiled. I laughed, and for the next four weeks, Bertha and I were friends. For a while, she appeared perfectly sane to me—that is, until I told her that I would be cycling out of that part of the hospital. Upon hearing the news, Bertha shut me out and resumed shooting her imaginary enemies. She seemed as psychotic as ever. But the experience taught me that health and illness are locked in a battle within us all, and that no matter how ill a person may be, there is always a degree of health within, as well. That healthy aspect of the patient is the part that a healer seeks to strengthen in the patient's struggle to overcome disease.

From Niagara, I went on to graduate school to work with emotionally disturbed children. Behind all my studies was a deep desire to find the root causes of disease. I always believed that if I could find the cause, I could somehow pull the disease out by its roots. After graduation, I worked at Rome City Hospital, in New York State, as a graduate nurse for three months, and then went to Boston University, where I received a master's degree in child psychiatric nursing, which made me a clinical specialist. I practiced for three years in child psychiatry and also taught in a nursing school.

As a nurse, I learned quickly how the power of touch helped my patients. Whenever I held patients' hands, or rubbed their backs, the effect was most powerful and obvious. They relaxed. Gradually, fear diminished. The patient trusted me more and felt more comfortable with what lay ahead. It's remarkable how much safety is communicated simply by touching a person. Is this why we instinctively touch our children to reassure them? I wondered.

In 1972, I worked at Boston University's Child Guidance Center and Infant Development Unit, which later became Solomon Carter Fuller Mental Health Center. I worked with families in lower socioeconomic brackets. Many of the mothers in this group gave birth to premature babies, many of whom died. The infant mortality rate was exceedingly high. These preemies were often placed in the neonatal intensive care unit, where they were kept on life-support systems. Their mothers were often afraid of all the machines. That fear created a kind of wall between the mother and her baby.

One of the practices I instituted was to get the mothers to touch and stroke their babies for extended periods of time. This helped the mothers overcome their fear of the machines. Even more importantly, the stroking helped the children to develop far more rapidly and thus lowered the risk of premature death. We worked directly with the infants, too, many of whom were deformed. We started passive exercise programs that resulted in remarkable improvement in their development of motor skills and coordination.

Premature babies are often no bigger than a small fist and far more shriveled than the fingers of an old man. They are vulnerable and delicate. Yet there is something that emanates from these tiny, vulnerable infants that I can only describe as radiant energy. You feel it when you touch such an infant or place your hand near her body. As your hand gets within a few inches of the child's head or back, you can feel a certain energy coming off her body. Your hand tells you something is there, but you cannot see it. At first, I wasn't really sure what I was sensing. The only thing I could call it then was "spirit" or "energy." Since I had no training in these areas, such words made me uncomfortable. I could find no rational place for my perceptions.

Anyone who has ever worked with children will tell you that the experience is transformative. One of the things you learn is that a child's view of life is radically different from an adult's. Children are thrilled to have you near and are very open to your touch. They don't have the same defensive or skeptical walls around them that adults have. Children let you in. I began to wonder if this high degree of receptivity, openness, and acceptance actually enhanced the healing process, because, despite their obvious vulnerability, children often make the most miraculous recoveries against incredible odds.

A few years later in my career, I became fascinated by the effects of diet on health. At age twenty-nine, I entered nutrition school to learn about holistic health and nutrition. I also realized that nutrition was an area that all of us could control, to some extent, and therefore gave us the power to heal ourselves. This idea resonated with me, in part because of the food I ate as a child. At that time, the organic and natural foods movement started to pick up steam.

At nutrition school, I began to realize that I possessed a certain degree of extrasensory perception that gave me insight into a person's inner condition. I discovered that when I looked at someone with the intention of understanding his health, I could sometimes perceive certain events taking place within the person's body—and even his organs. When I touched the area where a patient's liver is or lay my hands on his abdomen, I would get an image of the inner condition and whether or not the person suffered from some form of physical or emotional pathology. I also started to concentrate and pray while touching patients. Very often, the person would tell me that his or her pain or inflammation had noticeably diminished with my touch. This recognition profoundly altered my life. It also gave my previous experiences with touch far greater meaning.

In 1982, I went to the healing and educational center Interface, in Boston, for training in therapeutic touch. I knew right away that this approach was right for me. It was as if all my training and so many of my experiences had already formed the foundation for this work. I had been prepared, so the minute I walked into that classroom, nothing that was taught seemed odd, or bizarre, or in any way out of the ordinary realm of human experience. The training also gave me a language to describe my feelings and experiences, as well as a set of techniques to use in my practice.

Afterward, I actively sought spiritual experience and instruction and learned some of the healing methods of Native Americans—including those involving therapeutic touch. I am particularly grateful for my ongoing study with Oh Shinnah Fastwolf, an Apache, and Twylah Nitsch, a Seneca. These two Native American women supported and encouraged me; each gave me a more holistic worldview through the Native American understanding of life. They taught me how to do energy work, how to shape my intent, how to use imagery to heal, and to learn patience with myself as I proceed through my own life journey. Oh Shinnah taught me the importance of using ritual and prayer, not only to become more receptive to healing energy but to keep focused during the process. Twylah helped me with my technique. But more importantly, she stressed patience and the need for me to remember who I am. Twylah maintains that each of us, on an unconscious level, possesses all knowledge, including the knowledge of our own personal spiritual identity. Learning is actually remembering, and the ultimate memory is to recognize your true spiritual self.

I try to convey to you the essence and practice of all these teachings in this book. As we journey together through it, I hope you will learn how to enhance your healing abilities and your extrasensory perception so that you can help yourself and others. Some chapters will contain exercises that will help you focus your energies as you learn healing touch.

Healing Begins with Respect and Faith

During my many years of study, I have witnessed and helped to bring about many remarkable recoveries, as I will report throughout the pages of this book. I also learned ways of understanding and sensing the energy body, or life force, that exists around all people. But what my teachers gave me first was the right attitude for approaching this practice. The healer doesn't heal; he or she facilitates a process that is active and implicit within all of us. The seeds of healing exist in the person in search of help. It is important that the recipient of healing touch be open and respectful of this healing process. In a certain sense, we must be like children—open, receptive, and ready to learn. By maintaining an open mind and spirit, the recipient allows the energy that flows to him or her to be taken in and utilized efficiently.

A reverential attitude toward the healing process is the basis of all traditional healing approaches, and still is throughout the world. Healing is not seen as a lucky mix of chemical processes in most cultures, but is considered an expression of the harmonious joining of heaven and earth. Healing rituals are practiced in many cultures to evoke greater faith, which in turn triggers the healing forces within the person who is seeking help and within his family and community.

The scientific studies from which I report that prove the efficacy of therapeutic touch show that people benefit from healing touch no matter what they believe. My experience has shown, however, that those who are more open and receptive make quicker progress. For this reason, I always maintain that *healing is a gift you give yourself,* because you must receive this enhanced life energy and allow your body, mind, and spirit to utilize it for whatever purpose you need. You marshal these enhanced energies for your own purposes. Something inside of you accepts and embraces the healing process.

As Norman Cousins wrote in *Anatomy of an Illness:* "Drugs are not always necessary. Belief in recovery always is."

We live in a time when bridges between orthodox and alternative medicine must be built if we are to have a truly humane and effective health care system. Medicine and health care are now in the throes of a revolution. Today, more and more people are seeking the counsel and treatment of alternative medical practitioners of acupuncture, massage therapies, herbalism, diet, and other traditional healing methods. Healing touch is among those practices gaining credibility with both the lay public and medical professionals. Indeed, Western society's worldview is changing dramatically as science proves the wisdom and the efficacy of ancient healing approaches. This trend will continue as more and more people seek creative ways of healing old and intractable disorders. I hope that this book, *A Gift for Healing,* will inspire people to utilize this practice and in the process embrace a larger understanding of healing—and themselves.

Part One

Learning the Language of Energy

1

⁂

The Science
of an Ancient Art

healing power flows from your hands.
This power can help people overcome sickness, negative beliefs, and old and useless habits. It can heal wounds, reduce pain, boost energy, improve psychological health, and help to manage and heal chronic illness. Healing touch, or what has been known in the West as the "laying on of hands," has been used as a medical treatment technique in virtually every traditional culture. Healing touch can also serve as a powerful adjunct to conventional medical therapy. Today, scientific studies consistently prove its power to heal, though researchers still don't understand how or why the practice works.

In the broadest sense, healing touch is the act of consciously directing life energy from its infinite source, through the practitioner, to the person in need of assistance. It is done with the specific intention of giving love, support, and help in overcoming a physical or psychological problem. This conscious transfer of energy can be facilitated and enhanced through an assortment of techniques and by deepening your understanding of the practice.

Today, healing or therapeutic touch is being taught in eighty colleges and universities in the United States and is being utilized by

medical professionals around the country. My own profession of
nursing is the leader in this movement, in large part because nurses
traditionally offer emotional support, including solace and compassion, often in the form of touching. For all practitioners of healing touch, the practice has become an outgrowth of our desire to
help people in times of crisis or pain.

To understand the *how* and the *why* of healing touch so that
we can utilize its therapeutic value, we must open up to a larger
view of ourselves and of life. In a sense, we must go beyond the
restricted definition of life that is imposed upon us by our modern
culture. We must view our lives in a more traditional way—that is,
in the way people have seen life through most of human history: as
a physical, emotional, and spiritual whole connected to other lives
and to the greater life of our natural environment.

We must also view health in a similar way. Rather than seeing health as merely the absence of symptoms, we must see it in a
larger context—again, as a condition of wholeness or integration
of body, mind, and spirit within the greater cultural and natural
environment. Each of us represents a vast potential to grow and
develop emotionally, psychologically, and spiritually. Our world
demands such growth and development. Indeed, our health may
be predicated on our ability to reach down continually into the
psyche and bring forth and develop the unique skills and characteristics that lie deep within us. Yet, few of us realize our potential, in part because many of our better characteristics are hidden
within us, repressed or denied by fears and false beliefs. These repressive emotions act as walls of energy or blockages between our
potential or true self and our own conscious minds. Thus, we confront the world with only parts of our character, strength, and
spirit available to us.

Besides preventing self-realization and self-understanding, energetic barriers can also block life energy from flowing through the
body. In the traditional model of health, the entire body—and each
of its parts—depends upon the optimal flow of life energy to function properly. When barriers to the life force deprive certain parts

of the body of life energy, these cells, organs, and tissues consequently become weak, sluggish, and stagnant, and gradually degenerate. With time, these conditions can bring on some form of disease. The illness may be called one name or another, but the true underlying source of the physical or mental problem is a diminution of the life force flowing to that particular part of the body. Therefore, deep healing begins by a restoration of the life force to areas of the body that are deprived of life energy.

Healing touch can assist us in dealing with all of these issues by removing the blockages, or repressive barriers, that prevent energy from flowing. Thus, it can restore energy to parts of the body deprived of life force. In the same way, healing touch can help us arrive at a deeper self-understanding and lead to a fuller expression of those talents and the creativity that lie within us.

After a single session of healing touch, the recipient invariably feels refreshed, stronger, and clearer, as if he or she has just had a very restful nap. With repeated sessions, the health effects of healing touch are remarkable. Acute physical symptoms and long-standing chronic complaints are reduced or disappear.

The psychological and spiritual transformation is equally impressive. Gradually, the blockages that have kept the person from experiencing and understanding himself or herself are removed from the energy field, and hence from the person's life. Old, restrictive beliefs are shed like a skin that the person has outgrown. The person lets go of illness-inducing behavior patterns and sees more clearly how to live in more health-promoting ways.

One of the goals of healing touch is to help people become more aware of who they truly are and incorporate that awareness into daily life in practical ways. I call this "expanded integrated awareness." Only by grounding that awareness in practical daily activities can any of us truly integrate ourselves. With time, we free ourselves from self-limiting attitudes and develop a healthier and much greater picture of who we truly are.

Healers who today use traditional healing arts often incorporate a wide variety of therapies, including diet, herbs, acupuncture, and the laying on of hands, to strengthen the physical body and the life force within the individual. In my own work as a nurse practitioner, I use many healing modalities, often blending modern medical science with traditional healing practices. Over many years of practice, I have used healing touch extensively, relying on its remarkable powers to restore body, mind, and spirit to good health. This book is an outgrowth of my practice and strives to strike a balance between the often necessary use of medical treatments and ancient or traditional healing.

In this book, I'll talk about what scientific research has to say about the ancient practice of healing touch, but for the most part I'll be approaching the subject with the same understanding, respect, and spirit that traditional healers have applied since the birth of civilization. No other explanation better articulates how the practice actually works, and no other set of attitudes better prepares you to apply its principles.

The practice goes by many names. Dolores Krieger, Ph.D., R.N., a scientist and nurse and one of the pioneers of healing touch, and practitioner Dora Kunz have coined the term "therapeutic touch." Some refer to it as "a healing," and still others call the practice "healing through the auric field." Usually, I refer to the practice as healing touch, though all of these terms are essentially interchangeable. The reason is that whatever terms we use, the underlying principles are the same. Simply put, the practitioner of healing touch serves as a conduit, or channel, for a powerful healing energy that flows through the practitioner to the person he or she wishes to help.

Today, the practice of healing touch is being restored to a place of respect, thanks largely to the many medical, scientific, and lay practitioners who are using healing touch to help people overcome every sort of illness and problem.

This book will teach you how to use healing touch. It will show you how to make use of an energy that, at this moment, is flowing through your entire being. To the extent that it is possible, I will explain how therapeutic touch works and why it works. The book is intended for those of you who want to rediscover the healing power in your hands and utilize that power at whatever level you wish. You can apply healing touch to help yourself, your friends, and your loved ones. Or, with practice, study, and continual self-refinement, you can become a practitioner of this powerful healing tool.

As with most of the healing arts, healing touch makes its greatest demands of the practitioner. Throughout this book, I will be challenging many commonly held ideas and assumptions. I will be asking you to appreciate, at a much deeper level, the perceptions and abilities that arise from your senses, especially those that reside in your touch, and your intuition.

The Undiscovered Power of Touch

To greater and lesser degrees, all of us take our senses for granted, but perhaps no sense is more overlooked than our capacity for touch. Ironically, touch offers us a ceaseless and staggering amount of information every instant of our lives. Consider for a minute that right now your hands are providing you information about the book you are holding—the thickness of its pages and the sharpness of their edges, the resistance offered by the book's binding, the book's weight, and the slickness of its cover. If you are sitting, the nerves in your buttocks and legs are sending signals to your brain regarding the design and relative comfort of your chair. The temperature around you is conveyed by the air touching your skin. Your skin is also providing you information about the clothes you are wearing and the press of your feet against the floor. Touch provides you with a sense of place—not only with the gross matter that you touch but also with the warmth of the sun on your skin, or the push of the wind in your face, or the textured resistance of the soil beneath your feet. It tells us the temperature of water, the softness or coarseness of a person's skin, and the fine details of every surface we encounter. Without the ongoing sense of touch, you would be completely "out of touch" with the physical universe.

Each of us is introduced to physical life through the touch of our parents, the first and most essential way in which a mother and father communicate love to a child. Touch is also a fundamental means of communication between people.

On some level, all of us recognize that touch can convey healing power, especially if it is expressed with love. It is this very awareness that makes a parent want to rub or kiss a child's bruise, or hug a child who is emotionally or physically hurt. Indeed, loving touch is essential to our development. If a child is not given enough loving touch, the endocrine system will be impaired and the child will not grow properly. At the University of Miami Medical School, researchers found that premature babies experienced a 50 percent increase in weight gain when they received three fifteen-minute sessions per day of touching. The babies who received the touching were calmer, more active, and required fewer days in intensive care than those who did not receive the additional touching. Children who are abandoned and remain untouched frequently suffer from what medical doctors refer to as "failure to thrive." In fact, many elderly people who live alone and do not experience regular touching also develop this same syndrome.

The need to be touched continues through our lives. A hug, a kiss, lovemaking, and a rewarding pat on the back or shoulder—all of these are examples of how touch is used every day to communicate love, support, reconciliation, and even healing.

Somehow, we are able to discern a person's attitude and nature in his or her touch. Something almost tangible and full of information passes between us when we shake hands, touch someone on the shoulder, or hug someone. Indeed, our ability to receive information through touch is so refined that blindfolded parents are able to identify their newborn babies amid dozens of other infants merely by touching the children. By actively making such information conscious, we begin to open up to our incredible capacities of perception. We begin to open up to a larger definition of life that encompasses tangible and intangible connections to others.

Healing touch requires an even greater degree of sensitivity than touch or massage therapies, because the practitioner does not physically touch the recipient but passes his or her hands just over the person's body. As I will describe in detail later on, I sometimes touch the physical body to help move blocked or stagnant energy. For the most part, however, I perform the bulk of the treatment on the field itself, which is to say, slightly away from the actual physical body. The practitioner is seeking to heal and strengthen what traditional healers call the "life force," a complex web of energy that surrounds and permeates the human body.

Our culture has little understanding of how a person can influence the health of another human being without physically touching him or her. Our current worldview, which is based on the scientific objective model, insists that the world is made up of separate objects that have no relationship with each other unless they physically interact. This way of seeing life prevents us from understanding the subtle but powerful forces that link us all. It also prevents us from seeing how the practitioner of healing touch can act as a conduit for a powerful healing force that can be transferred from one person to another.

To better understand the process, let us first turn to the language and philosophy of our ancestors, and then see how modern science, in spite of its preconceptions and prejudices against ideas such as the "life force" and "human energy field," is validating this philosophy in the laboratory.

Beneath the Flesh and Bones, a Living Energy

Every traditional culture, whether it be Chinese, Japanese, Asian Indian, Greek, or Native American, sees life as an entity unto itself—a life force—that resides in physical objects for a certain amount of time. This life force is actually a vast and limitless energy, much like a river without beginning or end. That flow of life energy manifests as individual people, animals, insects, plants, and inanimate objects, such as rocks. The ancient Chinese called this infinite life force *chi;* the Greeks called it *pneuma;* the Asian Indians *prana;* the Japanese *Qi,* and Native Americans just referred to it as the Flow of Spirit.

Whatever the name, the flowing of a universal life force from the creator of the universe to each living thing is seen as the basis of physical, psychological, and spiritual health in virtually every traditional culture. Your body is infused with this life force. It surrounds and permeates every cell, organ, and sense. It is like a great ball of energy within which your body resides. As long as the life force flows through the human body, all the organs, systems, and senses function optimally. Illness is caused by a diminution in the flow of the life force. Without a free flow of life energy, organs function at lower rates of efficiency. Blood and lymph flows stagnate, waste accumulates, and illnesses manifest themselves.

No matter what therapies a traditional healer depends upon, he or she essentially is treating the life force itself. Wherever the life force is weak or deficient, the traditional healer attempts to make it strong; where it is too strong or excessive, the healer attempts to balance or modulate it. Restored to its optimal flow, the life force will assist the body's natural healing functions to restore health.

According to the traditional way of thinking, a person's way of life affects the degree to which he or she absorbs the life force, and thus enriches or impoverishes his or her existence. Practices that strengthen the life force within the individual eventually formed the basis for religious and spiritual life. For this reason, virtually every religious tradition depicts its spiritual teachers as having a glowing countenance. Evidence of the powerful life force emanating from spiritual figures abounds: In Buddhism, the Buddha radiates a golden glow; in Christianity, Jesus is shown with a glowing halo around his head. In the Bible and other religious books, these figures control the flow of that life force to bring healing to others (see, for instance, Mark 5:28–34).

Archaeologists have discovered in the Dead Sea Scrolls that the Essenes formally trained people in the laying on of hands, and that certain people within the Essene community possessed a marked ability to perform healing touch. Cave paintings of healing practices done by Native Americans depict the laying on of hands. Healing touch has been used throughout Asia. In fact, all Taoist philosophy, acupuncture, and the martial arts are based on developing a mature understanding and utilization of this underlying life force for health, wisdom, and personal power.

Growing Scientific Support

Today, scientists are validating this ancient wisdom. When researchers examine the effects of healing touch in the laboratory, they report consistent and even remarkable results.

At McGill University, in Montreal, Canada, Dr. Bernard Grad found that the wounds of laboratory mice that received healing touch healed faster than similar wounds on mice that did not receive therapeutic touch. Dr. Grad also found that plants that received therapeutic touch grew faster and stronger, and produced more chlorophyll, than plants that did not receive such treatment. Dr. Krieger reported that hemoglobin—the oxygen-carrying substance in human blood—increased in patients receiving therapeutic touch. Since hemoglobin is essential to life and healing, this suggested that therapeutic touch enhanced the body's capacity to heal itself. Other studies have supported such conclusions. Daniel Wirth, at the John F. Kennedy University Graduate School for Professional Psychology in Orinda, California, demonstrated increased wound healing in twenty-two of forty-four male student volunteers who were given five minutes of therapeutic touch treatments after having surgical incisions.

In 1987, Dr. Janet Quinn reported a significant improvement in immune function among subjects receiving therapeutic touch. Among her findings was an enhanced ratio between CD4 cells—the helper T cells that direct the immune response against an antigen—and CD8 cells—the cells that shut off the immune system. (The enhanced ratio of CD4 and CD8 cells is particularly important for people with HIV and AIDS. These people typically suffer from a diminishing number of CD4 cells and a stabilizing or increase in the number of CD8 cells. The drop in CD4 cells causes the immune system to rapidly decline, while the increase in CD8 cells causes the system to shut off, or to simply fail to respond in the presence of a pathogen or cancer cell.)

Studies have shown that those people receiving healing touch have increased alpha brain waves, characteristic of people in a meditative state. Such deep states of relaxation are associated with diminution of stress, improved respiration, better hormonal balance, enhanced bowel function, lower blood cholesterol levels, and heightened immune response. It's important to note that healing touch works on plants, animals, and humans (both in infants and adults), a fact that weakens the argument that the whole phenomenon is caused by a placebo effect. Also, there are no harmful side effects to such treatment. Healing touch is safe and highly effective. These and other studies reveal that something more than nerve fibers is involved in the exchange between the practitioner and recipient.

Developing a Scientific Model for the Energy Field

Not only are researchers demonstrating in the laboratory that healing touch works, they are also finding evidence for the underlying mechanisms that may explain *why* it works. Scientists are proving in the laboratory that the human body is animated by a complex web of electrical energy and that this underlying energy can be enhanced to bring about healing.

Among the leaders in this field of research is Robert Becker,

M.D., an orthopedic surgeon and formerly professor at Upstate Medical Center, Syracuse, N.Y. Dr. Becker and his colleagues have shown that a variety of techniques can boost the body's underlying electrical currents, which in turn strengthens the body's healing mechanisms, including the immune, endocrine, and nervous systems. Among the techniques Dr. Becker has shown to be effective at strengthening the body's energy system are acupuncture, certain dietary practices, and healing touch.

In his book *Cross Currents: The Perils of Electropollution; the Promise of Electromedicine* (Jeremy P. Tarcher, 1990), Dr. Becker reports that laboratory evidence is providing a picture of how healing touch may work.

"I have seen remarkable results obtained in a number of life-threatening circumstances," writes Dr. Becker. ". . . Since we know that the body uses electrical control systems to regulate many basic functions and that the flow of these electrical currents produces externally measurable magnetic fields, it does not require a great leap of faith to postulate that the healer's gift is an ability to use his or her own electrical control systems to produce external electromagnetic energy fields that interact with those of the patient. The interaction could be one of those that 'restores' balance in the internal forces or that reinforces the electrical systems so that the body returns toward a normal condition."

Dr. Becker and others have shown that by boosting the body's underlying electrical currents, the immune system and vital organs are also strengthened. Researchers have also demonstrated that the very act of healing is electrical in nature. That is, when the body is injured or ill, it struggles to increase the electrical energy flowing to the site of the injury or illness. This research forms the basis of a potentially revolutionary form of health care that scientists are calling "electromedicine." It has the potential to link modern science with ancient healing practices to create a truly unified medical system.

The basis for such healing, Dr. Becker has demonstrated, is the electrical body that surrounds and permeates the physical body.

Dr. Becker has shown that this energetic body, which he calls (as does Rupert Sheldrake, author of *A New Science of Life* and *The Rebirth of Nature*), a "morphogenic field," contains a unique intelligence that controls the growth, development, and health of cells and tissues.

As he describes in *Cross Currents,* Dr. Becker came by this discovery after performing a series of remarkable experiments on salamanders. These animals, you will recall, have the ability to regrow in perfect detail a new leg, an eye, an ear, half a heart, as much as one third of a brain, and most of a digestive tract.

The researchers at SUNY severed the tail and leg of a salamander, and as the animal grew new cells at the places of the amputations, Dr. Becker took some of the growing cells that were developing into a new tail and placed them on the stump of the amputated leg. You would think that these "tail cells" would continue to grow into a tail because DNA had already programmed them to do so. Remarkably, the new tail cells that were placed on the stump of the amputated leg became a new leg. The leg was complete in every detail, including skeletal bone, muscle, and nerves—all in perfect order!

On another salamander, Becker reversed the process: He took cells that were being used to grow a leg and placed them at the site of the amputated tail, and they grew into a perfectly developed tail. Becker was able to show that new cells, taken from any amputation site on the salamander's body and placed elsewhere at a new site, will become that new part of the body, whether heart, brain, or intestine. The question, of course, is: What made these cells become a leg, a complex organ by any standard, after they had already begun to grow into a tail? What changed the orders of the DNA?

The researchers were able to refute the notion that this change occurred locally, that is, at the site of the amputation by orders conveyed through local nerves. In fact, the researchers demonstrated that the nerves were "completely silent," which is to say, they transmitted no nerve impulses and no information. According to the reductionist view, the new-growing cells that were coded to grow a tail should have produced a tail—unless there was some larger intelligence that understood the salamander's body as a whole. This larger intelligence, which contains a blueprint of the animal's body, recognized the need to grow a new leg, and reordered the tail cells to produce a leg.

Through a series of additional experiments, Becker discovered that there was indeed a larger intelligence that existed as an electrical field that surrounds and infuses the salamander's body. Becker proved that this larger electrical body, a "morphogenic field," actually organizes and orders the DNA to produce whatever the body needs at a particular site. He proved that the information is passed from this morphogenic field to the animal's body, which triggers the appropriate DNA response and in turn produces the appropriate organ.

The morphogenic field also plays a role in the healing powers of acupuncture and healing touch. The field directs more life energy to specific parts of the body that need healing. Becker demonstrated that whenever a person is cut, injured, or suffers from an illness, the body increases the flow of direct-current electricity, which provides the essential energy for healing, to the injured or diseased site.

Acupuncture and therapeutic touch, to name just two forms of therapy, actually facilitate the focusing of additional energy to wounds and parts of the body that are diseased. Practitioners of healing touch perform this function by acting as conduits of life energy, which passes from the universal source, through the practitioner, and on to the recipient. In other words, the practitioner of healing touch performs the same function that the body itself is attempting to perform. The big difference is that, very often, the practitioner is able to boost the energy, which helps to overcome blockages to the life force and, in many cases, speeds the healing process.

Anyone Can Use Healing Touch

You can use healing touch to help a friend or family member who may be struggling with a chronic or acute disease or disharmony. With continued exposure to healing touch, you may also want to become a practitioner of this powerful healing tool. Those who have no intention of becoming a professional practitioner, however, must make a commitment to following all the steps in the practice, especially centering (see chapter 6). Working with someone who is ill can be extremely debilitating unless you are centered and know your limits. You also should be aware of the kinds of imbalances you will be treating and how to address these disharmonies. Specifically, you should know how to pull energy away from the field and direct it toward the individual. Finally, no session should be longer than thirty minutes, especially if you are new to the practice. Chapters 2, 3, 7, 8, and 10 provide instruction for time of treatment, sending and pulling energy, assessing the field, and using healing touch for specific imbalances. Read these chapters carefully before you employ the practice.

Joining the Modern with the Ancient for a Truly Holistic Healing Model

Scientists are on the threshold of learning a great deal about the electrical field, or energy body, that surrounds and infuses the physical form. But they have just scratched the surface. In order to have a working picture of this field, we must rely on the model given us by traditional healers and religious and spiritual teachers. This teaching, which I use in my own practice, has not been proven by science and likely never will be until we have scientific equipment with the sensitivity to measure this very subtle energy. Even if science could analyze this energy, it could not measure the ineffable qualities of the field, as it is understood by traditional people. That understanding extends too far into the realm of spirit to be comprehended by the current scientific method. Nevertheless, we need a picture of the energy body, which this model provides, to understand and perform this work. As you perform healing touch, you will develop your own experiences and understanding. For many of you, the model itself may change. You'll develop your own images of the character and topography of the energy body. But for now, let's see the practice in action and then explore the ideas and models that have served healers for more than ten thousand years.

2

The Healing Process

Wendy, a young woman on the verge of being crippled by multiple sclerosis, was twenty-eight when she first came to see me. Just before her first appointment with me in the spring of 1992, her doctor had informed her that her disease was worsening and that she should purchase a wheelchair immediately. In all likelihood, he said, she would be restricted to it by Thanksgiving. He also warned her to spend a week in the hospital to receive intravenous treatments of prednisone, a corticosteroid drug that suppresses the immune system and reduces inflammation. Prednisone has many side effects, however, including the weakening of bones and the encouragement of osteoporosis. Wendy wanted to try some other form of therapy first and eventually found her way to me.

I began by performing weekly treatments of healing touch and putting her on a program of dietary supplements. Before I recommend such supplements to any of my patients, I take a thorough medical history and advise them to get a thorough physical examination by their medical doctor if they have not already. I then do a complete blood analysis, from which I usually suggest dietary changes along with taking additional dietary supplements. These food supplements are prescription items in the wholistic field. They can only be dispensed by licensed health-care professionals. In Wendy's case, I suggested a program to clean her liver and support her digestion and nervous system.

At the time, Wendy suffered from many of the standard symptoms of MS, including the shaking of her limbs, stammer, weakness in the legs, shuffling of the feet, chronic fatigue, and a tendency to drop objects that she held in her hands. Her condition was complicated by asthma and sinusitis, which frequently caused labored breathing and wheezing. The muscles in her neck and shoulders were exceedingly stiff and hard. Conversely, her arms were weak and flaccid. In addition, the third and fourth fingers of her right hand were bent rigidly into the palm and could not be moved. In general, her fingers were numb and tingly, but the third and fourth fingers of the right hand had no feeling in them whatsoever.

Immediately, I realized that an excessive amount of Wendy's life force was bound up and blocked in her shoulders. These blockages prevented the life energy from moving down into her arms, hands, and legs, causing her limbs to get progressively weaker and, in the case of her fingers, progressively number. In order to help Wendy, I would have to free the energy that was locked in her shoulders and back and move it down into her arms and the lower parts of her body.

In a very deliberate manner, I began by removing the blocks to her energy and making it flow more freely throughout her field. This involved a kind of slow and gentle scooping action over her upper back. Whenever I pulled away the blocked, excessive energy from her back, I would literally send it up into the air. I asked Wendy to visualize the energy from her heart moving up into her throat, down each arm, and into her fingers, tendons, and bones. I then turned my attention to her arms, hands, fingers, and legs, and sent new energy into these tissues, tendons, and bones. As I worked on Wendy, my hands became very hot, an indication of the intense energy and circulation that was emanating from them, as well as the energy I was taking off her shoulders and neck.

After treating Wendy for a few weeks, an image came to my mind during one of our sessions. I saw a little girl sitting on a large black box with her thumb in her mouth. It was clear from the image that the little girl wouldn't open the box to explore it—but couldn't get off the box and leave it, either. She seemed stuck.

This image jumped into my mind with such clarity and force that I knew it had to be some kind of key to my treatment of Wendy. Very gently, and without any pretense that I "knew" something about her, I shared the image with Wendy and asked if it meant anything to her. Remarkably, the image of a little girl sitting on a black box had come to her as well. It seemed that as I worked on her, the image had passed from her field to mine, at which point I was able to make it conscious. At each subsequent session, Wendy and I engaged in the process of discovering what this image might mean to her and her healing. We explored many emotional issues that might lie within that black box. After each of these discussions, I would perform healing touch on Wendy.

We concluded that the black box symbolized Wendy's unconscious and that it held repressed emotions. The little girl indicated that Wendy had been emotionally traumatized at some early stage in life. Inside of the adult Wendy was a little girl who was suffering emotionally but was unable to deal with all the pain that was locked inside of her psyche. That pain had prevented the little girl from moving on and developing more fully. It manifested in the adult by preventing her from feeling physically when she was confronted with highly charged emotional situations. Hence, certain aspects of Wendy's consciousness were stuck in some preadolescent stage of development. These repressed and unexamined emotions within her psyche were stored in the black box upon which the little girl in the image sat. We also realized that those emotions, and the events that had triggered them, contained information and experiences that had to be examined and integrated into conscious life by the adult Wendy if she were to be healed.

In addition, I concluded that the energy that was stuck in her shoulders had originated in her heart chakra. Once it became blocked in her shoulders, it was unable fully to infuse her lungs, neck, arms, and hands.

Wendy characterized her emotional life as "going numb." She then suggested that perhaps her whole disease process was analogous to the way that she had gone numb emotionally.

I agreed, but only partially. I told Wendy that no one is to blame for his or her disease. On the contrary, no one fully understands all the reasons why he or she becomes ill. I stressed that in order for Wendy and me to work effectively, we must recognize that health and illness are mysteries that cannot be fully solved, but to which we must surrender.

Healing Is Transformative

This is an important concept to maintain as you read this book. The mind convinces us that we must *intellectually* understand the healing process in order to be healed, but that is merely the mind's attempt at maintaining control of the process itself—a veritable impossibility. True healing, especially from a serious disease, almost always involves personal transformation. Such healing includes confronting and changing deeply ingrained habits that have long been used to cope with life. This can be difficult since, very often, the habit was developed to help the person deal with emotional or psychological pain and survive it. Such habits once served an important purpose but now are no longer appropriate to the current situation or stage of life. By changing old ways of behaving, we renew ourselves and our lives. Thus we move into the future with new attitudes and more revitalizing ways of dealing with life— the past, present, and future. Since all of us maintain habits to cope with life, we are all growing and shedding behaviors at various stages of our development. No one, therefore, can be fully to blame for his or her illness, any more than healthy people can take full credit for being physically well.

Nevertheless, Wendy's own analysis of the numbness she experienced in her emotional life and in her physical body could be used as a therapeutic tool. "To feel is to heal," I suggested. "Perhaps this is some kind of guidance or mantra that you can use to encourage your recovery."

The energy work was having a very beneficial effect on Wendy. Increasingly, she felt strong enough to explore her emotional pain, to open the black box and examine its contents. At the same time, she was making excellent progress physically. In general, multiple sclerosis is marked by steady degeneration of the nervous system and the life-sustaining organs. The disease process is punctuated by plateaus that represent temporary periods of physical stability but that give way to another round of further degeneration of the nervous system and the organs it supplies. MS tends to worsen until any one of a number of life-threatening conditions that can eventually snuff out a person's life sets in. For this reason, MS is considered "incurable."

Contrary to all that was expected, Wendy was not experiencing the same type of steady decline. For one thing, she was walking regularly, and her gait was not weakening. In fact, we were working so well together that we were becoming hopeful that the work could slow the degenerative process somewhat and perhaps significantly improve her condition.

Entering the Healing Triangle

Wendy and I had entered what I refer to as the "healing triangle," an enhanced state of mind and body composed of three characteristics: patience, intention, and imagination (see diagram 1). As I continue to do this work, I am convinced that there is no disharmony on this planet that we cannot overcome. Yet, we need certain characteristics if we are to prevail and restore harmony to our lives. The first characteristic needed is patience, which contains within itself perseverance, humility, and concentration. According to *The American Heritage Dictionary,* patience is "the capacity of calm

DIAGRAM 1. THE HEALING TRIANGLE

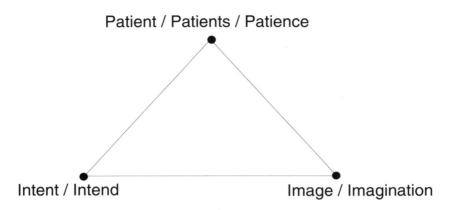

Patient / Patients / Patience

Intent / Intend   Image / Imagination

endurance." Patience gives us the strength to stay focused on our goal, to remain calm, and to endure in right action. Patience allows us to perform every task calmly and thoroughly so that the accumulation of these actions leads inevitably to our goal. Wendy demonstrated patience by allowing the healing process to unfold naturally and organically. If she was tired, she rested. If she didn't rest, she developed numbness in several parts of her body. As she honored her healing process and allowed it to progress at its own pace, her body became stronger and her bouts of fatigue and numbness became shorter.

Implicit within patience are humility and openness. Neither Wendy nor I had an agenda or schedule as to when she would begin to improve, or even what form the improvement would take. Rather, we were open to whatever her body decided to do with the energy being channeled through me to her. We knew we were seeing significant signs of improvement when she was able to distinguish by feel what kind of coin she was holding in her hand while her eyes were closed. She also became able to attend exercise class regularly and do all of the exercises. As Wendy improved, her gait was more stable and she no longer had numbness in her legs and feet. However, if she became overtired and did not rest properly, her gait would lag and the numbness return. Overall, we were en-

couraged by her progress and felt a renewed sense of patience and
faith in her healing process.

The second point on the triangle that Wendy and I utilized is
intention. Again, the dictionary tells us that to intend is to have a
"clear purpose; an aim that guides action . . ." Such characteristics
imply a strong will—the willpower to move toward a goal in the
face of doubt. At the outset of the relationship between the healer
and recipient, the healer is usually the one with the clearest intention and the strongest belief in what she or he is doing. The recipient may come to you simply because, as in Wendy's case, you are
the only alternative to a wheelchair and prednisone treatments. Yet,
the recipient may be filled with doubts. He or she may not have any
belief that the practice can be of benefit. In this case, the patient
needs strong intention toward his or her goal and the honesty and
the willingness to objectively assess the effects of the practice.
Meanwhile, the healer must also have strong intention and the will
to move forward in the face of her own doubts. Oh, yes, even the
healer must deal with doubts: Can this person get well? Can the
practice help him or her? Can I perform the practice adequately so
that this person benefits? These are just a few of the doubts that
creep into the heart of every healer who truly wants to help others.
To move beyond such doubts, the healer, too, needs clear intention.

With time and her physical improvement, Wendy began to
believe in healing touch, as well. Once she saw the results, Wendy
and I were working together with strong patience and intention.

Finally, patience and intention combine to create a higher possibility, which exists initially in the world of image and imagination, the third leg of the healing triangle. Imagination that arises out
of the practice of patience and intention creates possibilities that
were not initially apparent, nor originally seen or even dreamed of.

The healing path described by the characteristics that com-
prise the healing triangle is a very different path from that traveled
by those who are ill and act out of fear. Some people who act exclusively from fear have little patience and no clear intention (except to escape the illness). Trying to rush the healing process toward

a preconceived goal obscures one's ability to see the possibilities for creating wellness that may be implicit in the situation. On the other hand, by maintaining patience and acting with clear intent, we invite the magic of healing because we are open to the third element in the alchemical mix: imagination.

Many adults believe imagination to be something that resides mostly in children, something one grows out of. We're taught to grow into realism. Be realistic, we are told. We even shame one another by telling our friends to be realistic. It's like saying "Grow up" or "Act your age."

This "adult" way of thinking limits our creativity and, in the process, limits the possibilities for our healing. Fortunately for all of us, imagination cannot be killed or completely wiped out of our faculties, for it is a fundamental part of our humanness. It fuels our creativity. So, although we have unspoken rules about how we can apply our imagination, and while we are selective in how we use it, we can relearn how to gain access to it.

Using our imagination to aid the healing process is not a modern practice. Traditional peoples around the world always have been highly imaginative in their ways of healing, and are just as effective in treating many kinds of illnesses and disorders. Healing touch and other forms of energy medicine, such as herbs and nutrition, have been healing people since the dawn of consciousness. Today, science is recanting its condemnation of these practices, yet in us there is still that subtle training that works against our rightful claim to these and other forms of healing and also prevents us from using our imagination to conjure images of health and wellness.

Bad health, on the other hand, you can be imaginative about. Bad health, you can predict; you can even be clairvoyant when it comes to predicting your own bad health. "I think I'm about to be sick" is a perfectly legitimate thing to say. But people look askance at those who are already ill but say "I feel very strongly that I'm about to get well." We tend to offer a patronizing smile to the person who says words like that. Many people—especially health professionals—are threatened when people talk imaginatively about their imminent good health. The reason for this is that people tend to trust their assessment of bad symptoms, such as nausea or headache, but the prediction that you're going to get better because you're experiencing positive symptoms is often categorized as wishful thinking or "unrealistic" optimism.

Imagination is the gateway to seeing yourself and your world in larger, unrestricted terms. Imagination is also the basis for the positive messages that you send to your cells, organs, and overall body: "I am healthy" is a very positive message to your cells. It can even program them to act in ways that promote health. Imagination is the mother lode that you can tap into—like a big vein of gold in a dark mine—that can yield all kinds of rich and even magical possibilities. The third element in the healing triangle, imagination, points the way upward to good health. Imagination is an essential ingredient in every recovery, no matter what type of therapy is utilized.

We must remember, however, that what we imagine may be smaller than what can be achieved or is intended by the Creator. Our imagination has been put down for so long that we must acknowledge that perhaps greater possibilities exist than even those we can imagine. Think of imagination as the opening of your arms. It is the reaching up and welcoming the possibility of the unexpected, even the magic, that life provides for rebirth.

The Triangle Becomes a Pyramid

The triangle, of course, is a two-dimensional object, an abstract design that has height and width but no depth. When traditional people utilized the triangle to create spiritual temples, shrines, and symbols for healing, they gave the triangle a square base by adding two points, one in the front and another in the back, thus creating a pyramid. To carry our triangle metaphor one step further, therefore, I want to add two more points to the triangle's base to create a healing pyramid. These two points are gratitude and faith, two virtues that are so intimately related that each one gives rise to the other (see diagram 2).

Gratitude, as the pioneer stress researcher Hans Selye pointed out, has the power to instantaneously change your entire attitude toward life. Once you look at your life with gratitude, everything around you suddenly has an extremely important value. You notice the beauty of nature, the smiles of your loved ones, the goodness in your friends, and the endless blessings that you have received in life. You recognize that at so many vitally important junctures in life, situations whose outcomes were extremely tenuous nevertheless turned in your favor. One can hardly experience gratitude and feel the weight of its many revelations without wondering about the source of it all and the ultimate benevolence of that source. Like Plato and Socrates, we are forced to wonder if there isn't some force

DIAGRAM 2. THE HEALING PYRAMID

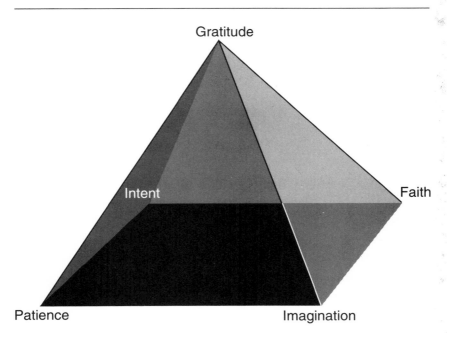

for good behind life's events. The more we consider that source, the more we come to have faith in it. Thus, gratitude leads inevitably to faith.

As Wendy and I worked together, she began to talk about how much she had learned from healing touch, and even from her illness. She had learned how to honor and respect her body, to rest it when it needed rest, and to nourish it with better-quality food and drink. The more intimate she became with her body, the more she marveled at its endless mysteries. That intimacy and wonder gave her even more gratitude for her body and greater faith in the ever-unfolding healing process.

I could not help but be grateful that Wendy had come into my life. I had learned so much from working with her and had gained so much more confidence in my abilities and in the efficacy of the practice. These were irreplaceable gifts she had given me, gifts that had changed my life.

Healing Is a Gift You Give Yourself

One day in June, while working on Wendy, I felt overcome by a strange calm sensation, a feeling of tremendous well-being. I was moving the energy out of Wendy's back and neck, down her arms, and into her hands. I then turned my attention to her hands, especially her right hand, where the third and fourth fingers were bent inward with almost a spastic quality. I was very focused and aware only of her hand and curled fingers. Suddenly, I was moved to hold her hand and her third and fourth fingers, and then, very gently, I straightened them. Wendy's hand opened and her fingers stretched out to their full length. Slowly and cautiously, she began to flex her fingers, moving them back and forth. These fingers had been rigid and immovable for months and now they were straight. For a moment, I couldn't believe what I had just witnessed and participated in. I looked at Wendy in disbelief. "You opened your hand," I said.

As if she were reading my mind, Wendy said, "Yes, Deby,

you really opened my hands." She started to cry. At that moment, I felt that God was moving through me. I wasn't questioning anymore.

From that time onward, Wendy made tremendous progress in her healing. I worked on her regularly for the next three years. Her legs got stronger, and she was able to stay on her feet and walk for longer distances before she became tired. She never needed a wheelchair, nor did she undergo prednisone treatments. Her hands and sensory perception continued to get stronger. Today, Wendy is the active mother of three children. She has completed a course that qualifies her as a nurse's aide, and now has a rewarding career and a family life that express the free-flowing energy of her heart. She has regained not only the ability to use her hands without artificial assistance but also her sensitivity to the size, shape, and texture of objects, which she can now identify with her hands. She can pick up coins and actually feel them. The tingling in her fingers is significantly reduced. Her nails are pink, an indication that the circulation in her fingertips is greatly improved. Whenever she overstresses herself, her legs get numb, but as long as she walks and exercises within her limits, she is quite functional.

I still see Wendy from time to time for energy work, but not on the regular basis that I did in the beginning of our work. Just before we stopped seeing each other regularly, another image of her jumped into my mind. I saw her walking through a forest toward a radiant sun that was pouring light through the trees directly in front of her. To her immediate left and right was darkness. I shared this image with her and the two of us talked about it at length. We decided that the light was the path of healing, but behaviors that did not support her healing were deviations from that path, a detour, left or right, into the darkness that is illness.

The healing pyramid teaches us that we must accept the energy that the practice of therapeutic touch provides if the larger possibilities of the healing process are to occur. We must enter into the healing pyramid, so to speak. We must cultivate patience, intention, and imagination. We must experience gratitude and through gratitude develop faith. This is our part in the drama that is healing. And because we have an essential part in the healing process, we must understand that healing is a gift we give ourselves. We strive for patience, we maintain clear intent, and we open our arms to the possibilities that we may not at first see; we are transformed by gratitude, which ultimately gives us the gift of faith.

EXERCISE

1. Use a dictionary and thesaurus and list each word from the healing pyramid and its various meanings on separate index cards.
2. Read each card before a healing session to begin to activate the healing triangle and healing pyramid.

3

Using Your Hands to Heal

Humans have built civilizations, created great works of art, and healed one another with their hands. So much of our advancement as a species is based on a simple yet singular belief: that what the mind envisions the hands can create. The hands are the instruments of the imagination, and if the imagination is inspired by God, then the hands are the tools of the divine. The hands are themselves great works of art. They possess beauty, power, and utility. In the hands, raw strength, miraculous precision, and musical dexterity become one. The hands can build bridges, sculpt stone, type, tie flies, and perform surgery. All the powers of our minds, hearts, and souls are concentrated in our hands, which is why they are capable of reshaping the world. Who can deny that the hands possess a unique and even awesome power?

That power flows from your hands, and you can use it to heal. All you need is to develop your understanding of this practice and your confidence in its efficacy, and open your heart with love and understanding so that the life force can flow through your hands freely.

The Body Electric: On the Brink of a Medical Revolution

When I talk about the hands as radiating electromagnetic energy, and about the electromagnetic field that surrounds the body, I am not talking about something mystical or even speculative. I am talking about a scientific fact. The body is an electrical unit, and like all electrical units it is surrounded by an electrical field. Electricity makes your heart beat, your muscles expand and contract, and your nervous system send messages across tiny fibers of tissue. Within your brain, electrical impulses fire across the neurons, making every thought, mood, and physical reaction that you experience possible. In short, there isn't a single event that takes place in your body that isn't dependent upon an electrical charge.

A little more than five decades ago, scientists began photographing this human electrical field. In 1939, a Russian scientist by the name of Semyon Kirlian accidentally shocked himself with a high-voltage generator and saw an electrical flash discharge from his hands. Amazed by the brilliant release of energy, Kirlian created a camera that could photograph the electrical discharge coming off his fingers. In these photographs, that discharge appears as a halo full of spikes around the perimeter of the hands. For the next twenty years, he and his wife worked together in an attempt to discover if the electrical discharge being given off by the hands could be used as a diagnostic tool. Is it possible, the Kirlians wondered, that photographic images could be used to determine health and illness? The Kirlians mapped out an extensive set of images that they said could be used to determine various disease states. Meanwhile, the images were so startling that many scientists argued that these pictures were photographic proof of the body's "aura," which traditional healers and mystics had been talking about for millennia. Others maintained that these images were nothing less than physical evidence of the soul.

Western scientists didn't know what to make of the Kirlians' photographs and dismissed them as meaningless—at least until recently. Today, scientists at the Massachusetts Institute of Technology, the State University of New York, and other research centers are studying the body's electromagnetic field to find out "what can be seen through the new window," in the words of MIT biomagnetic researcher David Cohen. One of the reasons for this breakthrough in interest is that some scientists now report that the "aura" given off by the body changes according to the person's inner state.

In the late 1970s, biophysicist Leonard W. Konikiewicz and his colleagues at the Polyclinic Medical Center in Harrisburg, Pennsylvania, showed that negative feelings, such as apprehension and animosity, weaken the intensity of the inner corona given off by the hands. Conversely, joy and sexual excitement make the corona stronger. Further research demonstrated that the corona changes according to the physical condition within the body, such as the stage of the menstrual cycle and the person's overall physical health. A person with cancer, for example, gives off a brighter and more diffuse corona than a person in normal health. Researchers of Kirlian photography have long maintained that a tight, bright corona is a sign of health, while a larger, more diffuse corona is a sign of disease.

American biochemist Glen Rein, who at the time of his research worked at Queen Charlotte's Hospital in London, used Kirlian photography to study tissue samples from women with breast cancer, and compared them with samples from healthy women. Rein found that the light intensity emitted from the tissues of the women with breast cancer was greater and larger than that from the tissues of healthy women. Rein went on to show that the hands of cancer patients also discharged more electromagnetic energy than those of people in good health. Some researchers speculate that the increase in energy released from cancer patients reveals that the body is in a state of degeneration, and consequently can no longer hold the life force in its grasp. Hence, the energy is released in greater quantities and shows up on Kirlian images as a larger, brighter, and more diffuse corona.

My own experience with cancer has given me a slightly different understanding of this phenomenon. The cancer cells, or tumor, are consuming the life force at such a rapid rate that they are responsible for this discharge of excess energy that is perceived in Kirlian photography. The life force was being drawn away from healthy cells and siphoned off to the cancer. This causes a general breakdown of the body, or the loss of physical and energetic integrity, which is revealed by Kirlian pictures as the excessive or unhealthy glow that radiates from the fingertips.

Other experiments have shown that the intensity of the corona also changes according to the environmental factors a person finds himself in. These factors include the temperature in the room the person is in, those who are present in the room with him, and the feelings of those present. In other words, the relative strength or weakness of the field depends a great deal upon both the inner and outer conditions of the person being examined. (This is one reason why I stress in chapter 6 how important centering is and how vital it is that you, the practitioner, be aware of your inner condition when you do this work.)

Scientists all over the world are now taking energy medicine to new vistas. Some of the work is far ahead of that being done in prestigious universities, such as MIT and SUNY, but it nevertheless describes where scientists may be looking in the years ahead. One such pioneer is Harry Oldfield, a London scientist who has developed a technique called "electronography." Oldfield's technique is to send a low-energy electromagnetic field through the body, which absorbs some of the field and radiates the rest back at a sensitive device that can detect a spectrum of frequencies being emitted from the body. Oldfield maintains that each organ has its own frequency, or vibratory rate, and that it can be detected and measured to determine the health of that organ. He has shown that when a person is thinking about something pleasant the body's electrical field is stronger. When a person thinks of something depressing or frightening, the field becomes significantly weaker.

Oldfield's work was reported in the spring 1986 issue of *Advances,* the prestigious journal of the Institute for the Advancement of Health. Writing about the technique, Clive Wood, Ph.D., a physiologist who teaches at Oxford University, experienced Oldfield's method firsthand. "Oldfield asked if he could scan my jaw and accurately located some recent dental bridgework that he could not have known about," wrote Wood. "Scanning my solar plexus, he asked me to think of something unpleasant. I thought about the dentistry, and within seconds the needle allegedly monitoring the energy output fell almost to zero. The thought, he said, had altered the relationship between the energy frequencies going into and coming out of my body. If it was a trick, it was a good one, but he had no reason to deceive me."

While Oldfield and others work on the outer rim of electromagnetic medicine, many highly regarded scientists are demonstrating the more fundamental fact that the body is not only an electromagnetic unit but that it can direct energy to heal. As I pointed out in chapter 1, Robert Becker at SUNY showed that all healing involves an increase in the flow of electromagnetic energy to the impaired part of the body. Becker's and Oldfield's work, when looked at together, may explain how an increase in positive thinking results in a stronger immune response: Positive thoughts may trigger a stronger electrical field, which may in turn boost immune function. This research may also explain why such practices as biofeedback and positive imaging have such healing effects.

That the body is an electrical unit, and that health is dependent on electromagnetic energy, is now well established. You have the power not only to heal yourself by boosting your own electrical field but also to help others by boosting theirs. That power radiates from all parts of your electromagnetic field. You can use your hands to direct that power to others.

"Turning On" the Hands

Once you center yourself, the next step is to "turn on" your hands, meaning to get the energy flowing powerfully from your hands. To do that, you must become conscious of the life force flowing through you from a higher source, or the Universal Healer. That energy flows to you from the cosmos above and the earth below, the two poles of existence. It fills your field and your entire body and flows like a powerful current to your hands. Your hands have the power to direct this current of healing energy to your client.

In this chapter, we are going to perform several exercises so that you can experience the healing power that flows from your hands. We'll begin simply by focusing on the palms of your hands. Turn your palms upward and see if you can sense an energy resting in your palms, as if a very light ball were sitting in each of your hands. Many people can sense this energy right away, but don't be troubled if you cannot. It takes time to develop an awareness of energy as an entity unto itself—your own as well as another's. Now, let's explore that energy a little further.

First, rub your palms vigorously together for about one minute. With your fingers and palms flat and straight, hold your palms facing each other and keep them about eight inches apart. Now, slowly bring your palms toward each other. As you do, see if you can sense the energy being compressed between your palms, as if its density is offering your hands some resistance. Now, move your hands away from each other until they are about a foot apart. Note that it's slightly easier to move your hands away from each other than it is to move them toward each other. Do this a couple of times and gauge the relative resistance you feel as your hands go toward each other and away.

Again start out by vigorously rubbing your palms together for about one minute. This time, however, change the posture of your hands so that each hand is cupped, as if it were holding a ball. Gradually, move your hands toward each other in the same way you did earlier. Do not let them touch, but hold them about four inches apart. This time, see if you can sense a greater resistance between your hands than you could when your hands were flat. A cupped hand will sense energy easier than a flat palm will. You may also feel heat or a radiating type of energy between your palms. What you are feeling are characteristics of the energy itself.

If you are having difficulty feeling the energy in your hands by rubbing the palms together, try this exercise. Extend your hands directly out in front of you, at about shoulder height, with your palms facing upward. Quickly, open and close each hand thirty or forty times. Bring your hands together slowly in a cupped position and try to feel the energy between your hands. Many people perceive the energy between the hands as a spongy ball. The rapid squeezing of your hands awakens the secondary chakras located there.

Once you have established this sensitivity in your hands or "turned your hands on," ask a family member or friend to allow you to feel the energy around them. Your pets or plants also make good energy subjects. Do not touch the person but bring your hand within eighteen inches of his or her body. See if you can sense the density of the field. Move your hand a little closer and see if you can perceive the energy radiating from the body. If you can feel it, you will note that the field becomes firmer as your hand moves closer.

As you do these exercises, part of you will clearly sense the energy in your hands or radiating from another person's body. At the same time, another part of you will doubt your experience. It isn't your senses that are in conflict, but your competing definitions of what is real. As I said earlier, healing touch forces us to confront our current beliefs and definition of reality. In a way, I had an advantage over many people who begin this practice because I had already seen the power of touch to heal in my nursing practice. Each time I would stroke a person's hand, or touch an arm or a shoulder, I could feel my patients relax. It was as if the tension that had gripped their bodies was suddenly released.

Keep in mind that tension in the tissues of the body is the basis for many illnesses. Tension is nothing more than an increase of energy—and sometimes excessive energy—that has manifested in muscles and connective tissues, such as fascia.

Building the Spongy Energy Ball

Here is a meditation designed to increase awareness and the healing power in your hands; it will show you how to use that enhanced sensitivity to "feel" another person's energy field. First, become aware of the energy flowing to you from the Universal Healer, who sends it forth from the cosmos above and the earth below. See the energy fill your field and flow in great rivers of energy through your body. You are imbued with the power that the Great Healer is sending to you.

Now to expand the hand exercise from the previous page, rub your hands together vigorously until you can feel the warmth generated by the friction. Rubbing the hands together awakens the energy centers in the palms of your hands. Slowly allow your hands to separate until they are about twelve inches apart. Once they have reached that point, slowly bring your hands together, all the while feeling the energy compress between your hands. One of the first things you will notice in this exercise is that it is easier to separate your hands than to bring them together. It's as if something is pushing your hands apart. As you bring your hands toward one another, you can sense a certain resistance between your palms, as if the energy is being compressed and is thus getting denser. Whenever I do this exercise (and I do a form of it every time I work on a person's field) I am aware of a powerful ball of energy that now resides between my hands. I sense it as spongy and radiating light, about the size of a basketball (see diagram 3).

While maintaining that heightened sensitivity and awareness of the energy in your hands, walk up to a family member, a friend, or a coworker and gently bring your hand to within about eighteen inches of his or her shoulder or back. (Do not do this exercise without first asking the person's permission.) If the person is a spouse, your child, or a close and trusted friend, you may bring your hand a little closer. Do not touch the person, however. See if you can sense the density of the field around that person. Feel the energy radiating from his or her body. Later on, we'll define the field's

DIAGRAM 3. THE SPONGY ENERGY BALL

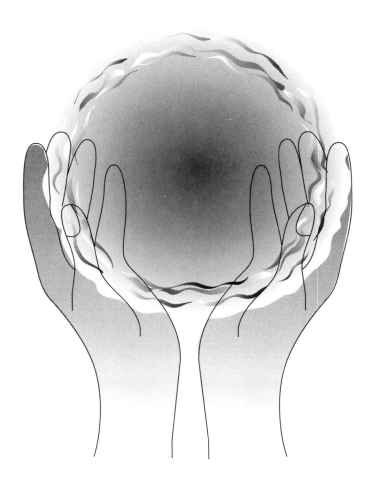

characteristics, but for now simply see if you can sense the energy that radiates from another person's body. If you can, you will note that the field is clearly palpable and even gets firmer as your hand moves closer to the body.

The more you become aware of your hands, the more you realize their remarkable power both to receive and to send energy. You can give energy to another person in the form of that ball of light that radiates from your palms. And you can receive energy—

and the information that is transmitted with it—when you shake hands or touch another person.

Relieving Pain: Jack's Story

Several years ago, I was providing nutrition counseling to a middle-aged man named Jack. Just after we began our work together, Jack suffered a heart attack and immediately underwent coronary by-pass surgery to restore blood and oxygen flow to his heart. At the time, surgeons were using part of the saphenous vein in the leg to replace the coronary arteries that supply the heart. One day after the surgery, he came into my office for our scheduled visit, and after we finished talking about his diet, I asked him if there were any other problems. Jack told me that his leg and ankle were both swollen and still very much in pain after the surgery. When I examined both, I saw that his ankle ballooned above the opening of his shoe, his foot was so swollen that he could barely put on his shoe, and his leg was inflamed and raw at the site of the incision. I offered to do healing touch on his leg. Jack balked. He didn't know anything about therapeutic touch and was skeptical. He preferred the more practical dietary recommendations I was giving him. "The practice can be effective against pain and swelling," I said. "It's worth a try."

"Let's do it, then," Jack said.

I asked Jack to remove his shoes and lie down on the table, where I began the treatment. I started by sending healing energy to the incision in Jack's leg. I then moved down to the ankle and removed the stagnant energy from the area of the swelling. I had expected only to be able to reduce Jack's pain, but as I continued to do the work, Jack's ankle felt less swollen to me but since his shoes were off, I couldn't judge the swelling adequately. However, I continued the treatment—removing stagnant energy from the ankle and sending the tissues healing life force. When I finished the treatment, Jack got up and tested his leg and found that the pain was gone. He walked around the room in amazement. "God, I can't believe this," he said. "I could never tell the doctor about this. He'd never believe it." He then put his shoes on, whereupon we both discovered that the swelling in his ankle had diminished noticeably. Both of us were now amazed. Jack walked around the room, shaking his head and saying, "This feels great. I can't believe it. I can't tell anyone about this. They'll think I'm crazy."

I continue to see Jack for nutritional counseling periodically. Although I do not provide energetic work for him, his wife, who later became my student, does.

Experiencing the Energy

This exercise will give you the experience of feeling the energy in your hands. It's a good exercise to perform before you work on someone's field.

EXERCISE

1. Hold your palms face up with arms slightly extended from your body.

2. Rapidly open and close both palms thirty to forty times.

3. Bring your slightly cupped hands slowly toward each other in front of you, noting the "spongy" ball of energy between your hands when they are about four inches apart.

Sending Energy and Pulling It from the Field

In my energy work with Wendy, I was essentially opening blocks and balancing the energy in her entire field. Her arms, hands, and legs were the areas that were deprived of energy, while her shoulders and back were burdened with blockages. I had to be able to remove energy where it was excessive and send it to places where it was deficient. It is not hard to determine where the energy is excessive or deficient, even before you become sensitive and experienced in being able to "feel" the energy with your touch. Remember that quality and quantity of energy within the field are generally replicated in the body itself. In Wendy's case, there was lots of blocked and excessive energy over her back and shoulders, which was manifested as rigid muscles in her neck and upper back. As for the field itself, I could palpably feel the energy when I moved my hands over and through this part of her field. It was dense and even heavy; it felt as if my hand were moving through a viscous substance that was full of resistance. Her arms, hands, and legs were deficient of energy, which was clearly reflected in the fact that these parts of her body were weak, and became more deficient when Wendy became overwhelmed with emotions of anger and fear. She would become immobilized—metaphorically speaking, she was unable to move off her black box and move along her healing path. Her fears prevented her from imagining her own good health and therefore prevented her from using the power of the healing triangle. When I worked on the field over these parts of her body, the lack of energy was palpable. The field felt distinctly empty, with no sense of charge, vitality, or density. This was a strange feeling for me as a practitioner of healing touch, because I had come to expect some reassuring sense of presence in the energy field.

My basic approach to Wendy's problem was to pull the energy out where it was blocked and excessive, and push the energy into the places where it was deficient. So, to help you get a feeling for working on pulling and pushing the energy, to help you experience the different sensations of therapeutic touch, try each of the following exercises.

You'll need a friend or partner to help you with this exercise.

EXERCISES

First, sit opposite each other in a straight-backed chair with your feet flat on the floor and your knees almost touching those of your friend. Take a minute or two to breathe deeply and center yourselves.

Now, rest your arms and hands on your thighs with your left palm facing upward and your right palm facing down. Have your partner place her right palm on top of your left palm and her left palm under your right palm. (For this exercise, you may actually touch each other's palms.)

Before you begin sending or receiving energy, you and your partner should try to determine how the energy is flowing between you. Does it go out your left hand and into your partner's right? Does the energy pass from your partner's right hand to your left? How does the energy that you receive from your partner affect your body? How does it travel through your body—that is, does it enter your right hand, for example, and travel up the arm, through the shoulders, and out the left hand? Try to feel the movement of energy before you try to affect the energy. Don't worry if you can't feel the flow of energy. Most important, don't think. Just feel. It takes time and practice to become sensitive to the movements of this energy.

Sending or Pushing the Energy to Your Partner

Once you have tried to establish the direction of the energy, see if you can direct it with your hands and mind. Decide between the two of you who is going to send the energy and who is going to receive it. Before you start to push the energy, take some deep breaths to center yourself. Decide which hand you are going to push the energy out of—the left or right. Now, use the exhalation of your breath to send the energy from the palm that you've chosen to send with. As you exhale, visualize the energy going out of your palm and into the opposite hand of your partner. The person who is receiving should stay in neutral mode and be sensitive to the energy. Visualize the line of flow—that is, see how the energy travels through your partner, such as from her arm, across her shoulders, down her other arm, returning to the hand opposite your own. Feel your other hand receive the energy. Ask your partner whether or not she can feel the energy flow. Take turns pushing with different hands. Also take turns receiving and sending the energy.

In general, sending energy to your partner or client will raise, or boost, the recipient's life energy. You send energy to places that are weak or deficient of Qi, or life force.

Pulling the Energy from Your Partner

The next energy flow to learn is pulling the energy. Pulling the energy will diminish the life force in an area; you do this in places where the energy is excessive. Repeat the previous exercise, but instead of pushing energy with the exhalation, visualize pulling the energy out of your partner's hand as you inhale. Try to determine how the energy is flowing within yourself and your partner. Where is the energy coming from that you are pulling from your partner? Is it coming from her shoulder? Her back? Her neck? Ask your partner if she has any physical sensations while you are pulling the energy from her.

Stopping the Energy Flow

Finally, let's try to stop the energy from flowing between you. Visualize the energy remaining at a state of rest between you and your partner. You are both closed to each other. Shut off. Determine how this feels and compare it to the previous exercises.

These exercises will help you learn how to master the ways in which you can direct energy through your hands. You can practice sending and receiving energy all day—whenever you shake a person's hand, send your energy or receive his or hers. When you touch another person on the shoulder or the arm, try to sense the person's energy or send some of your own. In short, try to expand your sense of touch. It's actually a lot easier than you think. Try not to make the practice excessively intellectual or difficult. All you need to do is experience and practice it.

Whenever you are sending or receiving energy, you will get images and impressions. As with the images I got when working with Wendy, these thoughts can help the healing process. At first, these impressions may be formless, but pay attention to the first thought that comes into your mind. It is usually correct. You may have a clear sensation that energy is moving out of your body to the recipient, yet your mind immediately attempts to squelch such a thought. You may hold your hand near a person's shoulder and immediately feel that you are able to sense the vibration coming from the person's field, yet your mind will automatically doubt what you are sensing. Learn to trust your initial perceptions and your expanded sense of touch.

In order to augment your practice, try to determine where the blockages exist in the people you see on the street or at work. Examine their fields and note the way they walk, or bend, or hold themselves. See if you can determine whether the left side or the right side of the field is stronger or weaker, whether there are blockages over the shoulders or neck or lower back. Try to "feel" the energy of a person you are sitting across from, and note any changes that take place in the person's field as you interact with this person.

With time and practice, all of these exercises become second nature. Your study of energy can go on all day long and for the rest of your life, with beneficial effects on your own and others' health.

Keep the Treatments Short

In general, healing touch sessions are short—anywhere from five to thirty minutes, depending on the age of the person and his or her health. The general rules are as follows: The younger the patient, the shorter the treatment time. And the more severe the disharmony of the person, the shorter the treatment.

For example, treatment for infants up to one year of age usually takes only thirty seconds. For a child of this age, you would do gentle healing touch over the area of disharmony or over the general body, especially in the case of premature babies or infants who are struggling with some type of systemic problem.

Ages one to five usually are treated for one minute (or for however long the child will sit still).

Very ill patients (especially those who are bedridden) are treated for no less than five minutes but no more than seven minutes. You can apply the treatment daily.

For those who suffer from acute illness (such as the first stage of a cold), the general rule is that less is more, meaning that a few minutes of healing touch will promote healing without overwhelming the body. If you work on a person with a cold or flu too long, you may trigger even stronger symptoms and more suffering than would otherwise have occurred. Colds are actually the body's attempt to eliminate accumulated waste and toxins, especially those that have been taken in from the environment, such as can be found in the air, water, and food. Over time, these waste products accumulate in the fluid between tissue cells. Tension in the muscles, fascia, and other tissues prevents the waste from moving into the lymph. Tension also prevents the lymph from moving the waste out of the tissues and into the liver for elimination. Hence, waste accumulates. This toxic environment in the tissues provides the right conditions for a virus or bacteria to flourish and to bring on a cold. Cold symptoms—such as sneezing, coughing, runny nose, frequent urination, diarrhea, and fever—are all the body's efforts to cleanse the system of toxins and to destroy the virus or bacteria. The symptoms are, in fact, the body's answer to the problem. By performing a long healing touch session on someone with a cold, you can trigger an even deeper discharge or elimination of waste products, and thus intensify the symptoms and cause more suffering. Thus, a cold or flu can be extremely acute in a twenty-four to forty-eight hour period. In other words, you will increase the suffering of the patient significantly. Treat this type of disharmony for five to seven minutes. You can apply the treatment daily. (For more on treatment of individual disorders, including the common cold, see chapter 10.)

One of the most difficult things to realize, especially when you are first starting out as a healing touch practitioner, is how powerful

DIAGRAM 4. TRANSFERRING OF ENERGY FROM THE ENERGY BALL TO THE SHOULDER

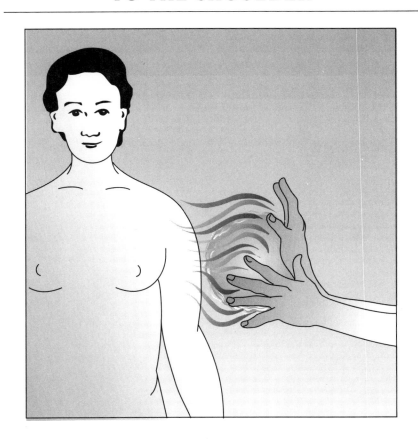

healing touch really is. You are sending another person the power of the life force, the basic energy that keeps the entire body alive (see diagram 4). Once the body accepts that energy, its own healing forces are boosted dramatically. What the body does with such energy and power is now up to that person and the Great Spirit.

Your hands have power. But as I intimated in the opening paragraphs of this chapter, that power flows from the mind and heart. And thus, your hands pour forth healing energy or fall inert by the images your mind and heart permit. You can limit your healing ability, or you can participate in a drama far greater than any of us can imagine. What mighty works these hands can perform, if only we have the faith to let them do their divinely inspired labor.

4

❀

The Energy Field

The vast majority of us can sense another person's energy field. In fact, very often the field is so palpable that most people perform mental and linguistic gymnastics in order to express in rational terms what we sense intuitively but cannot adequately explain. Thus, we refer to some people as having a "strong presence" or a "weak presence." We describe people who are thin or frail as having "a delicate energy." "He's a lightweight," someone says of another. "She fills up the room when she enters it." We don't really mean that a person is so wide that he or she "fills the room." We're talking about our clear perception of a person's energy field and all the information we derive from such perceptions.

Each of us senses the energy body and the consciousness that each energetic field contains. Some people radiate discipline, for example, or wisdom, or power, or danger. Others appear bathed in shadows, no matter how much light is in the surrounding environment. Some people have a very stable energy. Without saying a word, they put you at ease, make you feel relaxed and calm. Others have a very unstable field. Within minutes—sometimes even seconds—you feel the restlessness of their energetic body, their instability, their "static" electrical condition. "He was nervous," we might say to a colleague or friend later on. "How do you know? Did you see him shake?" the friend might ask us. "No, but I could sense it," we say. Just as a lie detector works by measuring the electrical fluctuations within the body, so you and I react to the changes in another person's electrical field.

We are taught from childhood to censor such perceptions as irrational. Nevertheless, when someone sends out a powerful thought or feeling, you receive that thought or emotion—and very often make it conscious. Someone's sexual energy, for example, can be very strong and palpable, even when that person has made no overt advances. Violence and danger are other powerful forms of energy that emanate from the field and affect us consciously. More subtle waves of energy also radiate from the field, though we tend to reduce them to generalities. "I get good vibrations from this person," we sometimes say. Or, "I got really bad vibes." Yet, there is so much more to be gleaned from a person's field.

When we allow ourselves to observe the brightness of one person or the darkness of another, we recognize that the relative amount of light emanating has nothing to do with his or her complexion, or skin color, or hair, or clothes. Think of the auras of Nelson Mandela or Martin Luther King, both black men, and note the kind of radiant energy that emanates from them. Think of Mikhail Gorbachev, the Dalai Lama, John Kennedy, Pope John Paul, Mother Teresa, or Margaret Thatcher—all very different in coloring, complexion, and physical stature, but all radiating a powerful light that seems to shine far beyond their physical bodies. The energy field gives us all our power, abilities, and health.

Sometimes, we can actually see wisps of this energy, especially if a person is sitting against a white wall in normal indoor light, as if little flames of light were dancing around the person's head. If you allow your eyes to go slightly out of focus when you look at someone, the energy body will become even more visible. This occurs, in part, because letting the eyes go out of focus shifts the emphasis of sight to the rods, or those cells within the optic nerve that perceive low-intensity light. The counterparts to the rods are the cones, another group of cells within the optic nerve that perceive bright light and color. The auric field is a low-intensity light and consequently is more visible to the rods. Watch the energy move in flamelike patterns around the head and shoulders. It appears very much like hot pavement emitting heat on a hot summer day.

Another way to see the aura is to note the fragments of light and color that move around a hand or arm as the person makes a gesture. Sometimes, when the light is right, you can see the field chase after the hand, like gossamer light, as the person raises the hand to his head or lowers it to the table or the arm of the chair. The aura seems to be left behind as the hand moves, as if the hand were leaving a trail of light in its wake.

Your energetic field makes an impression on people, too. Though it is impossible to know exactly how you affect others, we affect those with whom we interact. As I will show in chapter 10, the field sustains personality characteristics and patterns of behaviors that can be positive or negative. These are energetic patterns, streams of energy or blockages that maintain our choices and behaviors. We also tend to attract similar kinds of people into our lives over and over again. If you reflect on the similarities among the people you attract and the consistency of certain of your experiences, you begin to see that these attractions are not coincidences but are responses to nonverbal, energetic patterns, messages we transmit. Healing touch can strengthen patterns—if we regard them as positive—or change behaviors—if we want to be free of them.

The Soft Resilient Field: A Model for Understanding

Think of the field as having the consistency of a big ball of cotton candy. In health, the field is soft, pillowy, and resilient. Each filament of energy within the field is like radiant spun sugar. Unlike the cotton candy, however, the filaments in the field are uniform and in perfect relationship to each other.

Shaped like an egg, the energetic *you* is a sphere of energy that surrounds and fills every cell of your corporeal body. The energetic body also extends about two to four feet beyond your physical form. It is radiant with all the colors of the rainbow. It is this energy that people are referring to when they use the word *aura* or talk about an auric field. The energetic you maintains your physical health and, indeed, the life of your physical body for as long as you are on this earth. According to the healers and mystics of both East and West, the energy body does not die when the physical body dies. Just the opposite: When the energetic body decides that its purpose on earth is complete, it leaves the physical body to return to the energetic or spiritual world. At that moment, your physical body ceases to function and returns to the earth as disparate elements. The consciousness that you know to be the real you, the "I" inside of you, lives within the energy body, which lives on eternally.

Chakras: Wheels of Energy

Embedded within the field are seven wheels of energy, known traditionally as *chakras*. These chakras are arranged vertically in the center of your body, from the base of your pelvis to the top of your head. Each chakra provides life force to a specific set of organs, tissues, and eventually to an endocrine gland. In addition, each chakra is a center of consciousness, providing emotional, psychological, and spiritual capabilities to the body, mind, and spirit.

The chakras are energy tunnels that swirl uniformly, like eddies of water. These perfect tunnels of energy are widest at the outside of the field and then funnel into the body to an endocrine gland. At the point where the chakra intersects with the body, it is about the size of your palm. At the endocrine gland, the funnel reverses itself, becoming larger and wider as it swirls from inside the body, out the back, to the outer reaches of the field. The chakra tunnel does not disturb the uniformity and flow of the energy fibers or filaments in the field but actually feeds them and helps to maintain balance and order within the field.

The seven primary chakras are located in the following locations (see diagram 5): the first chakra is found at the base of the pelvis and is known as the root chakra; the second is located at the center of the lower abdomen, about three or four fingers below the navel, and is called the sacral chakra; the third chakra is located at the solar plexus; the fourth chakra is located in the center of the chest, and is known as the heart chakra; the fifth chakra is located at the throat and is known as the throat chakra; the sixth chakra is found between the eyes, just an inch above the eyebrows, and is known as the chakra of the brow, or *ajna;* the seventh chakra is found at the top of the head and is known as the crown chakra. (For more on chakras, see chapter 5.)

In addition to these seven primary chakras, there are secondary chakras located on the palms of the hands, the backs of the knees, and the soles of the feet, and twenty tertiary chakras on the tips of the fingers and toes.

Seven Layers of Life

The energetic body is composed of seven layers. Each layer corresponds to a specific aspect of consciousness. The layers have a certain density that becomes more diffuse as you move away from the physical body; it is more dense and palpable as you move closer to the physical body.

In health, there is good communication among the layers of the field, so that each level influences the other six. All seven levels of the energy field are intimately connected and interdependent on each other (see diagram 6). For example, thoughts create emotions (and emotions create thoughts). Indeed, one cannot have a thought without the production of hormones, which can trigger emotional changes. The quality of that thought will determine the character of the emotion and the physical response we experience. Memory can

DIAGRAM 5. THE SEVEN CHAKRAS

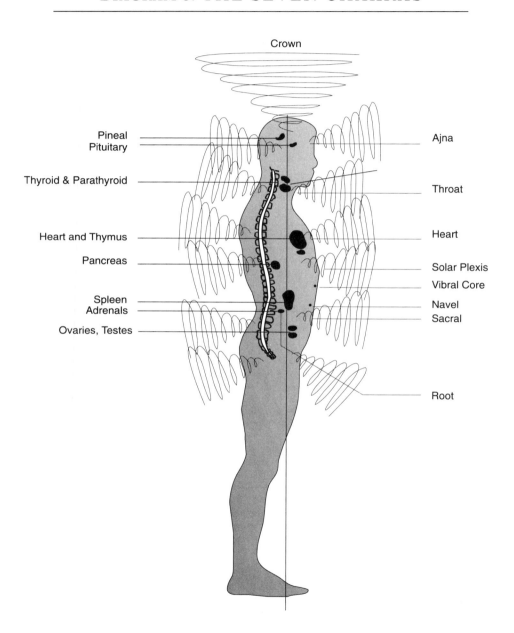

Crown

Pineal
Pituitary

Ajna

Thyroid & Parathyroid

Throat

Heart and Thymus

Heart

Pancreas

Solar Plexis

Vibral Core

Spleen
Adrenals

Navel

Sacral

Ovaries, Testes

Root

DIAGRAM 6. THE SEVEN LAYERS OF THE ENERGY FIELD

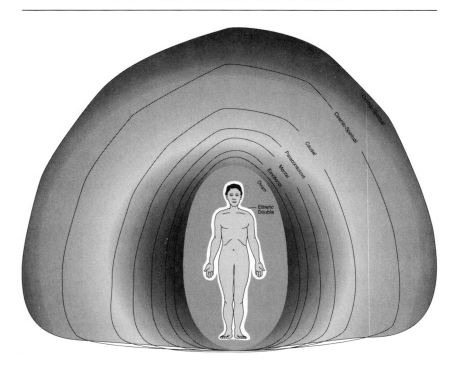

elicit compassion, fear, or emotional pain, all having different effects on the physical body as well as on various layers of the field. Because of this interaction within the field, you and I are able to experience a wide array of information at the same time. We can have an intuitive insight, for example, while, at the same time, we process that information intellectually and experience the joy that such a revelation brings. In this way, insight and joy give us a true sense of our direction.

The seven layers of the energetic body are as follows:

The First Layer: The Etheric Body

Often referred to as the aura or corona, this layer of energy is joined directly to the physical body. Every cell, tissue, and organ is infused with the ovum or etheric body, receiving the life force from this most intimate part of the field. The ovum or etheric body is often depicted in spiritual art. Another image that I often use to describe the etheric body is the waves of heat that come off a road on a hot summer's day. This ovum holds to the physical body and moves around it in much the same way, and is the easiest part of the field to perceive with your touch. All you have to do is hold your hand within a few inches of a person's body and you can perceive its powerful radiant energy. Whenever you kiss a baby, your lips perceive this layer in the field; often, a baby's etheric body is so palpable that it seems to have an almost liquid quality.

The etheric body, which extends between two and six inches from the body, is often referred to as the "etheric double" because all the organs are replicated in the etheric form. Indeed, your entire body is a physical manifestation of the etheric body. Rudolf Steiner, the German philosopher, writer, and psychic who created the Waldorf schools and Steiner medicine, said that all the physical organs are formed out of their exact replicas in the etheric body. The physical heart, for example, is formed out of the etheric heart. Your heart is an exact double, even a product of, the etheric heart in your auric field, which continues to send life force to the physical heart for the lifetime of the organ. All organs of the body are similarly nourished by the etheric body.

People who suffer an amputation frequently experience "phantom limb" phenomenon, which is the feeling that the hand, arm, or leg that's been lost is still present and can even be felt. The missing limb is indeed present in etheric body, and even provides vibrational feedback to the rest of the auric field, giving the faint physical impression that the missing limb exists. (It is this same auric field that is responsible for instructing salamanders to regrow amputated limbs, as cited in chapter 1.)

Humans are not the only living creatures with an etheric body. All plants and animals have the same corona, or golden glow, surrounding and permeating their every cell and fiber. The golden aura captured on Kirlian photography is this etheric body that surrounds the physical form. This is the part of the field that, in humans, salamanders, and all other living things, directs biological functions.

The Second Layer: The Emotional Body

From this level within the field, all our emotions, desires, joys, pains, sufferings, and passions emerge. Emotions are a form of radiant energy without physical form. The astral body and its emotional nature are common among all animals. Indeed, the lower or primitive aspects of our emotional or astral body link us with the animal kingdom. Yet, as Steiner and others have pointed out, only humans have an ego, the "I" that serves to organize all our human characteristics—including emotions—and subject them to higher levels of consciousness. We are required by this higher organizing center, the "I," to integrate our emotions, desires, and passions with the higher levels of our energetic field as well as with the physical body. As we all know, this is one of the most challenging aspects of life.

Emotions affect the body through the nervous, endocrine, muscular, and immune systems. Indeed, as every teenager quickly learns, you cannot experience an emotion without an instantaneous glandular reaction. Each emotion appears in the field as a charged constellation of energy. Depending on its nature and quality, an emotion can emerge within the field like a flower opening to the sun or like an explosion that showers the field with ecstatic or destabilizing energy. If the emotion is joy, the field opens and expands, sending energy radiating throughout the entire electrical and physical body. Immediately, the body experiences a flood of life force; every pore seems to open to the sun. The light within you is expanding, brightening, and opening up to the infinite energy that surrounds you and is channeled through your energetic field. In this moment, you are more alive than ever because you are experiencing love—the love of the universe for you!

That energy, that love, is always present, but changes in the field—caused by beliefs, perceptions, attitudes, and most of all, fear—cause the field to shut down or be injured. But when the moment of joy arrives, you open and experience the light that is all around you. The part of you that opens, specifically, is your heart, or your heart chakra, a whirling flower of energy over your heart. You experience this opening and are filled with the light of love, which in turn floods your field and your physical body.

The healing that can take place in that moment can be miraculous. Depending on how much life force is penetrating your field and physical body, that love can overcome barriers or forms of stagnation that are currently causing physical symptoms and disease. Love, hope, joy, and feelings of well-being—all of these are generators of energy within you that cause the field to expand and open, and result in similar openings within the physical body.

You have experienced the electrical quality of emotion hundreds—even thousands—of times. Think back to your first date, the first time you touched the hand of a boy or girl whom you liked. Something tangible, electric, and altogether wonderful passed between you. Think back to your first kiss. Need I say more?

If, on the other hand, the emotions are negative, the opposite effects take place. Small to moderate degrees of anger or conflict cause the energy within the field to become erratic. It is an irritating energy that causes similar nervous, muscular, and hormonal irritations in the body. Great anger, fear, or hatred wound the field, causing rifts, holes, walls between layers, and great storms of energy within the field that wound even further. When an angry patient arrives, the field feels to me as if it is hard and pushing outward, as if it is pushing people away. Anger also causes the field to have jagged edges, as if it contains knives that are being fired at me. Frenetic, unfocused energy, on the other hand, feels like static electricity, or little spikes of energy.

Changes within the field cause immediate changes within the body. For example, the well-known fight-or-flight reaction occurs when fear stimulates the adrenal glands to secrete adrenaline, which in turn becomes epinephrine, dopamine, and norepinephrine, chemicals that trigger an incredible array of thoughts and physical reactions, among which are increased heart rate, respiration, blood glucose, and muscular activity. Fear depresses immune response, increases heart rate and respiration, and causes heightened muscular activity. If the fear becomes chronic, cholesterol levels are elevated significantly, hormones—especially catecholamines—become heightened and imbalanced, respiration becomes shallow and tense, and muscles remain tense and sometimes go into spasm.

Conversely, positive emotions—such as love, hope, joy, and feelings of well-being and security—all strengthen immune response and make the physical body better able to fight off disease. In this case, the emotions are smooth and flowing. What most people do not realize is that these changes—both positive and negative—originate in the electromagnetic field that surrounds and permeates the body, and that many come from the astral layer of the field.

Emotions, of course, are directly linked to our thoughts, which exist in the next level up within the energetic field. Even unconscious emotions—those emotions whose sources still lie unrecognized in the unconscious—create thoughts of which we are conscious. For example, we may be angry at someone and have long internal monologues with ourselves, yet never realize the deeper reasons for our anger; perhaps we are really angry at ourselves or at someone whom the person in question reminds us of. Indeed, it isn't until the emotions and thinking work in harmony— that is, until our emotions are allowed to emerge and our thoughts are made free to investigate the sources of these emotions—that we understand our emotional world.

All of us have experienced the "energetic" nature of emotion, though we find it hard to use words to describe the experience. For example, remember the last time you were embarrassed. This emotion, which we usually try to keep hidden, nonetheless causes a variety of physical responses: the ears and face redden and become hot, the scalp may twinge a little, and our hands may begin to sweat. We experience palpable changes in respiration and heart rate and, overall, we shrink just a little. Shame, another powerful and negative emotion, often causes the face to become pale and the whole body to physically fold upon itself. Again, we feel ourselves shrinking energetically, as if we were being drained of energy. Guilt is another emotion that we experience as a kind of wound in the heart; at the same time, we experience an inexplicable loss of energy.

The loss of energy that occurs whenever we experience guilt, shame, or unresolved anger is referred to as a *leak* in the field. The boundary that maintains the integrity of the field is torn. Through that tear, energy leaks and is lost. We experience guilt as a loss of integrity, personal protection, and a blurring of our own boundaries. We are no longer capable of protecting ourselves from another person's judgment of us. It's as if we have absorbed another person's assessment and made it our own. The boundary that supports our sense of self is injured, allowing energy to be lost. We experience a palpable diminution of the life force, with all its familiar and well-known weaknesses: fatigue, self-condemnation, loss of direction, and a weakened sense of self. Anyone who has ever witnessed a child being yelled at by a parent or some other adult has seen the child react as if he or she were being hit. The child may visibly recoil in an attempt to escape the verbal and energetic blows.

For the healer, the emotional layer of the field is an essential part of the healing process because most illnesses are very often rooted here. Old traumas and long-standing emotional wounds will appear as areas of dull thick energy, like stones or boulders or scar tissue. Often, I experience blocked energy on the astral plane as having an almost tarlike viscosity. For more recent wounds, you may experience patches of heat or swirling, active, even pulsating energy. (I'll talk more about the specific feelings associated with blockages later in this chapter and farther on in the book.) When the practitioner of therapeutic touch begins to work with these stagnant forms of energy, all the old emotions will begin to emerge at first, though with less intensity. Recipients of healing touch may re-experience events that took place long ago or find themselves thinking of specific people or situations that were forgotten or repressed. Unexpected images can come to mind, even for the practitioner while he or she is performing healing touch. Eventually, if healing touch is continued, the person can be freed of these memories and emotional blocks. The energy can flow smoothly again and healing can occur.

After the healing touch session is complete, a meditation or guided imagery can help the person repattern the emotional plane. This will help close wounds and establish new and healthier habits.

The size of the astral field is determined by the emotions, thoughts, and intentions of the person in question. People deal with emotions in so many different ways, but among the most common is to repress them, which has a shrinking effect on the field. Also, people who are driven by selfish or egotistical motives tend to have smaller, darker energies on the emotional plane. You will feel such a person's energy field as thin, close to the body, and insufficient to hold another person's feelings, hopes, or desires.

Rudolf Steiner offers an insight into the power of love to affect another person's energetic field. He states that whenever you maintain a loving thought for someone, such as when you are conducting a session of healing touch, your thought escapes your own energy field as a "form of light" in the shape of a flower, which enters the person it is intended for in the astral and etheric fields. It then directly strengthens the recipient's field, causing increased vitality, health, and happiness. Simply sending a thought of love has this effect, says Steiner, no matter what the distance between you and the person you wish to help. Thus, energy work is accomplished no matter whether or not you use your hands. Often, your intention alone is sufficiently powerful to change another person's condition.

The efficacy of one person's healing thoughts on others, even those at a considerable distance, has been demonstrated in many scientific studies. Randolph Byrd, M.D., a cardiologist, used a computer to divide randomly a group of 393 coronary patients at San Francisco General Hospital into two groups. Group 1, which was composed of 192 patients, was prayed for each day by a separate group of people who came from a variety of religious faiths. The members of group 2, composed of 201 patients, were not prayed for. No one connected with the study—including the patients, doctors, and nurses—knew who was being prayed for and who wasn't (this is called a double-blind study). As for the people who prayed for group 1, each member of the prayer group received the first name of several patients, along with descriptions of the patients' condition. That meant that each member of group 1 had five to seven people praying for him or her each day for the ten-month study period.

The findings, published in the *Southern Medical Journal* (July 1988), were so startling that they convinced even many hard-core skeptics. After ten months of following both groups, Dr. Byrd and his colleagues found that the patients who were prayed for were five times less likely to need antibiotics (evidence of improved immune function) and three times less likely to develop pulmonary edema (a condition in which fluid fills the lungs as a consequence of inadequate pumping of the heart). None of the members of the prayed-for group required endotracheal intubation, while twelve of the members of group 2 required the procedure; and fewer members of group 1 (the prayed-for group) died.

Other studies that have examined the influence of prayer have shown similar results. Like healing touch, prayer has been shown to affect the health of plants, fungi, and bacteria. Research has demonstrated that people can use prayer effectively to inhibit the growth of fungi, even at a distance of fifteen miles.

The power of prayer demonstrates the importance of your intention while you perform healing touch. In short, send those you work with your love and make your healing touch sessions an act of prayer.

The Third Layer: The Mental Body

The third layer of the field is responsible for intellectual function, the conscious and unconscious mind, and many memories. The conscious mind, of course, refers to those aspects of ourselves and our environment of which we are aware. By unconscious, I mean the personal unconscious—those thoughts, memories, and dreams that have been repressed or forgotten but that exist just beneath the surface of our consciousness. Higher layers of the field relate to the archetypal world, elucidated by Plato, Swiss psychiatrist Carl Jung, and others.

The mental body coordinates physiological activity, including conscious and autonomic functions. It gives you the ability to, say, drive your car many miles while you think of everything but driving and yet arrive safely. Biofeedback and relaxation techniques allow a person to gain access to the mental body and to make unconscious and autonomic functions conscious and accessible to mental control. Dr. Krieger, a nurse researcher at New York University, and others have demonstrated that during a healing touch session, both the practitioner and the client experience an increase in the production of alpha brain waves, the electrical patterns associated with deep states of meditation. Such alpha states are associated with deep relaxation, slowed heart rate and respiration, and expanded perception, including experiences such as extrasensory perception.

Among the important contents of the mental body, especially from a healing perspective, are the unexamined ideas, beliefs, judgments, and concepts that give rise to our behavior and can inhibit our growth. Beliefs, judgments, and attitudes that no longer serve our current state of maturity and development exist as blockages to circulation of energy within the field. They stand rigidly in the way of new information, fresh insights, and larger belief systems. Like boulders in a stream, or knots of tension in muscles, they block circulation of energy within the field, preventing renewal and new understandings of life. Even worse, these unexamined judgments and beliefs feed the conscious mind and cause behaviors that are inappropriate to our current situation. They prevent us from seeing situations in a fresh, new light. Racism, sexism, and various beliefs of superiority or inferiority are all examples of blockages in the mental plane. Beliefs that you are weak, or talentless, or "always wrong" (or "always right") are also unexamined judgments that impede health and development. The insistence "I can't do that" is an unchallenged belief that becomes energetic patterns in the field. These patterns prevent the free circulation of energy within the field, which limits our freedom and our creativity and affects our health.

Many psychological projections reside here in the mental layer. An example is the person who projects the notion that powerful people are ultimately selfish and seek to prevent him or her from rising to higher levels of responsibility and success. People who insist on being victims of every difficult situation, or those who try to manipulate others because they fear being forthright or honest in their relationships, are commonly blocked on the mental plane.

As a practitioner of healing touch, you will release these blockages from your loved ones' or clients' fields. When that occurs, you will frequently hear people start talking about their frustrations, their projections, or their unexamined beliefs from a whole new perspective. Some will have revelations of how they have limited themselves. Others will simply feel tremendous relief or a new sense of personal power and identity.

Once some of the long-standing beliefs are released, far more creativity emerges. Great relief and flexibility are felt. The person feels empowered simply because he or she has been unshackled of beliefs that have prevented him or her from seeing the vast array of possibilities—and opportunities—implicit within situations.

The Fourth Layer: Paraconsciousness

Jack Schwarz, author of *Human Energy Systems* (E. P. Dutton, 1980), calls the fourth level the layer of paraconsciousness. The fourth level contains all the extraordinary abilities, such as intuition, extrasensory perception, image projection, spiritual sight, and clairvoyance. In addition to these abilities is one's capacity for compassion. Rudolf Steiner maintains that one form of intuition is the ability to join with another person, to feel his life condition, to know his pain and suffering. Out of such intuition comes compassion for another human being.

Here, Steiner gives us an insight into how intuition actually works. Intuition is the ability to experience the true connection that exists among all people—and indeed with the Great Spirit or Tao or God. When we experience that unity, we open ourselves to the information that is passing constantly through the cosmos in the form of energy. On a one-to-one level, you can experience connectedness simply by listening and feeling another person's life force. Various forms of Oriental diagnosis teach methods of developing intuition by allowing the client's energy to contact your own field so that you are able to touch your client's energy body with your own field. In this way, you can understand the person in a deep and intimate way. (In chapter 7, I provide methods and exercises for doing this, as well as ways to release any of your client's energies that you might have picked up during your session.)

We practice this awakening to connectedness whenever we perform healing touch. During a session, the practitioner channels universal energy through himself or herself to the client. The practice is based on the fundamental unity among the cosmos, the practitioner, and another human being. By doing this, you are living in the awareness of connectedness, which accelerates the development of your intuition and the fourth level of the field. No ESP or clairvoyance or spiritual sight is possible without a deep connection to the oneness—either with another person or with the cosmos itself.

Your ability to allow your intuition or the fourth layer within your field to guide you depends on how clear and unobstructed the lower layers currently are. By removing obstructions from these levels of our being, the fourth and higher layers can influence the mental, emotional, and etheric bodies. Consequently, our feelings of connectedness and intuition automatically improve.

The Fifth Layer: The Causal Body

Traditional approaches to the field maintain that there is a place within all of us that knows why we are here on this earth. This layer of the field contains the knowledge of your life's purpose, your many talents, and the lessons you wish to learn while you are on this earth. The causal layer contains the knowledge that awakens in you, if only faintly, when you encounter people with whom you have agreed to work out specific tasks, accomplish goals, and overcome barriers before you came to the earth. On this layer of the field, your soul's plan for this lifetime can be found.

Virtually all religions have taught that reincarnation, or the transmigration of souls, is the foundation of life. This is true of Buddhism, Taoism, early Christianity, and the Kabbalistic teachings within Judaism. We live multiple lifetimes on this planet so that we can learn and evolve to higher states of being. In the process, we accumulate knowledge, which we use in each succeeding lifetime to help ourselves and others. In addition, we make mistakes and incur karmic lessons, or debts, that we wish to propitiate. All of this is done so that we can develop greater and greater love, knowledge, and understanding of the meaning of life. Life itself is an inextinguishable resource; it cannot be destroyed, and so continues to manifest in the forms that best replicate the consciousness associated with that particular life form. The physical body perfectly replicates the consciousness of the being within it, and serves to manifest in physical form all the abilities and lessons that each individual soul wishes to experience, express, and learn. All such information about your individual lifetime, as well as all previous lifetimes, is contained within the causal body, the fifth layer of the field.

Traditional spiritual and religious beliefs have taught that expressing your innate abilities, working with those people with whom you have made spiritual and karmic agreements, and learning the lessons that you came into life to learn are the sources of your greatest joy. All of them combine to move the spirit closer to its ultimate goal: complete union and harmony with God, Tao, the

Great Spirit, or whatever name you wish to call the source of all life.

It is important to recognize that you do not have to believe in reincarnation to serve as a practitioner of healing touch. On the contrary, all you have to do is to care deeply about the person you are trying to help and to serve as an instrument for the universal love and energy that will pass through you to the person you wish to help. There need be no greater understanding or conceptualization than that.

The Sixth and Seventh Layers: The Cosmic and Spiritual Consciousness

The sixth and seventh levels of our beings represent our most intimate links with what each of us recognizes as God, the Great Spirit, or the universal creative force. Obviously, all aspects of the field and the physical body are directly linked to the divine universe, but the sixth and seventh layers actually *know* it and are consciously in direct contact with it. Consequently, these layers offer us the experience of direct union with God. They sometimes are able to resonate within our consciousness when we are deep in prayer and meditation. It is this level of our beings that is being experienced when a person is said to have a momentary enlightenment.

Not much is known about these levels of the field, simply because they are so rarefied and lofty that very few people consciously experience them and then write about their experiences. What we do know is that the sixth and seventh layers of the field possess a tremendous force of energy that, when it grounds in the body, can create a host of psychological disorders if the person is not prepared for such an experience, or if the body itself is not in sufficient health.

The Dead Sea Scrolls lend credence to this theory and point to the fact that the early Hebrews were well aware of the power of these upper levels of the field. The scrolls were produced by a sect of Jews called the Essenes, who ventured out into the desert, to a place called Qumran, where they prepared for the coming of the Messiah. One of the ways they prepared was to observe strict dietary

laws that conformed to their traditions. But some scholars maintain that the Essenes also were purifying themselves with the intention of creating a familial line of great constitutional strength; such
a family would eventually produce a son whose physical powers
were sufficient to hold the energies of the sixth and seventh layers of
the field.

It is well known that the Essenes placed great emphasis on the
physical constitution of every member of their sect. They believed
that a person's physiognomy, or physical characteristics, could be
read to discover the spiritual development of that person. The Messiah was to possess the purest physiognomy, reflecting both his
great constitutional strength and his spiritual inheritance. Rudolf
Steiner also maintained the same belief, writing that the Hebrews'
strict dietary and lifestyle laws enabled them to produce a body that
was capable of carrying the sixth and seventh layers of the field, or
the Christ spirit.

Layers Interact with Each Other

In order to better understand the topography of the field, I've described the layers individually, but this separation does not reveal
how the layers interact, influence each other, and function as one.
While each layer of the field has its own unique function, strengths,
weaknesses, talents, and abilities, it must work in coordination with
the entire field in order for us to express our talents and abilities and
learn about life. The person who has a gift for music is using his or
her entire field while playing an instrument, clearly beginning with
the physical body and including the first layer (the etheric body, to
coordinate the voice or the muscles used to perform on an instrument), the second (placing the depth of feeling in the music), the
third (providing the intellectual ability needed to learn the music
and express it with nuance and precision); the fourth (experiencing
music's power to unify people in harmony and sound), and the fifth
(music is part of a particular person's life plan and expressing that

plan provides the greatest of joys). If the musician truly reaches great heights, he or she has the potential to express the divine sound—or, as Pythagoras called it, the "music of the spheres." All the layers of the field must work in harmony if the person is to truly express his or her gifts.

The Central Tube: The Channel of Spirit in You

After several years as a practitioner of healing touch, I realized that in addition to the standard layers, there is another characteristic of the field, which I call the central tube (see diagram 7). This tube, or channel of energy, runs down the center of the physical body itself. It originates at the very top of the head, where the spiritual life force enters the body, and runs down the center of the body through the neck, down the center of the digestive system, to the very base of the sex organs, where the energy can pass out of the body and where the earth's energy can enter into it. Along the tube are found the seven wheels of energy, or chakras, each of which fan out and en-rich the organs in that particular area of the body. This is a kind of spiritual channel running from top to bottom.

Energy runs like a river through this tube. Blockages within the tube often appear as eddies of energy and can prevent energy from flowing cleanly through this essential channel. The most fre-quent problem I have found among those with blockages in the tube are emotional conflicts, specifically the problem of integrating concepts of the head with the emotions and instincts of the heart and lower organs. As we will see in chapter 5, specific aspects of consciousness are located within the seven chakras that are located along the tube. The chakras represent (among other things) specific aspects of our human psychology. People who have great difficulty integrating the head, the heart, and the sexual-survival instincts often have blockages in the tube. Life force that would otherwise flow smoothly among these three centers is blocked, causing the mind to behave as if it were separated from the emotional and

DIAGRAM 7. THE CENTRAL TUBE

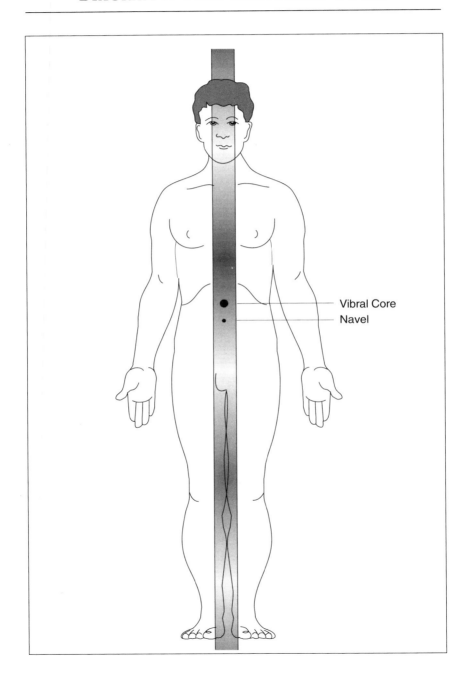

Vibral Core
Navel

sexual-survival centers. Such a person is continually in conflict over what he or she thinks versus what he or she feels or secretly wants, or is instinctually drawn to.

By eliminating these blockages, we can help the person integrate the higher and lower centers of the psyche and restore the brightness and clarity of the mind.

In the center of the body, just below the solar plexus and just above the umbilicus, is the center of being, known as the *vibral core*. Here, spirit and matter join and become one. This is where the vital healing energy flows from the practitioner to the client. The energy originates from the creator of the universe but flows to the practitioner, who sends it forth from the vibral core. Thus, healing energy flows from the universal source to the practitioner's vibral core, then to the practitioner's hands, and then to the client's vibral core. Twylah Nitsch maintained that the vibral core is where the father spirit (energy) and the mother earth (matter) mingle to create our essential humanness. When the healer and client work together, their energetic bodies mingle and become one. That oneness is established between their vibral cores. This vibrational union harmonizes the two people and directs both of them in the healing process.

The Body Is the Product *of the Field*

Most of us believe that health and illness reside entirely in the physical body. Indeed, all of Western medicine is based on this fundamental belief. Hence, the principal forms of treatment in the modern armamentarium are drugs, surgery, and radiation—all directed exclusively at the physical body. Ancient and traditional healers stand this belief on its head. Our ancestors taught that the physical body is the *creation* of the energetic field, which itself is part of the larger spiritual world. In the same way, health and most forms of illness begin in the energy field and ultimately manifest in the physical body. There are exceptions to this, such as when we are exposed to a toxic chemical or a pathogen in the environment. But even these examples are not so clear-cut as you may believe. Your ability to ward off a chemical or pathogen depends to a great extent on the strength of the energetic body, which supports your immune system and organs of elimination. When these systems and organs are functioning optimally—thanks in part to a powerful life force— you are able to avoid many of the toxic side effects of modern life. This, of course, is demonstrated every day, as some people effectively ward off the toxic effects of their environments while others do not.

In the vast majority of cases, the physical manifestation of disease is the last stop in a process that began in the energetic field. Whenever a blockage manifests in the field, life energy is prevented from flowing optimally to the body or to a specific place within the body. When numerous blockages manifest, the flow of life force is diminished. As I have said, without life force the body cannot survive. Without optimal life force, the body cannot sustain health.

There are many reasons why blockages or other types of injuries to the field can manifest. Psychological and/or physical trauma commonly injure the field. Many such energetic wounds can be healed, however, unless a belief system sets in that supports the continued existence of the wound. The most damaging belief, of course, is fear. All of us have beliefs that support our fears. We believe that certain types of people or situations are particularly threatening. Or we believe that we are inadequate to handle certain conditions in life. Such beliefs change our behavior and alter the energetic field that supports our lives. They cause us to develop patterns of energy within the field. These patterns eventually manifest as blockages, or tears, or even leaks—wounds that prevent us from experiencing our own boundaries and allow our life energy to drain from the field (I'll discuss patterns of energy, blockages, and leaks in greater detail in chapter 7). In any case, strong beliefs—and especially fear—are usually at the bottom of all illness. For example, a certain person works too hard because he believes that unless he works seven days a week he'll fail to please his superiors; perhaps he believes he'll be fired or he'll be broke. In the end, his fears and his excessive work manifest as imbalances in the field that prevent life energy from flowing to the body, which in turn contributes to illness. Someone else is afraid to experiment with life, fearing that any deviation from the "tried and true" will lead to mistakes or "sin" or retribution. Thus, she never comes to know her true nature, desires, and abilities. Ultimately, such a rigid approach to life contributes to frustration, anger, and disease.

Yet, sickness should never be seen as a punishment for mistakes or imbalances. All of us become sick and all of us will die and none of the illnesses that we encounter is regarded by traditional healers as "punishment" for anything you or I might have done. We may speculate as to why one person became ill, or why another died in this or that way, but such speculation is just that: It is a guess, a hunch based on partial information, which leads inevitably to inaccurate conclusions. As Paul wrote so eloquently in 1 Corinthians (13:12): "For now we see through a glass darkly; but then face to face: now I know in part, but then shall I know even as also I am known." Remembering that we know only in part is a good exercise in humility, especially for a healer. Practitioners of healing touch are not so interested in knowing why people become ill as much as we are in addressing the blockages in the energy field.

Ultimately, sickness is a mystery that each of us must confront and derive our own conclusions and enlightenment from. Sickness and health hold their own unique gifts that we must discover for ourselves. On the higher spiritual levels, illness is another way to develop greater understanding of life and compassion for ourselves and others.

The Real You Behind Your Eyes

Susan, a fifty-year-old married woman with two children, came to me in 1986, overweight and suffering from edema, yeast infection, allergies, swollen hands and feet, and a swollen, distended stomach. She had skin rashes, was regularly fatigued, and was often irritable and depressed. She also suffered from regular insomnia. Susan had followed numerous weight-loss programs with no lasting effect. She kept losing and regaining the same twenty-five pounds. As for the skin rashes, she applied topical ointments that provided temporary relief but no lasting cure.

When Susan first came to me, I placed her on a diet that would eliminate many of the foods to which she had intolerances or sensitivities. But her previous experience with diets had made her resistant to yet another regimen. I usually wait until after the diet and nutritional therapies have strengthened the underlying organs before I begin a program of healing touch, but in Susan's case I decided to start early in our treatment program.

"After the first couple of energetic treatments, I started to feel better," Susan said. "The first thing I noticed was that I slept better and I was generally more relaxed. What was surprising was that I also began to feel better about myself. I started to have a better sense of my own power. I didn't know why I had these benefits. All I knew was that I felt better. And I was certain my improvement had to do with the therapeutic touch."

Shortly after Susan began seeing me, her husband suffered a heart attack. This occurred right before Christmas, and the stress of that event hit her family like a tidal wave. "After my husband had the heart attack, he had a triple bypass operation. Naturally, we were all upset. I went to Deby a lot then to help me relax and get me through the crisis. It was amazing how helpful this practice was to me. I really felt something good happening whenever I had a session. I felt lighter, stronger, more relaxed. I was able to maintain a consistent positive attitude through some pretty rough times." It wasn't just her attitude that was improving. All her physical symptoms, including the edema, the yeast infection, and the rashes, were disappearing.

Because Susan felt she was benefiting so much from the practice, she had me perform healing touch on her whole family, including her husband, Don. "Deby did therapeutic touch on him right up to the time he went in for the operation," recalled Susan. "It made his outlook brighter, more positive. It built him up, made him stronger before he went in for the surgery. After the surgery, Deby did therapeutic touch on my husband's leg where the surgeons removed the vein that would be used for his bypass graphs. Normally, the leg would become swollen and painful, but after therapeutic touch, he healed quickly and had no swelling or pain."

After several weeks of healing touch, Susan had no trouble following a healthy diet, which relieved her food intolerances and caused her to lose weight. Her weight fell to 125 pounds, which on her five-foot, five-inch frame was ideal. All the bloating left her, as did her yeast infections and the extended bouts of irritability and depression. Today, Susan has turned her experience with therapeutic touch into a new vocation. She continues to study this powerful healing tool and is practicing therapeutic touch at a local chiropractor's office two days a week. "One of the main benefits I received from healing touch was a big change in self-esteem. The longer I do this practice, the stronger I feel. I just feel better about myself. I used to be a housewife and a mother, and when my kids got bigger, I started to feel that there was nothing left for me to do. This practice gave me a bigger view of myself and I realized that I could help people with it."

Like many people who begin practicing therapeutic touch, Susan soon discovered that she could actually experience the energy field that surrounds all of us. "When I'm working on someone's foot, let's say, I can feel the energy coming off the person's foot. Sometimes it feels like I'm lifting the energy off and away from the foot.

"It takes a certain leap of faith to begin using this practice, but as soon as you commit to doing it, your confidence grows because you can see and feel the very tangible results."

EXERCISES

Here's an exercise that you can perform during early evening—it's best at twilight—that will help you see the auric field around your hands. Turn off all artificial lighting and lie on your back on the floor. Raise your hands a foot or so above your head and join your fingers in a relaxed weave. Now, very gradually pull your hands apart so that your fingers gently and slowly separate as your hands move in opposite directions. As your hands slowly separate, relax your focus gaze between your hands so that you are looking at the space between your hands and at the ceiling of your room. Slightly blur your vision (as I explained in a previous section). You will likely see streams of soft light between your hands and fingers. The light will appear much like vapors that surround your hands and dance between your fingers.

As discussed earlier in the chapter, ask a friend or partner to sit in a well-lighted room against a pale or white wall. But instead of just concentrating on the field, carry on a conversation with the person. While you are looking at him or her, slightly blur your vision while you gaze at the light around his or her head and shoulders. Note the wispy quality of the light. It seems to move in flame-like motifs around the person's head. Also note whether the quality of the wisps change as you converse.

Often, we have trouble experiencing energy because we identify exclusively with the body. Here's a meditation that can help you see yourself as more than your body, more than your emotions, and more than your intellect.

MEDITATIVE ALIGNMENT EXERCISE
(Attunement)

1. Sit in a chair or on a pillow on the floor with your back straight and your body comfortable and relaxed. Breathe deeply and establish a deep rhythmic pattern of breathing (Breathe in a

regular pattern for approximately one to three minutes). Slowly draw your attention away from your environment and focus on the in and out movement of your breath. Let go of all your thoughts.

2. Bring your attention into your physical body. Take some time to notice where you are holding your tension. Breathe deeply and evenly into the tension and visualize the tension stretching out and becoming relaxed. See the area of tension becoming smooth and supple. Then say to yourself, I have a physical body and I am more than my physical body.

3. Now bring your attention into the emotional body. Take some time to become aware of your feelings. Take a personal inventory of what is going on within you. Notice your feelings; do not judge them or try to change them. Then breathe into those feelings and visualize yourself letting go of them; see them fade from your consciousness and say to yourself, I have an emotional body and I am more than my emotional body.

4. Move your attention into your mental body. Take an inventory of your thoughts. Notice the amount of activity going on in your mind. Breathe deeply and slowly and quiet the mind. Release all thoughts and arrive at a place of stillness. Take a moment to experience the stillness, then say to yourself, I have a mental body and I am more than my mental body.

5. Focus your attention at the top of your head and say to yourself, I am a center of pure creative awareness and higher spiritual will. Allow yourself to fully experience that statement. Feel its power and the grace that flows to you from this recognition.

6. See yourself as an energetic field, a living energy, that has consciousness and love. That love flows to you from an infinite source; it can never be extinguished. You can send that energy to others to help them in endless ways, including helping them to heal. Say to yourself, I am in the flow of power. I am a channel of power and that power is love.

EXERCISE
Feeling the Field

1. Stand face-to-face with your partner at a little more than an arm's distance from each other.
2. Extend your arm directly out from your side, toward your partner's shoulder, but still well back from your partner. Keep your elbow bent slightly.
3. Cup your hand loosely and gradually bring your hand toward your partner's shoulder.
4. As your hand approaches your partner's shoulder, move your hand slowly through his or her field, slightly raising and lowering your hand a few inches, so that you can delineate the various layers and densities of the field. Feel the field with your hand. Note the changes in thickness, temperature or patterns as your hand perceives as it moves through the field.

5

❀

The Chakras: Spheres of Energy, Consciousness, and Life

I f you take your hand and place it gently over your heart, allowing your fingertips to touch your shirt ever so lightly, and then slowly rotate your hand in a clockwise direction, as if the clock face was sitting on your chest with the numbers facing outward, you will feel comforted. If you continue to rotate your hand in that gentle, circular way, you will feel your body relax and get warmer. Gradually, you will likely experience a strange communion with this part of your body, as if your heart area were smiling at you in gratitude. Breathe deeply and allow that smile to warm your entire inner being. Many people who do this exercise eventually start to cry. They cry because they feel comforted, relieved, and overwhelmed with gratitude, as if they were being welcomed into a realm in which all their burdens could be put down, a realm in which they were embraced by an unconditional love. (Try doing this exercise by reversing the motion of your hand over your heart. Note the difference in the feeling.)

When you do this exercise, you are applying healing touch to your heart chakra, the sphere of energy that governs your heart and thymus gland and a specific realm of your consciousness. In doing this exercise, you get a small glimpse of the unity of your body, mind, and spirit. You also recognize that you have the power to gain access to your spirit and influence it in healing ways. As you progress through this book, you will learn many other techniques for healing your body, mind, and spirit through simple yet powerful methods of healing touch.

For the practitioner of healing touch, a knowledge of the chakras is an indispensable diagnostic tool. The chakras also are the sites at which great healing can occur. We can understand people according to their chakra imbalances, but more important, we can do so much for them by working with the chakras through healing touch. Finally, the chakras demonstrate the importance of your intention, for your intention reveals the chakra from which you are expressing yourself. As we have seen, your actions will have very different effects on the recipient, depending on the chakra by which you are motivated. If you, as a healer, are acting from your heart chakra, you are channeling the energy that can utilize all your other abilities—the furthest reaches of your mind and your deepest, most practical wisdom about survival. Ultimately, the chakras prove what the poets have always taught: that the greatest integrating and unifying force in life is love.

The information I provide here on the chakras comes from my own experiences and from numerous other investigators in this field, especially from Swiss psychologist Carl Jung, spiritual teacher Ram Dass, and numerous experts on Sanskrit, Ayurvedic healing, and traditional Eastern Indian spirituality.

Chakras: Where the Body, Mind, and Spirit Are One

Nothing illustrates the unity of body, mind, and spirit better than the chakras. *Chakra* is a Sanskrit word meaning "wheels" or "circles of movement." The chakras are spirals of concentrated life force—vortices of energy, as they are referred to by some. They are arrayed in a straight line on the front of your body, starting at the very base of your spine (at the perineum) and extending to the top of your head. The seven primary chakras are located as follows: The first is found at the base of the spine; the second a few inches below the navel; the third at the solar plexus; the fourth over the heart; the fifth over the throat, at the larynx; the sixth between the eyebrows; the seventh just above the crown of the head. Each of the seven primary chakras radiates downward into your physical body and outward through the seven layers of your energy field. Each chakra is shaped like a cone or a spiral, with the pointy end entering the body and the ever-widening end spiraling outward into your energy field.

In addition to these primary chakras, you also possess smaller, secondary chakras on the palms of your hands, the backs of your knees, and the soles of your feet near the arches. There are even smaller tertiary chakras located on your fingertips and on the toe tips. You use the second and third chakras in your hands to direct energy during healing touch, and you use the second and third chakras in your feet to ground yourself while performing the practice.

As you will notice shortly, the function of each of the seven primary chakras corresponds roughly to the seven layers of the field, so that the activities of the first layer of the field (the etheric layer) correspond to the first chakra; the second layer of the field corresponds to the second chakra; the third layer with the third chakra, and so on.

One of the functions of the chakras is to act as funnels for the life force. Each of us is continually bathed in an unlimited flow of electromagnetic energy, or the life force that sustains our lives. We breathe in the life force, receive it through the five senses, channel it through the field, and draw it into us through the seven chakras.

The chakras can be understood on several levels. On the gross physical level, they channel life force to particular organs and en-docrine glands. Indeed, when you look at the illustration of the chakras (see diagram 8), you'll notice that they correspond with the most active parts of the body—the brain, eyes, speech center, heart,

DIAGRAM 8. THE CHAKRA LOCATIONS

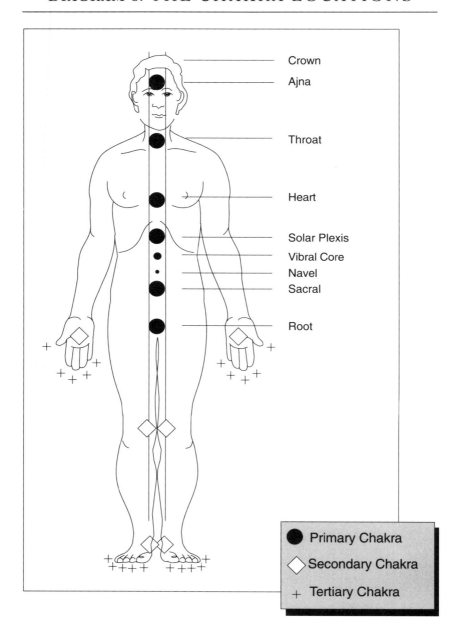

Crown
Ajna
Throat
Heart
Solar Plexis
Vibral Core
Navel
Sacral
Root

● Primary Chakra
◇ Secondary Chakra
+ Tertiary Chakra

middle organs, digestion, endocrine glands, and sex organs. These areas, obviously, require a great deal of energy. But we can say the reverse as well: that in their enormous activity, these same areas of the body generate the most energy. These are the parts of the body that give rise to thoughts and ideas that, in turn, shape our world; they recall memories that sustain relationships; they drink up light and color; they masticate and digest food; they pump and cleanse the blood; they procreate and sustain life. In short, they are the basis upon which we experience life—and even participate in its creation. Little wonder, therefore, that ancient sages correlated these parts of the body with special vortices of energy that would sustain such important functions.

But there is much more to these chakras than the purely physical. These seven zones also carry with them profound emotional and psychological associations, of which virtually all of us already are aware. For example, on some visceral and well-established level of our knowing, each of us regards the heart as the center of the emotions. We say about some people "He has a lot of heart" or "She has the heart of a lion" or "He's a heartless soul." To express our deepest love, we might say "I give you my heart." Other chakra areas possess their own unique character and associations: the brain, for example, is regarded as the realm of intelligence, objective thought, and reason, even though the brain is directly linked to virtually every physical, psychological, and emotional aspect of our humanity. When trying to assess a person's character, we search his eyes for insight into his soul. We look at a person's bloated and enlarged stomach and on some intuitive level wonder if he's not perhaps a slave to his appetites. Sigmund Freud became a giant by articulating just some of the associations we have about sex and our sex organs. (Even Freud did not elucidate all that we know and believe about sex.) And as we all know, our associations with each of these areas go beyond the physical, energetic, and psychological. They bring us into the realm of spirit.

In fact, each chakra is the site of a specific consciousness, a realm that offers its own specific set of values. None of us has integrated all seven levels of consciousness into our being. You may be awake and motivated by two, three, or even more chakras, but it is the very rare being who is awake and functioning at all seven levels of consciousness.

Which brings me to an essential point. The one, two, or three chakras that might be most influential in your life dictate your physical and emotional needs, your values, and your spiritual awareness. The world today is being governed by the first three chakras. As a species, we are now struggling collectively to break into the fourth chakra and allow its values and consciousness to direct our lives and permeate our world.

The chakras, therefore, represent a kind of ladder of personal, psychological, and spiritual evolution. Each of us is attempting to move into the next higher chakra above the ones that now direct our worldview. Hence, the values and awareness implicit in the chakra that we are striving for represent our next step in growth and development. The chakras describe in ascending order how we proceed from the very rudimentary consciousness to an ever-enlarging viewpoint on life and ourselves.

As we will see, moving up the chakra ladder inevitably presents the greatest challenges life has to offer. Very often, one or more of the chakras are blocked or partially closed. That means that we are not being influenced sufficiently by the corresponding values and understanding that reside within that chakra. It will also mean that the life force will be diminished in that part of the body. Yet, even when one or another chakra is closed, it still functions in some limited capacity. It is still providing nourishing life force to its corresponding part of the body. If the chakra did not function on some level, we would soon be dead. Still, when a chakra is operating in a weakened state, the part of the body to which it corresponds is also weakened. In addition, the values and consciousness represented by that chakra do not influence us as strongly, if at all. Gradually, the related organs and glands may atrophy and eventually manifest some kind of symptom or disease. Also, our lack of understanding for the part of life represented by that chakra inevitably brings us into conflict and crisis.

By understanding a person's problems, and at which of the seven chakras he might be fixed, the practitioner of healing touch can understand why certain physical and psychological problems manifest. The practitioner will also know which of the seven chakras the client is struggling to integrate into consciousness, and therefore where the practitioner must concentrate his or her work.

As a practitioner of healing touch, you are doing more than working on physical health. You are working with the body, mind, and spirit, and in so doing, you are treating the underlying reasons we become sick in the first place.

Let's turn now to an examination of the seven chakras individually and collectively to better understand their role in our lives and in the practice of healing touch.

The First Chakra: The Root of Being

Referred to in Sanskrit as the *Muladhara,* or the root chakra, the first wheel of energy is located at the very base of the spine and encompasses the perineum. It provides life force to the adrenal glands, which in turn produce adrenaline for instinctual and instantaneous responses to exciting events or perceived threats. This chakra provides life force to the large intestine, rectum, bones, legs, and feet. It is also responsible for maintaining the nervous and circulatory systems. Physical symptoms that emerge when this chakra is congested, blocked, or closed include constipation, hemorrhoids, obesity, sciatica pain, arthritis, knee trouble, anorexia nervosa, and suicide.

The first chakra is responsible for grounding your life in physical existence. It is your instinctual center, your energetic and spiritual root on the earth, the source of your survival instinct. It keeps you rooted in the present moment and aware of possible threats to your existence. Any reaction related to your survival, including the flight-or-fight instinct, emanates from this center of consciousness. Conversely, any self-induced threat to existence, such as anorexia or an attempted suicide, is a breach of the values and consciousness inherent in this chakra.

Kundalini yoga and Ayurvedic medicine teach that the first chakra is responsible for maintaining our sense of smell. The human olfactory sense is quite developed, though we usually don't think of ourselves as good smellers. In fact, we can identify an object after smelling just nine molecules of the particular substance, which means that we can often perceive something at a considerable distance from our nose.

Our faculty of smell was developed as a means of self-protection. Smell allows us to perceive whether or not something is poisonous or somehow dangerous without having to eat it, for example, or to get too close to the object in question. (Cautious children and adults invariably place unknown or foreign foods under their noses before they dare taste something that they might find revolting or dangerous.) This relates directly to the chakra's overall responsibility for survival.

There is an enormous body of literature and mythology surrounding the seven chakras, and much attention has been paid to the first chakra. Out of this mythology has come our understanding of the consciousness and values that lie within this wheel of energy.

To begin with, this chakra is associated with the earth and the color red. It is characterized by cohesiveness, inertia, and a certain amount of stagnation. The first chakra makes us cautious, which is a kind of inertia. It encourages us to remain focused on our number-one priority, which is survival. And it prevents us from allowing too many contradictory thoughts and bits of information to enter our consciousness, which would break down the mind into fragments. This is part of its character of cohesiveness.

The earth chakra is symbolized by a giant black elephant that is holding up the world. In his writings about the first chakra, Carl Jung stated that the elephant, placed as it is at the very root of existence, symbolizes the enormous power and strength that supports human consciousness. The elephant symbolizes how strong is our foundation. Without such a foundation, we would not have the confidence and spiritual strength to develop awareness of ourselves and of the world around us. Yet, because the foundation is so strong, said Jung, humanity has the security and even the yearning to expand its awareness and thus to grow.

Yet, the first chakra mitigates our curiosity and growth by making us constantly aware of our need to survive. The first chakra is Darwinian in its nature. Survival of the fittest is its law, which means its impulse is to see situations and people in competitive terms. Hence, this chakra's energy is one of separateness and individuality. People who are dominated by the first chakra live in constant fear for their lives. They may affect a secure manner, but they evaluate all information and all people on the basis of whether or not they are a threat to life, livelihood, and possessions.

Hence, the first chakra is the realm of your separateness from other living beings and, indeed, your separateness in the universe itself. From this chakra, we experience our aloneness.

The Second Chakra: Sex, Passion, and the Water World

Referred to in Sanskrit as *Svadhisthana,* or the center, the second chakra is located a few inches below the navel at the region of the first lumbar vertebra. It provides life force to the ovaries in a woman, to the testes in a man, and to their related hormones. The chakra channels life force to the male and female genitals, kidneys, bladder, and circulatory system. It also serves a developing fetus with life energy.

This chakra is also responsible for governing the sense of taste and the deep vital breath. According to Chinese medicine, the kidneys make the deep breath possible. When the kidneys are strong and vital, they draw the breath deep into the bottom of the lungs.

When the kidneys are weak, the breath is shallow and the person is timid, nervous, and fearful.

Blockages, closure, or any impairment of the second chakra can result in illnesses related to the kidneys, bladder, sex organs, and the lower back. All emotional and psychological issues related to sex emanate from the second chakra, including how one expresses oneself as a male or female.

The chakra's main biological functions are the maintenance of the sex organs, the sex drive, the desire for physical pleasure, and all the social issues associated with entering into a sexual relationship. One cannot truly experience sex alone, and consequently the second chakra leads us from the individualized state articulated by the first chakra into the search for a mate and the realm of social interaction.

The second chakra is regarded as the center of the personality. In Japan, it is known as *hara,* or the center of gravity. Hara is the foundation upon which one maintains physical, emotional, psychological, and spiritual equilibrium. It is the center of power and vitality, say the Japanese. From hara, one maintains balance—no matter what the circumstances—and therefore controls himself and his environment without lifting a finger. All the martial arts—whether they emerged from Japan, China, or Korea—are based on strengthening and sustaining one's center of gravity, or the second chakra.

The second chakra is associated with the color orange and the water element. It is symbolized by the leviathan, or sea serpent. What the elephant is to the earth, so the leviathan is to the oceans. It is the embodiment of the enormous power and mystery that lies beneath the intimidating surface of the seas. Water, of course, connotes fertility, the womb, and the bodily fluids that carry sperm and egg. It symbolizes the unconscious mind and its infinite mysteries that lie beneath its waves. Consistent with this image is the fact that water and the serpent represent a primitive stage in the evolution of life on the planet, when living creatures inhabited the oceans exclusively. In writing about this chakra in his book *Alchemical Stud-*

ies (Princeton University Press, 1967), Carl Jung wrote: "We are reminded of the 'days of Creation,' of the time when consciousness arose, when the primordial unity of being was barely disturbed by the twilight of reflection, and man swam like a fish in the ocean of the unconscious."

The ocean is the mother of life on the planet, the womb from which we all emerged. Indeed, while each of us was in our mother's womb, we underwent a reptilian stage that replicated our earlier journey from the ocean waters to land.

Mythologically, the serpent symbolizes consciousness and choices. It was the serpent who introduced Eve to the "tree of the knowledge of good and evil" and encouraged her to eat its fruit. Once she and Adam had eaten the proverbial apple, their eyes were opened and they became conscious of their surroundings and their nakedness. In other words, they were suddenly more aware of themselves and their environment than they had been before. They understood good and evil, though they might well have been too immature at the time to do much with that knowledge. Nevertheless, mythology has consistently revealed the serpent as the symbol of wisdom and consciousness. In considering the second chakra, Jung wrote that the serpent "is the power that forces you into consciousness and that sustains you in the conscious world."

The serpent, of course, is a sexual image, and it symbolizes the central function of the second chakra: sex, sexual gratification, and reproduction. But as we all know, sex is never so uncomplicated as to be restricted exclusively to a simple act. Sex, as Jung says, leads us inevitably into greater awareness of ourselves and of others because it leads us into the complex and often contradictory world of relationships between the sexes. Such contradictions, of course, force us to stretch our understanding and increase our awareness of ourselves and others.

According to Native American and ancient Greek mythology, the serpent also symbolizes transformation, healing, and rebirth. The Native Americans saw the snake's talent for shedding its skin as a transformative process by which a living thing is reborn. Greek mythology depicts Hermes as carrying the caduceus, which is the winged sword wrapped by two intertwining snakes. The image of the caduceus, long regarded as the symbol of wisdom and healing, was later adopted by the medical profession.

The second chakra is a step upward along the evolutionary ladder because it reveals that the human has taken care of his survival and can now consider sexual relationships and even procreation. Such relationships don't happen until after we feel sufficiently secure in our environment to go out and make friends. Or, as Ram Dass writes in *The Only Dance There Is* (Anchor Books, 1974): "See, you've got your security under control and now you start to go into sensual pleasure and sexual desires and reproduction. You can't be busy reproducing if you're protecting your life, but the minute your life's protected a little bit, then you can concern yourself with the next matter, which is reproducing the species." Ram Dass points out that Sigmund Freud is the master spokesman for the second chakra.

Thus, the second chakra is concerned primarily with sex and the behaviors related to having sex or entering into a relationship in which you can have sex.

The Relationship Between the First and Second Chakras

Let's pause a minute and reflect on the first two chakras and how their value systems affect our lives in very different ways. Since it is concerned with the preservation of life and of separateness, the first chakra makes us aware of the dangers of life and our own aloneness. That aloneness makes us aware of our incompleteness and our need for companionship, love, and sex, which means it drives us to the second chakra. In its truest form, the pursuit of the opposite sex is based on love.

Sexual love is the union of opposites, man and woman, yang and yin, heaven and earth. In all traditional spiritual and religious practices—but especially those of the East—human sexual experience is regarded as the union of divine opposites. It is seen as the way for humans to glimpse the harmony and order that occurs when two halves of the cosmic puzzle come together in love. In the ancient Hebrew and early Christian traditions, the fact that sex was so pleasurable was considered proof that God is good. In yoga and Tantric traditions, sex permits two people to reenact, and thus participate in, the coming together of archetypes, cosmic deities. It is one way humans can participate in the divine drama, which is essential in the creation of life.

On the most basic and fundamental level, however, sex overcomes separateness. If it is expressed with love, it overcomes loneliness, isolation, and independence as well. In sexual love, we recognize the interdependent nature of life. Thus, if we are to enjoy sexual love, the consciousness of the second chakra must overcome the consciousness of separation, which is to say, it must overcome the consciousness of the first.

The Third Chakra: Power, Mastery, and the Ego

The Sanskrit word for the third chakra is *Manipura*, or "gem center." It is located at the solar plexus, or the region of the eighth thoracic vertebra. The third chakra is responsible for providing life force to the pancreas. It also funnels electromagnetic energy to the liver, gall bladder, spleen, and stomach.

The pancreas, of course, is responsible for creating insulin, which makes blood sugar available to cells as fuel. The third chakra is therefore associated with metabolism and the basic work of the cells of the body. Metabolism is, in fact, a tiny fire inside the cells. Like tiny factories, the cells burn glucose (or blood sugar) so that they can do their work. Hence, the third chakra has traditionally been associated with fire—or, in Ayurvedic medicine, with the fire element.

Blockages or closure of the third chakra result in digestive disorders, ulcers, diabetes, hypoglycemia, liver problems, and disorders related to the metabolism of blood sugar and fat.

Psychologically and spiritually, the third chakra is all about your personal power and self-mastery. Personal power and mastery are developed because you are required to refine yourself and mature. Hence, you are required to embrace the third chakra. Ram Dass states that the supreme spokesman for the third chakra is Alfred Adler, the Austrian psychologist whose philosophy centered around power as the central theme in relationships.

In addition to fire, the third chakra is also associated with the mind and the color yellow. This chakra is represented by the ram, which is the symbol for the zodiac sign of Aries, known for its strong will, courage, outgoing nature, leadership, and, indeed, its stubbornness. Aries is often joined with Mars, the planet of fiery passions, war, impetuousness, emotion, assertiveness, violence, courage, and activity. This chakra provides you with the capacity to assert yourself and your wishes and the power to fulfill what you set out to accomplish.

Hence, the atmosphere of the third chakra is all about passion, raw power, and an untamed mind.

Yet, the chakra is symbolized by the ram. Carl Jung points out that the ram is a sacrificial animal. This symbol reveals how personal mastery and power are actually achieved: by sacrificing the wild passions that are inherent in this stage of consciousness so that discipline, order, and concentration can prevail. The raw and naked power of the third chakra can make one behave like a wild goat: unruly, undisciplined, egotistical, and selfish. Life demands, in fact, that these characteristics be brought under control. Inevitably, we are thwarted in our wishes and are required to refine our self-expression and skills if we are to advance along our path.

When we are deeply frustrated, we often feel physical pressure or unease in the solar plexus. The third chakra is alerting us to the fact that our passions are unruly and that our personal power is being blocked or frustrated, perhaps by our own beliefs, perhaps by circumstances in the environment, or perhaps by both. There are two courses that can be chosen at this point. Either we can self-reflect, be creative, and apply a new approach to the situation, or we can push harder and force our will. This can lead to more frustration, anger, and resentment, which is why the third chakra is often associated with violence.

The Relationship Among the First, Second, and Third Chakras

Clearly, a progression of consciousness can be seen from the first, second, and third chakras. Having confronted our separation and aloneness, we are driven to sexual relationships, which joins us with at least one other human being and thus leads us beyond ourselves and our own priorities. The third chakra leads us back to ourselves, this time focusing on self-improvement and self-empowerment.

In a sense, the third chakra is an evolved first chakra: Both the first and third chakras are interested in you, the individual. The first chakra is more concerned with your survival, while the third is more concerned with the power needed to fulfill your desires. Yet, there has been an evolutionary step in between the first and third chakras, a step represented by the second chakra.

The second chakra leads a man and a woman into a sexual relationship, which typically results in children. As every parent knows, children force an adult back on himself or herself. They require the parents to love and develop their talents and skills in order to provide for their children's needs and survival. Parents are stretched by the demands of family to raise their children with love, order, and understanding. They must discipline themselves and even postpone their own desires to provide for those in their care. Indeed, they must sacrifice their own needs, and sometimes even their own lives. Women lose their lives in childbirth. Yet, they welcome pregnancy. Fathers sacrifice the attention and maternal love of their wives so that their children can enjoy such love and attention and thereby develop fully. Fathers, too, give their lives for their children. Ultimately, love demands sacrifice and self-development, which means that the second chakra leads inevitably into the third.

In a fundamental way, awakening to the second and third chakras—indeed, surrendering to them—means opening up to the worlds above the third chakra, because sex and self-development involve us in complicated relationships that ultimately require love.

Confronting the Crisis of the Third Chakra

The third chakra encourages us to utilize our own power, to be responsible for our own fate. Thus, it pushes us to realize our talents, our individuality, and to achieve self-mastery. Such a consciousness leads us inevitably to one of two crises.

The first is the crisis of demagoguery. The paradox of self-mastery—indeed, one of its pitfalls—is that as people progress in their development, an inevitable ego inflation sets in. As they become more skilled, more successful, they also can become more arrogant. They can indulge in the false belief that they are masters of their own fate. This can ultimately isolate them and destroy their lives. That is only one of the dark roads that the third chakra can lead us down, however.

The second is the one most of us find ourselves on—the road that leads to grief, sadness, and self-recrimination for not having achieved all that we wished for. Here, at the third chakra, are found many of our frustrations with ourselves. By the time we reach midlife, we often find ourselves asking very hard and critical questions, such as: Why didn't I do this, or become that? Why didn't I make better choices along the way? These questions precipitate a life crisis, very often a mid-life crisis, in which the imperatives of the third chakra—the overwhelming desire to become master of our own fate—force us to conclude that we have failed in life. We didn't master ourselves so thoroughly, we decide. We didn't become the great person we set out to be. Thus, very often we feel bitterness and grief, which becomes locked in the third chakra.

The healing of the third chakra depends upon our moving upward to the fourth, which beckons us to evolve to a higher point of view, to see life in larger terms. That growth step is a particularly difficult one, however, because our modern culture urges all of us to be independent, self-sufficient, and masters of our own fate. Our culture leads us to live according to the first, second, and third chakras. Yet, our healing lies in moving upward to the fourth.

It is love that leads us to the fourth chakra.

The Fourth Chakra: Awakening to Unity

Known traditionally by its Sanskrit name, *Anahata,* meaning "unstruck," the fourth chakra provides life force to the heart. The name of the heart chakra, Anahata, means to emit a cosmic sound that is heard beyond the realm of the five senses. It is a sound that is "unstruck," meaning it has no origin, yet it exists. Its location is the first thoracic vertebra, or the area of the heart. It also provides Qi to the thymus gland, the lungs, the arms, and hands. Problems related to the heart chakra manifest as symptoms in these organs and extremities, including heart disease, high blood pressure, asthma, and other lung diseases.

The central ethic of the heart is love in all its manifestations, but most of all as compassion. Compassion means caring for others, which leads to healing. Thus, the heart chakra is focused on altruism and improving the lives of one's fellow human beings. Healing begins with the heart, and healers themselves work from this chakra first if they are truly dedicated to helping others.

The heart chakra is the central conduit through which all the chakras express themselves. In this sense, the heart chakra is unique, but it demonstrates the universal need for love. Thus, all forms of healing, all forms of expression, all ideas, all information must be expressed with love and compassion if they are to do another person any long-term good. The heart chakra is therefore considered the matrix through which all the other chakras must express themselves.

Whenever a person's consciousness progresses from the third chakra to the fourth, he or she very often confronts some crisis in life. The reason is that the heart chakra, as I will explain shortly, brings about the most dramatic change in consciousness.

The sound of the heart chakra, Anahata, the "unstruck" sound of the cosmos, is the same sound that the Greek philosopher and mathematician Pythagoras called "the music of the spheres." It is a heavenly music that inspires and lifts the heart.

Tantric teachings refer to the fourth chakra as Purusha, "the essence of man," or the supreme man. In understanding the ideas and feelings associated with the heart chakra, one sees the ideal human being, or the Purusha.

In Ayurvedic medicine, the heart chakra is associated with the air element and the principle of touch. It is symbolized by the black antelope or gazelle, an animal known for its speed, lightness of being, and gentleness. Healing touch is done from the heart chakra.

From the heart chakra comes our ability to see the unity among people—indeed, the life we all have in common. As Ram Dass points out, the fourth chakra reveals to us that this shared life is, in fact, one life. From the perception of that shared life comes the recognition that what happens to you also happens to me. This brings compassion and the desire to work for the good of all people.

Everything that is understood in its unity and in collective terms comes from the heart chakra. Thus, Jung, whose psychology articulated the collective unconscious and the archetypal world, is a leading spokesman for the fourth chakra.

At this level of consciousness, the experience of our separateness and aloneness begins to dissolve. This is one reason why the fourth chakra is associated with air—because of its universality to human existence; indeed, its universality to all creatures that live on the earth. We all wish to avoid suffering and experience happiness. We all want to breathe the good air and receive what we need. Without this recognition, we are reduced to an existence governed by the first chakra, which is to say, by the law of survival of the fittest. In this case, we are little more than animals.

The heart chakra unites people in the mystery of love. I say it is a mystery because love has an indefinable power to unify one person with another; to unify a family, a community; to embrace humanity as a whole. As love grows, its circle widens, so that the unity of life is experienced ever more deeply.

The Relationship Between the Third and Fourth Chakras

Crossing over from the third to the fourth chakra is an enormous step in evolution, and it's not an easy one, writes Jung. It is fraught with obstacles and sacrifices. The identity that we associate as our true selves actually serves as an impediment to this step in evolution. Crossing from the third to the fourth chakra is like going from a very personal and self-centered view of life to a universal view. This universal view strips away something that each of us defines as our uniqueness. In a profound way, each of us is attached to our separateness, our individuality, and our desire for personal power. The illusion that we can control life and ultimately master all that life brings to us is exceedingly intoxicating. That illusion reinforces our individuality—we don't need anyone else, we tell ourselves. We can do it on our own. This cowboy mentality is especially deep in American culture and, as we all know, is at the root of many of our most profound social, economic, and ecological problems. All of these issues spring from the first, second, and third chakras. I do not mean to suggest that we ever stop being responsible for our actions and our own happiness, but at the lower three chakras, we see our happiness as having to be attained through struggle with other people or against situations. We do not see the larger forces of life that support us in our path and, in fact, support everyone's efforts at fulfillment. I am referring, of course, to the presence of the divine in all our lives.

Within the psyche is a larger divine presence known by many names, the most utilitarian being the higher self. This higher self is your true guide in life. Jung points out that the higher self, or what he refers to as the psyche, is evolving at its own pace and according to its own organic plan, and consequently will force us to confront the next stage in development with or without the acquiescence of the conscious mind and its organizing center, known as the ego. In fact, the higher self often causes a shift in consciousness at the very moment when we least expect it. This invariably precipitates a crisis. We are forced to acknowledge the limitations of our current values and our worldview, which means that we must grow to a higher perspective, not because we necessarily want to, but because we must in order to reestablish equilibrium, health, and happiness.

Once the psyche, or the higher self, forces us to awaken to the need to grow and embrace a new set of values, we must also recognize that we are no longer in total control of our lives. Obviously, if we were in control, we wouldn't be facing the crisis that caused us to review our current values. Indeed, the crisis forces us to recognize that we are in some way inadequate to whatever it is that we are facing.

This would be crushing—and often is—were it not for the fact that such a crisis is usually joined with an awakening to a new set of values, often whispered to us as if from some other quarter of our lives. We pick up a book that makes sense to us. We listen to a lecture that inspires us. We talk to a friend or a teacher who points the way. In some altogether mysterious way, life opens a door and we walk through it. Or, to put it another way, life awakens us to the fact that the values of the third chakra are no longer sufficient to guide our lives, and now we must turn to the consciousness of the fourth chakra. In doing so, we turn to the Great Spirit for help, and in some subtle and often modest way, that help guides us out of the crisis. In the process, we become conscious of the fact that the resolution of the problem did not come out of our own power, or personal mastery, but came instead from some mysterious outside source of help.

For many people, this crisis, which is so common at mid-life, becomes the source of rebirth, because the movement from the third chakra to the fourth is often based upon the letting go of the illusion of our own omnipotence and the awakening of larger spiritual forces that shape our destiny and can be turned to for help. The rebirth invariably occurs because it is based upon a new faith.

As Jung says, this crisis that stimulates one's growth from the third to the fourth chakra brings with it the recognition that the "psyche is self-moving, that it is something genuine which is not yourself." That, says Jung, "is exceedingly difficult to see and admit. For it means that the consciousness which you call yourself is at an end." Or, as Ajit Mookerjee put it in his book *Kundalini: The Arousal of the Inner Energy* (Destiny Books, 1982), "You are no longer master of your own house." You must now recognize that something larger is within you and that the identity you recognize as yourself is subordinate to this larger entity. This recognition is transformative, because it is an awakening to the presence of the Great Spirit in your life.

Paula's Story: Imbalances of the First, Second, Third, and Fourth Chakras

The difficulties in making this step are apparent throughout our society, especially in those who suffer from chronic depression. A few years ago, I began seeing a thirty-eight-year-old woman, whom I will call Paula, who suffered from chronic fatigue, depression, and heart palpitations. She came to me because she did not want to take the antidepressant suggested by her therapist and because she was having trouble implementing the changes her therapist was recommending. She was stuck, and the depression seemed to be getting worse.

Paula presented a host of physical characteristics that revealed where her problems were located: her face was dull, expressionless; her shoulders were rounded; her chest was concave. In short, her heart chakra, which sends energy from the heart up through the neck and shoulders and lights the face, was exceedingly weak. Some experience—or set of experiences—had injured her heart chakra. Paula had a weak sense of her own identity and integrity, and therefore could not establish healthy boundaries—a first chakra issue. Her boundary issues also manifested in her overly active sex life. Paula had trouble discerning when and with whom she should have sex and whom she should avoid sexually. Paula had trouble saying no to people; she could be talked into things too easily, and consequently she was taken advantage of. The effect of her profligate sex life was to create an injury in her second chakra, over her sex organs, which felt to me as if it were tender and raw.

She also lacked will—a third chakra issue. When she became angry, it was usually after the fact, and she wasn't able to express that anger to the appropriate person or in the appropriate situation. Instead, she turned the anger back on herself, injuring herself in the process. That injury was especially acute in the fourth chakra, which I soon felt was lacerated and wounded.

I worked on Paula's entire field for a two-year period, seeing Paula two to four times per month. I did several things during each treatment. I began by moving through Paula's field, removing blockages throughout the field. I also concentrated on opening the secondary chakras in Paula's feet, which would allow Paula to feel more grounded, safe, and empowered. It would also improve Paula's ability to receive the supportive, uplifting energy that flows from the earth.

Then I attempted to remove blockages that were concentrated in her first and third chakras. These obstructions existed in the chakras like bundles of stagnant energy—or what I refer to as stones, or boulders. The boulders prevented the life force from flowing freely through these chakras, thus weakening the chakras and the consciousness that was housed there. The effect was to give her a very blurred sense of self, and because the first chakra was weak, her very survival was called into question, a common occurrence in people who are depressed.

I tried to remove the blockages in the first and third chakras by gently reaching into the area of the chakra with my right hand. As I moved into the chakra, I rotated my hand slowly in a counterclockwise direction, as taught to me by my teacher, Twylah Nitsch. Twylah explained that this counterclockwise motion allows healing energy to penetrate the field. She further explained that once inside the chakra, I should reverse the motion of my hand, turning it clockwise, which would allow me to scoop out the blockages and pull them free from the chakra. Why must I turn my hand in these directions? I asked. All she would say is that this is how her grandfather taught her. My own experience has taught me that the counterclockwise motion provides the healer with a certain amount of power that enables the healer's hand to enter directly into the chakra and dislodge the energetic mass. At that point, the healer reverses the motion, that is, turning the hand clockwise, to move the energy in its natural direction and thus assist the chakra in eliminating the stagnant energy. When my hand was outside the chakra, I then visualized the blockage moving off my hand and into light to be transmuted.

Once this was done, I concentrated on sending healing energy to Paula's second and fourth chakras, the areas of her sex organs and heart, respectively. I finished each session by closing the holes and wounds that were in the field.

The effect on Paula was gradual but significant. In the early going, Paula told me that she had begun implementing the behavioral changes her therapist had recommended. This was something she had been unable to do before she started receiving energy work, and it reflected her growing sense of identity and self-empowerment. After a few months of therapeutic touch, her depression began to lighten significantly. "I felt that I could see the sunshine for short periods of time," Paula said. She started to have hope again.

These improvements increased steadily over a two-year period, until Paula was finally able to feel in control of her life and experience the lifting of her depression.

The Fifth Chakra: The World of Sound and Hearing

The fifth chakra, referred to as *Visuddha,* or "pure," is located over the throat, at the third cervical vertebra. It provides life force to the thyroid and parathyroid glands, as well as to the larynx, neck, shoulders, arms, hands, and ears. It is associated with the speech center and with hearing. Problems related to the fifth chakra include disorders of the thyroid and parathyroid glands, stiff neck, hearing impairment, colds, sore throat, tonsillitis, and all voice-related disorders.

The fifth chakra is the realm of communication. All forms of expression are under the influence of the fifth chakra. So, too, is the sharing and the synthesizing of ideas.

The fifth chakra is the transition into the world of ideas, symbols, and communication. The first three chakras are concerned with material existence and individuality. The fourth chakra represents a transition point into the higher realms, a doorway into the world of spirit. From the fifth through the seventh chakras, the levels of consciousness become increasingly focused on the matters of spirit and immaterial existence. Consequently, the consciousness of the upper three chakras is more and more rarefied, more subtle, and spiritual in nature.

Like the first and third chakras, the fifth represents a turning inward from the more altruistic and outgoing heart center. At the fifth chakra, the person moves into the inner world of energy, sound, and light—light, because words and ideas illuminate the darkness that is ignorance and show us the way to resolution of conflicts and reconciliation with one another.

The fifth chakra is associated with the element ether, which, according to Ayurvedic medicine, is the vessel in which all elements mix. The color associated with the fifth chakra is blue, and its principal concerns are sound, hearing, and communication. The animal that symbolizes this chakra is the moon-white elephant, a sacred mythological creature that represents the powerful and mystical base upon which the mind and the world of ideas are founded.

The quality of our communication—the temperament and meaning of our words—is a direct representation of our underlying consciousness. For most of us, the fifth chakra is the instrument of the first three chakras. If we are bound to the lower three chakras, we communicate from our separateness and our aloneness; we communicate from our needs for sex and for companionship; and we communicate from our will to power.

The consciousness of the lower three chakras is essentially dualistic, in that they make a clear distinction between you and me. They also tend to define people and situations as either good or bad. There isn't much gray in situations, nor is there much overlap in the recognition of people's needs. Consequently, there isn't much understanding. But once we enter the fourth chakra, our communication through the fifth becomes increasingly universal. Our words take on greater magnitude because they unite people in understanding and in love. People are no longer seen as necessarily good or bad, but as humans struggling to avoid suffering and find happiness.

The fifth chakra, however, has its own consciousness and values, which is the plane of energy and light. Words and sound are invisible. Their nature is immaterial, yet they move the material world and they change it. Words and sound are an expression of the spirit, and because words and sound have so much power, they give us a glimpse of just how powerful spirit truly is.

The word *Visuddha,* or "pure," indicates that the ideas and values native to the fifth chakra are pure and perfect and that those who reach the fifth chakra are able to express the purity and perfection of spiritual ideals. In his book *The Inner Life* (The Theosophical Publishing House, 1978), theosophist Charles Leadbeater wrote that those who reach the fifth chakra and embrace its consciousness are able to hear the heavenly sounds. Also, the communication of such people is guided by heavenly spirits. Such a person can communicate love, compassion, and a rare insight into spiritual truths.

The Relationship Between the Fourth and Fifth Chakras

The fifth chakra represents a new level of detachment unknown to the fourth. The heart chakra is still very much attached to the material plane, in that it cares so deeply for other people and for the life we all share. At the fifth chakra, one understands the impermanence of material life and can see clearly where permanence and infinite truths really lie. The fifth chakra represents the kind of detachment spoken of in Buddhism, in which the world is recognized as *Maya,* or "illusion." Hence, the crossing over from the fourth to the fifth chakra requires a further letting go of this impermanent world for the eternal world of spirit.

The Sixth Chakra: The World of Wisdom and Forms

Known by its Sanskrit name, *Ajna,* meaning "command," the sixth chakra is located over the forehead, slightly above the eyebrows, between the eyes. The sixth chakra provides life force to the eyes, much of the central nervous system, and the brain. It also funnels Qi to the pituitary and pineal glands, both endocrine organs located in the middle of the brain. These two glands work in harmony to support the individual and unified functions of the sixth and seventh chakras.

Most authorities say that the sixth chakra is associated with the pituitary gland, which is the master gland of the endocrine system. It controls virtually all endocrine functions and thereby influences the entire body, both in its everyday operations and in the body's growth and development.

The sixth chakra is said to control various states of concentration and consciousness. This is the realm of omniscience. Whenever someone breaks through to this level of consciousness, extrasensory perception, clairvoyance, visions, psychokinesis, and other paranormal experiences occur.

The sixth chakra is associated with the color indigo, according to Christopher Hills, author of the book *Supersensonics* (Destiny Books, 1975). Hills has studied and written exclusively on the chakras. The chakra is symbolized by Om, the cosmic sound. Om represents the alpha and the omega, the beginning and the end of all things. There are no elements associated with the sixth chakra, since it is beyond material existence. It is the world of cosmic law, harmony, perfect order, and vibration.

To better understand the sixth chakra, we should consider that the seventh chakra is the realm of undifferentiated oneness. In order for that oneness to give rise to creation, it had to bifurcate, or divide into opposites, so that it could create polarity, energy, and thus provide the underlying substance of the spiritual and material worlds. The sixth chakra is that realm of bifurcation and creation, where all things were created in their original perfection. At the sixth chakra, all paradoxes, all seeming contradictions, are harmonized. Yin and yang, man and woman, day and night, positive and negative—all opposites are brought together as one.

The sixth level is regarded as the archetypal world, or Plato's "world of forms." All seminal ideas exist here. It is said that the Godhead referred to in all religions is here at the sixth level, the realm of pure ideas. To tap into the sixth chakra means to glimpse the all-knowing and thus to have insight into the past, present, and future. For this reason, it is associated with intuition, ESP, and other parapsychological states of consciousness.

Thus, the sixth chakra is the world of perfect knowing, the world of wisdom. "The wisdom center (Ajna) shines with the light of Cosmic Consciousness and reveals the universe in its unified wholeness of being," says Mookerjee in *Kundalini: The Arousal of the Inner Energy.*

The Seventh Chakra: Oneness

The seventh or crown chakra is referred to in Sanskrit as *Sahasrara,* meaning "thousand," or the lotus of a thousand petals. It is located at the back of the head, slightly above the crown. Some maintain that it actually hovers above the head at this spot.

This chakra also nourishes the cerebral cortex and much of the central nervous system. Its primary function is to unify understanding and integrate all ideas and states of consciousness. The crown chakra is responsible for synchronizing all the human senses and faculties and thus making the world coherent.

Malfunctions that occur in the crown chakra manifest as depression, alienation, and the inability to learn or comprehend ideas, situations, and people.

The crown chakra is the transcendental state beyond consciousness, what the Buddhists call the Void and the Hindus call Brahmin. It is the ultimate oneness, the state beyond description.

The seventh chakra is associated with the pineal gland, an endocrine organ that serves to maintain mood, among other things. For centuries, mystics and philosophers regarded the pineal gland as purely a spiritual organ. They associated the gland with light, intuition, and truth. Indeed, many believed that the pineal gland was the so-called third eye, or the eye of intuition. Seventeenth-century philosopher René Descartes maintained that it was the seat of the soul. Yet, the organ remained a mystery to scientists, who until very recently thought the pineal had no function at all. New research has corrected that archaic assumption, however. The pineal gland, it turns out, plays an essential role in the maintenance of our circadian rhythms (biorhythms), brain chemistry, and mood. Remarkably, the pineal is, in fact, highly sensitive to light. When deprived of light, such as in winter, the pineal gland secretes abundant quantities of a hormone called melatonin, which consumes the chemical neurotransmitter serotonin. The brain uses serotonin to help create feelings of well-being, positive thoughts, and to enhance its ability to concentrate. It also is the chemical basis for deep and restful sleep.

When the pineal gland is deprived of adequate sunlight, it produces more melatonin, which in turn depresses serotonin levels. This results in a widely suffered disorder called Seasonal Affective

Disorder, or SAD. SAD is exactly that: a disorder in which people feel depressed, fatigued, and withdrawn. Most people who experience SAD suffer it in winter or when they are deprived of natural lighting for extensive periods. The cure is simply to increase one's exposure to sunlight or full-spectrum lighting. This causes the pineal to produce less melatonin, which makes serotonin levels rise and results in increased feelings of well-being, positive emotions, better sleep, and the removal of depression.

As for the pineal's reputation as the human third eye, even that remains something of a puzzle. According to *Atlas of Human Anatomy,* by Samuel Smith and Edwin B. Steen, "Some evidence suggests that it [the pineal gland] is a vestigial organ, the remnant of a third eye." Perhaps it was an organ that existed early in human evolution and there's more to the pineal function than we currently know.

The color associated with the crown chakra, says Hills, is violet, although many Eastern Indian traditions maintain that there is no color associated with the crown chakra. This chakra represents the ocean of life to which we all return. It is the ultimate and indefinable state of love and bliss.

The Energy Spiral
Harmonizing High and Low, Heaven and Earth

My experience has taught me that the system of Chinese acupuncture is absolutely correct in its assessment that life energy, or Qi, flows in channels, or what the Chinese refer to as meridians. But it does more than that. Energy also flows in spirals, or eddies, especially in the primary and secondary chakras. In addition, life force weaves among the seven chakras, connecting and unifying them into a fully integrated whole (see diagram 9).

As I mentioned earlier, each chakra provides a concentrated flow of life force to a specific part of the body. It also represents a particular type of consciousness that must be integrated into our being. Were it not for the spiral of energy, there would be seven

DIAGRAM 9. THE ENERGY SPIRAL

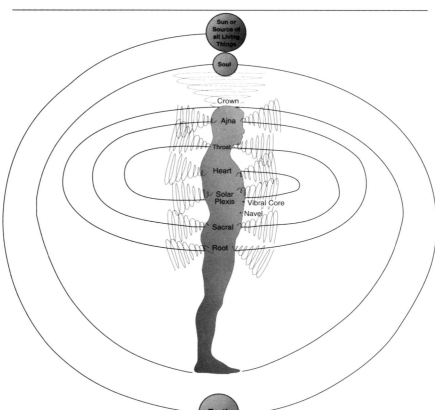

major subdivisions of consciousness operating in opposition to each other, much like seven heads of state running the same country. The net effect, especially on the physical and mental levels, would be chaos. Thus, the spiral of energy unifies the physical, psychological, and spiritual functions of the seven chakras and thus creates integration.

The spiral of energy has a distinct pattern, like a single line of threat that holds seven buttons in place on a shirt. The line itself begins at the heart chakra, emanating out of the heart and turning down and in to the solar plexus, or third chakra. There, it reenters the body and exits the back, where it loops upward and reenters at the back of the throat, or throat chakra. From the fifth chakra, or throat, the energy moves out the front of the body and loops downward into the second chakra, located in the area of the large intestines and sex organs. From there, it exits the back, turns in a semicircle upward, and reenters the body at the back of the head, at the sixth chakra, or third eye. From the third eye, the energy leaves through the front of the body and turns downward, again in a large semicircle, so that it enters the body at the root chakra, or at the base of the pelvis. From the pelvis, the energy arcs upward to the crown chakra, located at the top of the head. Within the crown chakra lies all the knowledge and life plan of the soul. Thus, the movement of energy through the chakra system is 4, 3, 5, 2, 6, 1, and 7.

Traditional people believed that the soul's journey on earth is already mapped out and that knowledge of one's life plan lies within each of us. Our challenge is to know ourselves and thus truly to understand why we are here on earth. The spiral of energy reveals this ancient wisdom in a very simple diagram. It shows that from the lofty heights of the crown chakra—the place where all self-knowledge lies—the energy turns downward to the earth, where the soul sojourns temporarily. From the earth, the energy spiral turns upward toward heaven, thus signaling our eventual return to our source.

Using the Energy Spiral as a Therapeutic Tool

This threadlike pattern unifies all seven chakras. It also joins individual chakras with their complementary opposites on the upper and lower parts of the body. Using the heart chakra as a center, we note that there are three chakras below the heart and three above. The spiral of energy begins at the heart and then weaves its way through each chakra, joining them in complementary pairs. For example, the root chakra, the lowest of the seven chakras on the body, is connected to the crown chakra, or highest, by the spiral of energy, thus joining the instincts to survive with the highest levels of ethics and universal love. The energy spiral exits the fifth chakra, located at the throat, and flows downward to the second chakra, thus unifying the voice and upper respiratory tract with the intestines, kidneys, and sex organs. From the second chakra, the energy turns upward to the sixth, or third eye, linking the lower intestinal function with the head and brain.

The energy spiral can be used as a diagnostic and therapeutic tool. If a client suffers from chronic headaches, I do not concentrate exclusively on the head and the area of the sixth chakra, but turn to the second chakra as a possible source of trouble. Very often, headaches have their source in the lower intestinal, kidney, and sex organ functions.

If a person suffers from chronic sore throats, a fifth chakra problem, I consider two other possible sources of the problem, neither of which are located in the throat. The first may be the area of the third chakra and middle organs—small intestine, lungs, liver, spleen, and pancreas. The third chakra provides life force to the fifth chakra via the energy spiral. If the third chakra is blocked, the fifth chakra will be deficient of Qi and will begin to manifest disharmonies. Dryness of throat, laryngitis, weak or breaking voice, accumulation of waste and mucus, and sore throat are common when Qi is deficient in the throat. In general, there is a feeling of emptiness in the field here; the person himself may experience this as weakness in the throat or lack of personal power. Therefore, when working on someone with chronic sore throats, I always clear the third chakra area, especially if there are chronic physical problems here as well.

On the other hand, the fifth chakra sends life force via the energy spiral to the second chakra, the area of the intestines, kidneys, and sex organs. If the second chakra is blocked, energy will build up in the throat, causing irritation, a buildup of mucus, the swelling of glands, and excessive heat.

The second possible cause of sore throats is repressed anger, held by the heart chakra (the fourth chakra). It must be remembered that physical illness often needs to be treated pharmacologically, which may include the use of an antibiotic or herbs. However, in order to truly heal a chronic sore throat—or any other disharmony in the body, for that matter—the underlying energetic imbalance must be treated. In the case of a sore throat, this means using healing touch to treat the second and fourth chakras. In addition, I also work on the chakras directly above and below the affected area, which in this case would include the sixth chakra.

A recent client of mine, whom I will call Sally, is a good example of how the spiral of energy can be used as both a means of diagnosis and guidance for treatment.

Headaches: When the Cause Isn't Just in the Head

Sally, forty-five-year-old wife and mother of two, suffered from regular headaches, migraines, overweight, and severe premenstrual syndrome (PMS) that included nausea and night sweats. Her gynecologist believed that Sally was entering perimenopause, which he felt brought on the night sweats and nausea. The physician further believed that the estrogen and progesterone Sally was taking to alleviate the perimenopausal symptoms was actually exacerbating her headaches. Sally was stuck. She didn't know whether to give up the hormones, which would allow her perimenopausal symptoms to flare, or to maintain the hormones that control the symptoms but fueled the migraines.

Unfortunately, her headaches and migraines were getting worse. She had to do something and eventually she came to me.

I saw Sally weekly for one year, during which time we made remarkable progress. The first thing that healing touch gave Sally was greater confidence in herself and a deeper sense of stability. She started to talk about her own behaviors that might be contributing to her problems, and by our third session together she realized that her headaches came on after she ate certain foods, which she immediately gave up.

By the second month of treatment, Sally's headaches were less frequent. By the third, her migraines were gone. Over the next five months, Sally experienced only one migraine.

One of the first things I noticed as I worked on Sally's field was that the energy around her second chakra, located over the lower abdomen and responsible for providing life force to the sex organs, kidneys, bladder, large intestine, and adrenal glands, felt irregular, as if the chakra did not have an integrated consistency. I felt clearly that this part of her field was swollen, while other areas were weak or even withdrawn, as if there were a gaping hole in the field. As I continued to work on her, I kept getting the image of an open wound over the area of the second chakra. This corresponded with the physical problems Sally was having in her sex organs and adrenal glands. Even more telling was the fact that this part of Sally's field seemed even more irregular and swollen to me whenever she had headaches.

From an energetic viewpoint, this made perfect sense, since the second and sixth chakras are related through the spiral of energy. Clearly, the source of her headaches was the imbalance in the area of her second chakra.

Whenever I saw Sally, I worked on her second and sixth chakras first. I sent energy to the second chakra and then closed the wound by moving my hands in a very gentle pattern, as if I were literally bringing together tissue that had been torn apart. Then I turned my attention to the sixth chakra, which was congested and blocked. Here, I drew energy away from the chakra, opened it up, and increased the circulation within this part of the field.

After a few months of treatment, the wound in the abdomen seemed to be less swollen and starting to heal. At the same time, Sally's headaches and perimenopausal symptoms clearly had been relieved.

It wasn't until the tenth month of treatment that Sally began to lose weight—now without effort. This happy circumstance coincided with what Sally experienced as a dramatic shift in consciousness. She reported feeling better able to express her needs. She had always had great difficulty asking for emotional or psychological support. She was a big giver, thinking that if she was loving and supportive of others, that same love and support would come back to her. Often, it didn't. Also, Sally had a hard time setting boundaries for others. Thus, she ended up feeling taken advantage of and being trampled on. As a form of compensation, and a way to relieve her tension, she overate. Now she felt much stronger in herself. Sally found herself asking for help or saying that she simply could not perform certain tasks at home or at work because she was already too busy. At times, she said she marveled at her newfound strength.

By the time we stopped our regular work together, Sally was steadily losing weight. She was far better able to handle the stress in her life and her headaches were infrequent to rare. Though Sally decided to continue to take estrogen and progesterone, she suffered only mild symptoms of perimenopause. Her migraines had disappeared.

The Chakras

CHAKRA 1—ROOT CHAKRA

LOCATION	Base of spine, perineum
GLANDS	Adrenals
ORGANS	Legs, feet, bones, large intestine
FUNCTIONS	Survival, grounding, life promoting, vital physical energy
MALFUNCTIONS	Constipation, hemorrhoids, obesity, sciatica, arthritis, knee trouble, anorexia nervosa

CHAKRA 2—SPLENIC OR SACRAL

LOCATION	Two to three fingers below navel, lower abdomen, first lumbar vertebra
GLANDS	Ovaries, testicles

ORGANS	Uterus, genitals, kidneys, bladder, circulatory system
FUNCTIONS	Assimilation, life promoting, emotions, sexuality, desire, and pleasure
MALFUNCTIONS	Kidney/bladder trouble, female and male organic and emotional sexual problems, lower back problems

CHAKRA 3—SOLAR PLEXUS

LOCATION	Eighth thoracic vertebra just below notch where ribs come together to form xyphoid process to navel
GLANDS	Pancreas, adrenals
ORGANS	Liver, spleen, stomach muscles
FUNCTIONS	Willpower, personal power, taking in of energy from outside of self, growth, healing
MALFUNCTIONS	Digestive troubles, ulcers, diabetes, hypoglycemia, liver disorders, fat metabolism

CHAKRA 4—HEART

LOCATION	First thoracic vertebra, heart
GLAND	Thymus
ORGANS	Heart, lungs, arms, hands
FUNCTIONS	Self-love, love toward others, taking in life nourishment in general, mental energy, consciousness, healing
MALFUNCTIONS	Heart disease (including high blood pressure), asthma and all lung disease

CHAKRA 5—THROAT

LOCATION	Third cervical vertebra
GLANDS	Thyroid, parathyroid
ORGANS	Neck, shoulders, arms, hands, ears (hearing)
FUNCTIONS	Communication, expressive energy, volition, will (discernment and power of choosing), synthesizing of symbols into ideals

| MALFUNCTIONS | Thyroid problems, hearing problems, stiff neck, colds, sore throats |

CHAKRA 6—BROW OR AJNA

LOCATION	First cervical vertebra in back (space between and slightly above eyes on forehead)
GLAND	Pituitary (working in harmony with pineal)
ORGANS	Eyes
FUNCTIONS	Seeing, intuition, synthesizing
MALFUNCTIONS	Headaches, vision problems, nightmares

CHAKRA 7—CROWN

LOCATION	Top of head and slightly back where soft spot on baby's head is located
GLAND	Pineal (working in harmony with pituitary)
ORGANS	Cerebral cortex, central nervous system
FUNCTIONS	Integration and understanding
MALFUNCTIONS	Depression, alienation, inability to learn or comprehend

A knowledge of the anatomy and physiology of the chakras and their relationship to the physical body is essential in the practice of healing touch. The chakras offer the healer a set of portals into the body, mind, and spirit of the person on whom we are working. These portals are concentrations of energy and, indeed, of life. Within the chakras are the roots of many old wounds, blockages, and patterns that must be released if healing is to occur. Thus, the chakras offer the healer not only insights into the person's past but great opportunities to assist the person's rebirth.

EXERCISE—THE CHAKRA SPIRAL
(refer to diagram 9)

1. Envision a beam of rainbow light coming out of your heart in an arc and entering your solar plexus.

2. See the light pass through the solar plexus out the back, curve upward, and enter the body at the back of the throat.
3. See it pass through the throat and arc downward into the second, or sacral, chakra.
4. Envision the light passing through the body at the second chakra, exit the back, and turn upward and reenter the body at the back of the head, at the third eye, or sixth chakra.
5. Through the front of the third eye, see the beam of light arc downward and enter the body at the first, or root, chakra.
6. Visualize the light passing through the root chakra, exiting the back, arching upward, and reentering the body at the crown chakra.
7. From the crown chakra, see the light moving down through the center of the body to the bottom of the feet.
8. Once the arc touches the bottom of the feet, envision your entire field being lit up by the rainbow light so that the field is radiant with color and light.
9. From the feet, send an arc of light to the earth.
10. From the earth, see the light re-enter your body in the feet and turn upward, exiting the crown chakra and returning to the source of light and life.
11. Feel the rainbow light fill up every cell, tissue, and organ of your body with radiant light. Each organ absorbs the colors of energy that it needs for health and vitality.
12. When you feel full of light and life, open your eyes and let your light shine. If you become fatigued or imbalanced at any time of the day, you need only breathe in this radiant light to be restored.

If you tape these meditations with your own voice and play the tape to guide you through these mediations, your healing will be more profound.

BUILDING THE ENERGY BALL

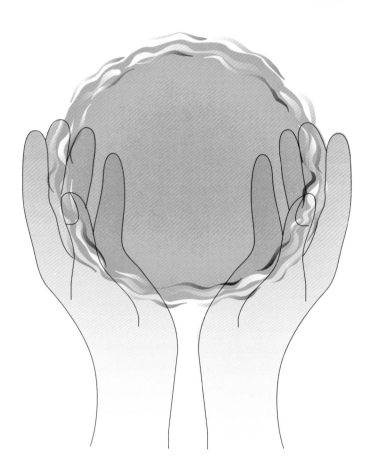

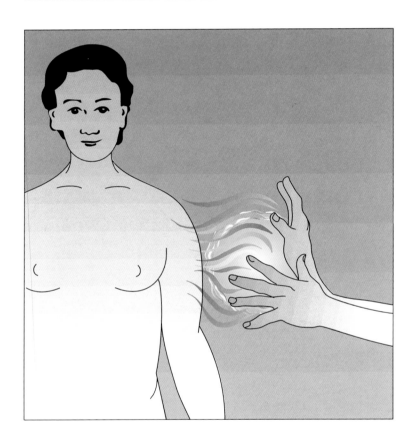

ENERGY FIELD

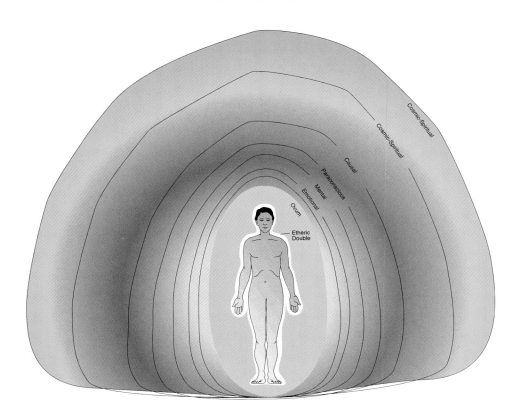

Cosmic-Spiritual

Cosmic-Spiritual

Causal

Paraconscious

Mental

Emotional

Ovum

Etheric
Double

CHAKRA LOCATIONS

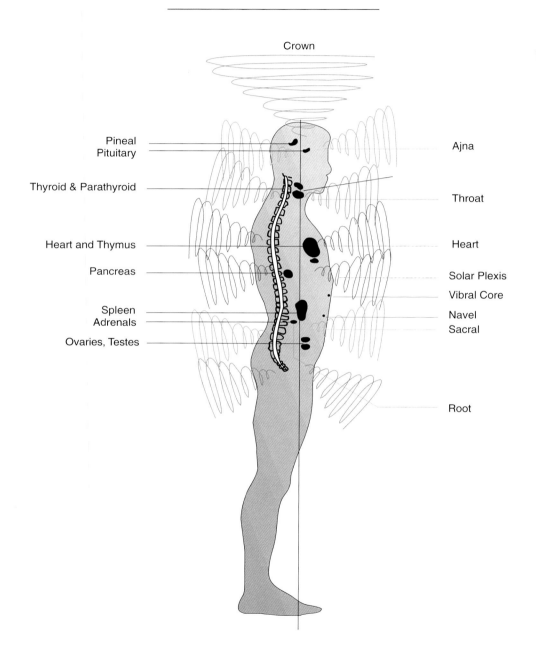

Crown

Pineal
Pituitary

Ajna

Thyroid & Parathyroid

Throat

Heart and Thymus

Heart

Pancreas

Solar Plexis

Vibral Core

Spleen
Adrenals

Navel

Sacral

Ovaries, Testes

Root

ENERGY SPIRAL

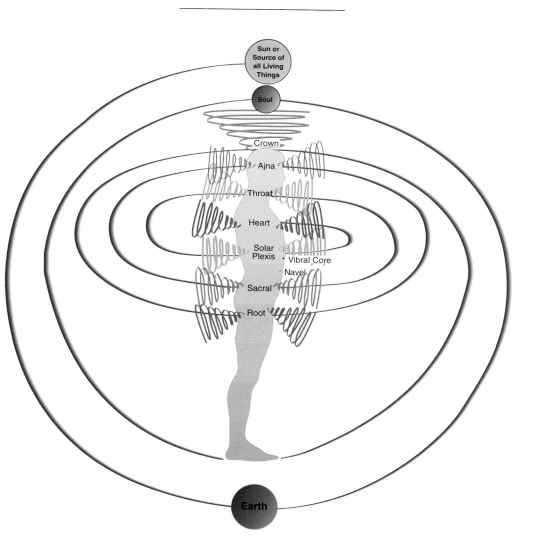

EGG MEDITATION

3-POINT MEDITATION

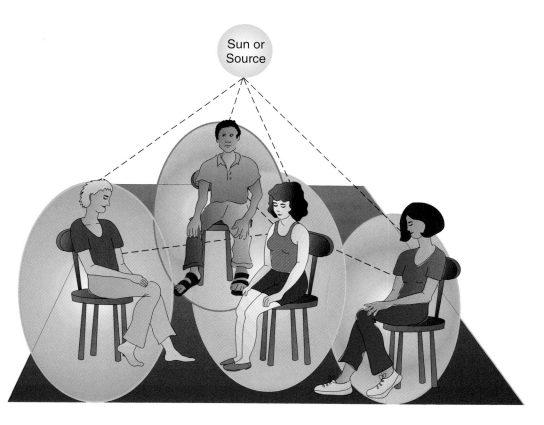

Sun or Source

RAINBOW DISK

Step 1

Step 2

Step 3

6

❧

Centering

C entering" yourself, in essence, means to shift your consciousness from the instability of everyday life to the
quiet calm of your own spiritual core. In the center of
your inner being lies a peace and stability that cannot
be shaken by events outside of you. As your consciousness becomes
ever more founded upon this inner spiritual base, you become more
tranquil, emotionally stable, and powerful in understated and balanced ways.

Typically, our awareness is subject to the volatile world of
everyday cares and concerns. Our physical, emotional, and psychological condition is predicated on events that take place outside of
us—on whether or not we had a good day at work, for example, or
how other people treat us. As people and events change, the quality
of your life rises and falls. The more attached you are to the events
and the behavior of others, the more reactive and unstable you
become.

To center yourself, by contrast, means to anchor your awareness in the spiritual roots of your life. To be centered in your spiritual roots means to shift your consciousness from life's daily
tumult to the center of your soul, the place within you that contin-

ually draws life energy from its universal source. Here, at your vital center, is the place from which your life truly springs.

Life itself is energy, and the source of energy is the One, the Great Spirit, the Tao. To attune your consciousness to the center of being is to align yourself with the will of the universe and to be nourished by its never-ending flow of life energy. (I will offer several meditations to help you achieve a centered state shortly.)

The effects of such a shift in awareness are transformative in every respect. Rather than being tossed around by the external travails of the ephemeral world, you are now grounded in the unchanging world of universal life force. Hence, you are at peace. The level of physical tension in your body drops precipitously. Scientific research has shown that people in meditation exhibit high degrees of alertness, concentration, and synchronicity between the left and right hemispheres of the brain. Heart rate and breathing patterns slow, blood pressure stabilizes, and skin conductivity decreases, a sign that circulation has improved. Dolores Krieger conducted a pilot study on practitioners of healing touch and found that they also achieved this same meditative state and thus experienced many of the same biological changes that sitting meditators undergo.

Various cultures and religious traditions have developed far-reaching understandings of what it truly means to be centered. The entire Japanese culture is founded upon the ethic that all behavior should flow from the vital center of being, or what the Japanese call *hara*. All the Japanese martial and cultural arts—from judo to painting to flower arranging to music—are meant to be expressions of the vital center. To be centered, say Japanese and Chinese philosophers, is to reconcile heaven and earth.

Perhaps for this reason, centering makes you acutely aware of yourself as a whole human being—that is, you become aware of your physical body, your emotions, and your spiritual consciousness as an integrated totality. Centering is a meditative act and an act of integration and harmony.

Virtually all traditional philosophy has recognized that we humans are being pulled constantly by the two archetypal extremes within our consciousness—the instinctual world of the physical senses and physical desires, and the intellectual and spiritual realms of ethics and ideals. These two archetypes cannot be balanced or harmonized by any intellectual or mental act. Indeed, as every adult knows, to settle this existential conflict through an activity of the mind is to settle it in favor of the mind, and thus to deny the needs of the body. Traditional peoples have maintained that the only way the two extremes can be reconciled and brought into harmony is to shift one's consciousness to the center of being, the vital center, which is beyond mind, concepts, and the changing standards of right and wrong. Here, in the spiritual center, lies the reconciliation of all opposites within life.

Carl Jung concurred with this view. In *Alchemical Studies,* he points out that the "center is compared to paradise and its four rivers." The four rivers connote the four directions of the earth, or the relative world. The place where the rivers converge and are joined, the center, is the place where the four cardinal directions are all reconciled and made one. "Nothing is more like God than the centre," writes Jung, "for it occupies no space, and cannot be grasped, seen or measured. Such too, is the nature of God and spirits." Indeed, Jung, like the great alchemists before him, most notably Paracelsus, maintained that meditation and the shifting of consciousness to the center of being brings about the perception of the invisible or spiritual world.

Jung quotes Gerard Dorn and his book on alchemy, *Theatrum Chemicum,* in which Dorn states that "all things which likewise fill no place because they lack body, as is the case with all spirits, can be comprehended in the centre, for both are incomprehensible. As therefore there is no end of the centre, no pen can rightly describe its power and the infinite abyss of its mysteries."

Perhaps because the center is the place of such "infinite mysteries," we recognize that from here springs all that is sacred into the material world. Thus, to center oneself means to approach the sacred or divine within.

Centering, therefore, is a meditative act that transforms you physically, psychologically, and spiritually. The practitioner of healing touch begins a session by centering herself. In this way, she places herself in right relationship with the universal energy and thus attains the right standpoint for participating in the flow of that energy.

This is the mental framework that the practitioner of healing touch attempts to achieve. When you are centered, you have no judgments about the person you are working with, nor do you have any attachments to outcome. You are not the source of the healing. You are not in control of what takes place. The energy flows from the divine source, through you, and to the recipient of healing touch. You, as a practitioner of healing touch, submit yourself as an instrument of that divine source. Whatever outcome occurs for the client is between the creator of the universe and the recipient. In a way, you, as the practitioner, are a witness to the outcome.

Elisabeth Kübler-Ross, M.D., in her essay "The Four Pillars of Healing," refers to the healer as a channel, or as she puts it "a conduit of a healing entity or force." Healers, shamans, and medicine men or women have referred to this same healing energy as Yahweh, Great Spirit, God, the Christed Energy, or the Higher Self. However one refers to it, it is this divine energy that creates the healing, regardless of the healer's technique. Twylah Nitsch, my Seneca teacher, also points out that the healer not only opens as a channel for the Great Mystery, but also must come from a place of faith and gratitude. No healing can occur without faith and gratitude.

As Dr. Kübler-Ross points out, healers do not heal. The very title "healer" is a bit of a misnomer, because the true healer is the Great Healer. The practitioner is more a facilitator, a participant, and a witness. He or she is not the source of healing.

This is often a difficult fact to recognize because, as a compassionate human being, you want to help others. Indeed, one of your primary motivations for doing healing touch is to be of service. Also, there is the added pressure that we all feel to prove that the practice works, that this is not a fringe or charlatan practice but a highly effective form of treatment. Yet, the essence of the practice is to surrender all control of outcome because the energy that you help to transmit will be utilized by the recipient's body however the body needs the life force.

In explaining the mysterious nature of healing, Dolores Krieger, a pioneer of healing touch, showed in her essay "The Timeless Concept of Healing" why a practitioner must ultimately surrender to larger forces that control the healing process. As healers, we cannot know every level of what the patient needs for complete healing. Dr. Krieger points out that just on a physiological level, the myriad biological functions are "exquisitely synchronized." When we add the emotional levels of healing, it becomes even more complicated. Therefore, when we approach our patients, part of our prayer must be, "Thy will be done." We have faith that the incredible human and divine energies come together to create the exact transformation for healing that is needed.

True healers have always understood their humble, yet essential role in the healing process. Even the Father of Medicine, Hippocrates, understood his position in the face of the mysteries that healing invokes. For all of his wisdom and knowledge, which at the time towered above all others, Hippocrates recognized that divine powers ultimately decided the final fate of every illness. As he said some 2,500 years ago, "The healing art involves a weaving of a knowledge of the gods into the texture of the physician's mind. The Art is held in honor by the gods, in its relations not only to bodily mishaps but to bodily conditions generally. For it is not by individual cleverness that a physician is effective. Although he has his hands on many aspects of an ailment, it may still happen that the cure comes about quite spontaneously. Of course whatever contributions the healing art is able to make should be accepted from it. But the path of wisdom in the Art lies in making final acknowledgment to Those Very Ones."

Thus, the most important attitudes that the practitioner must maintain toward a client, as well as toward himself or herself, are compassion, love, honesty (especially with himself or herself), and humility. This is how the practitioner of healing touch confronts the sacred drama that he or she is witness to and assists.

It is also why it is so important to begin every session of healing touch by centering yourself. By centering yourself in your own spiritual roots, you are not so easily distracted by anyone's emotions or desires, or even by the explicit needs of the client. Rather, you are respectful of the client and his or her relationship with the Creator. Once you are centered, you come into communion with the source of the energy that truly heals. Then, whatever that energy desires to happen will happen, effortlessly.

Being Present and Grounded to Be the Clearest Channel

Once you have centered yourself, of course, you must firmly maintain your center through the course of your healing touch session. To do that you must sustain your concentration and be fully present with your client. You can't suddenly drift off in your mind and begin to think about the many demands in your own life. Such wandering off will affect the flow of energy that is traveling through you to your client and thus make the session less effective. Also, the more you wander, the more you diminish the sense of the sacred. The client's awareness of the sacred is part of what allows him or her to accept the life energy that's being offered. The best way for you to sincerely invoke the sacred is through your own centeredness and concentration. Most forms of ceremony ring false and ultimately cast you in the wrong light. You are a professional practitioner who must maintain his or her professional standpoint. Yet, you are dealing with powers far beyond your comprehension, or mine, and therefore must be respectful of the true source of the healing energy that you transmit. As I pointed out earlier, the best and perhaps only way to strike the right balance between your earthly role and your heavenly ideals is to remain centered and focused. In the center, all paradoxes are reconciled, and the sense of the sacred is invoked without your doing anything.

In order to keep myself focused and centered, I do a visualization before the session and recite a prayer during it. Therefore, before you conduct your healing touch session, do the following:

First, place your feet firmly on the floor, about shoulder-width apart. Feel the energy in your legs and feet anchor itself in the floor. Visualize it going deeply into the earth so that the earth holds you in its embrace. Feel yourself being supported by the earth and nourished by the energy that flows upward from the Great Mother. At the same time, feel the upper levels of your own energy reach up into the heavens, just as the limbs of a tree reach into the sky. Feel the love of the heavens rain down on the limbs of your field and surround and envelop you. See the love and energy come up from the earth and mingle with that of the heavens. Visualize that energy channeling itself into your entire body and down into your arms and hands. See it flow from your hands. You now have the healing energy to channel to your client.

Before I turn to my client, however, I recite a prayer. I say this prayer over and over again throughout the healing session to remain focused on the work. I share this prayer with you as a basis for creating your own prayer, or for adopting it yourself. The prayer is as follows:

"Father, Mother, God, I place myself and this patient in your Holy Light for the Highest Good of all. I ask that You work through me to bring healing to this patient. From Thee, through me, to this patient. I ask that Thy Will be done, and I am grateful for this healing."

If you create your own prayer, I encourage you to include the phrases "for the Highest Good of all," "Thy Will be done," and a phrase of gratitude for the healing that is taking place. These phrases assist you in your efforts to surrender the outcome to the higher power or Tao. Remember, surrender is not giving up, but rather giving over control and outcome to the Great Mystery that is the true healer. By reciting this prayer, you are acknowledging your faith in the Creator and its power to heal. You are also offering yourself as a participant and a servant in that process.

Finally, as you do your energy work on your client, visualize the darkness, boulders, and blockages that are being released from your client's field as being absorbed into the light and love of the heavens, or ethers. The earth takes these energetic blockages, stones, and old patterns and dissolves them into the soil, transforming them into elements that support life and renewed growth.

Be sure to do the egg meditation, given below, before you begin to work with your client. This will protect you from the energetic imbalances and illnesses your client may be suffering from.

Before You Proceed, Know How You Feel

Your centering and grounding meditations will put you in touch with your physical body and your emotions. You'll know how you feel and, if you allow your emotions to fully surface, you will know why you have such feelings. Do not resist or repress such emotions, or the events that surround them, but rather embrace and honor these feelings. No matter what surfaces, whether it is anger, shame, humiliation, or conflict, try to examine the feelings and have compassion for yourself. Such emotions—and the events that triggered them—are part of what it means to be human. With continued meditation, you will be able to integrate these and other feelings. You will be able to see the courage you had to have to go through such events. In time, you will be able to honor yourself in ways that perhaps you cannot do now. You will also become more proficient at opening your heart and entering into a consciousness of non-judgment and acceptance.

However, if you cannot reconcile these emotions in the moment, or create peace within yourself, you are better off avoiding the day's healing touch sessions.

Powerful emotions, especially anger or hatred, are inappropriate to a healing touch session. There is a good chance that you will transmit such vibrations to your client. Or you may not be able to maintain your concentration and groundedness to protect yourself from your client's energy or illness. You are better off avoiding the whole interaction and postponing it to another day. In the meantime, work on yourself. Remember what I said in chapter 1: The greatest demands made on a practitioner of healing touch are those the practitioner makes of himself or herself. He or she must become more open-hearted, loving, compassionate, clear, and less attached to outcome. The practitioner must become more centered in the spiritual roots of his or her being, and thus clearer about who he or she is, who the client is, and who the healer is.

Being Centered Means Respecting Your Limits

As a practitioner of healing touch, you are performing an invaluable service to your client, to the healing arts, and to the world at large. You are providing your client with an enormous boost of healing energy, energy that is essential for the client's restoration and recovery. By offering this service, you are giving people a new tool to restore health, as well as a new approach to understanding, health, illness, and, indeed, life itself. Finally, you are serving as an instrument of love and healing, something in very short supply in our world today.

Yet, despite this incredibly important role, many practitioners of healing touch nevertheless feel they must be more, and in the process make the mistake of overstepping their own boundaries, and the client's. You must always keep in mind the scope of your practice in order to be effective in your job as a healer. Always remember that your central function is to serve as a conduit for healing energy. You promote the flow of the life force in other people. Whatever your client does with that energy is between him or her and God. The person already knows what he or she needs to be healed, though this knowledge may not be conscious. Nevertheless, you must release the client into the hands of the Universal Healer in order to do the most good. You are not responsible for the client's recovery, any more than you are responsible for the client's disharmony or disease. You are assisting the client in her or his journey through life and, specifically, in her or his attempts to get well. You are the helper, the server, the practitioner of a powerful healing tool. You do not have to diagnose or provide insight into the person's past disharmonies. You do not have to be a psychotherapist, or a medical doctor, or a nurse, if these are not your professions.

People will want you to be more at times. Indeed, you will be tempted to be more, in part because the practice requires so much faith, especially in the beginning when you lack experience and haven't seen the incredible effects you can have on people just by doing this seemingly simple job. This lack of experience may tempt you to fill the knowledge gap with promises or speculation. Resist these temptations with all your strength. Instead, become both a practitioner and an investigator of this practice. See for yourself what it can do. Fill up your life and your practice with real experience. Really come to know how the practice affects other people, how it changes lives and restores health. When you do this, your words will be based on what is true and real, rather than on what you think or have read. The practice works, but you must experience it working before you know in your heart that it works. Let yourself have that experience.

Follow these three rules and you will be safe in all situations:

1. Be honest with yourself; when you don't know something, admit it to yourself. Embracing your humanness is one of the most wonderful and transformative experiences you will ever have. The more you can do this simple act, the more you stand in the light of truth, the greater your own transformation, and the more powerful you become.

2. Be honest with your client; don't be trapped into inflating your role, or your knowledge, or your ego, even if it means making

the client uncomfortable temporarily. People naturally want reassurance, and you will want to give it. But sometimes that mutual desire can lure you into implying things, or promising things, that you cannot be certain of. It is better to say "I don't know" than to offer people promises that later turn out to be false or illusory. You are centered and powerful whenever you speak the truth, even if the truth is merely admitting your limitations.

3.   Respect yourself. You are taking up a role that, in other cultures and traditions, was among the most revered and honored functions in human society. Today, all practitioners of the holistic healing arts are pioneers, offering people powerful tools for establishing health. We are bringing back to the modern world the keys to health that temporarily have been forgotten. Slowly, but inexorably, holistic healing is being restored to the place of honor that was once the natural place for herbalists, acupuncturists, practitioners of Chinese medicine, Ayurveda, bodyworkers, shamans, and practitioners of healing touch. As long as you are clear about your practice and what you do, you are performing an essential service that is not being duplicated by any other profession. You belong in the healing arts. And you do not have to be any more than what you are. As you gain experience in this practice, you will learn firsthand that that is quite enough.

Meditations for Centering

MEDITATION #1

Sit in a chair with your back straight and your feet flat on the floor, hands resting on your knees. Relax. Take in a deep breath and begin an easy exhale, making an "aaahhh" sound with your voice box. After a few seconds (two or three), suspend the noise and the exhale without closing the throat. The throat should feel open as it did when you made the "aaahhh" sound. After a few seconds let the breath exhale. Repeat this two more times. You should notice by the third time that you are able to hold your breath longer. When you open your eyes the room should appear brighter. You are centered and probably in an alpha brain wave state.

MEDITATION #2: THE EGG MEDITATION

1.　Sit in a comfortable chair with your feet flat on the floor, hands on your knees.
2.　Take a few deep even breaths and then begin to breathe rhythmically. Concentrate on your breath. Watch the breath.
3.　Meanwhile, let go of all thoughts. If any thought enters your mind, watch it float into and out of your consciousness. Feel your consciousness enter more deeply into your body.
4.　Picture yourself enclosed in an egg-shaped bubble that surrounds you at a distance of about an arm's length. Feel the outer edge as kind of a strong, semipermeable membrane, something like a Plexiglas shield, that allows only positive, loving energy to escape your inner being and the bubble; the bubble only allows such loving, supportive, and positive energy to enter the bubble and embrace you, as well.
5.　Balance the front and the back of the egg or bubble so that the energy feels equal on all sides. This balances the output of energy between the front and back chakras.
6.　Maintain a steady, slow, rhythmic breath, noting any places in your body where you are holding tension. Breathe into that tension and release it.
7.　Notice your posture. Maintain your centeredness and an erect posture with your breath.
8.　See the protective energetic shield as a force of invulnerable love. It is designed to protect you, while it allows you to help others.

This meditation is not designed to place boundaries between you and your client, or between you and the world. Rather, it is designed to maintain the integrity of your own energy field, to close any leaks, and to allow you to focus the healing energy that you are channeling in your work. The egg meditation is designed to create a powerful sphere around you so that you will be protected from your client's energetic imbalances, disharmonies, and any illnesses the client may be suffering from. This bubble is composed of your loving energy, and thus vibrates at a rate that is not conducive to your client's disharmony or imbalance. Anything that your client sheds or releases during the session, therefore, will not be able to attach itself to you.

MEDITATION #3

In his book *Awaken Healing Energy Through the Tao,* Korean healer and teacher Mantah Chia provides a meditation that teaches us to circulate the Qi throughout the body. This meditation helps each of us, as practitioners, restore our own health and maintain balance and harmony. Once again, the responsibility of the practitioner—especially one who works with the transmission of energy—is to keep his or her own field clean and health strong.

Sit in a quiet, peaceful room, on a comfortable chair, with your back straight and your feet flat on the floor. Rub your hands, feet, arms, and legs with your hands. Rotate your neck. Place your hands in your lap with both palms up, your right hand resting on top of your left. Your eyes can be open or closed, though closing them will make it easier to visualize during the meditation. Then perform the following steps:

1. Look down into your body and smile down the front line of the upper part of your body. Smile into your eyes; smile to your face, neck, throat, heart, blood and circulatory system, lungs, kidneys, adrenals, liver, pancreas, and spleen.
2. Now smile down the mid-line of your digestive tract. Smile to your esophagus and stomach. Swallow your saliva and let it

carry the smile down into those organs. Smile down into your small intestine, down into your large intestine, rectum, and anus. Continue to swallow saliva and visualize it carrying your smile downward through your entire digestive tract.

3. Focus on the back of your body. Send your smile down the spine, vertebra by vertebra.

4. Release your jaws and touch the tongue to the palate.

5. Complete the meditation by collecting the energy at the navel. Spiral the energy inside the navel one and a half inches deep. Women should spiral the energy thirty-six times counterclockwise and twenty-four times clockwise. Men should spiral the energy in the opposite direction—thirty-six times clockwise and twenty-four times counterclockwise.

This inner smile will have profound changes on your life if done every day, as it begins to repattern the energy flow through your entire body.

The following meditation is designed to help you, the healer, center and clear your own energy.

EXERCISE #4—CENTERING AND CLEARING

1. Take some deep breaths, relaxing your mind, letting go of all thoughts and words. Feel the relaxed rhythm of your breath.

2. Picture a small globe of light that is your soul about six inches above your head. Above that, picture a larger globe of light that is the sun or the source of all living things (The Light of Love).

3. Slowly visualize a beam of light full of all colors of the rainbow from the source through your soul into your crown. Feel the crown chakra take the color that it needs to expand this area. Release what is no longer useful there into the Light of Love.

4. Drop the rainbow light into the brow of the third eye. Feel the color that is needed expand from the rainbow and be released

into the chakra. Feel the area expand and release what it no longer needs into the Light of Love.

5. Let the rainbow light descend into the throat chakra, filling it with light, expanding and releasing.
6. Fill the heart space, expanding and releasing.
7. Visualize the light moving into the solar plexus, expanding and releasing.
8. Next, visualize the energy moving down into the sacral chakra, expanding and releasing.
9. Now fill the root chakra with this light, expanding and releasing.
10. Split the light, seeing it travel down both legs, exiting through the arches in the feet, going deeply into the earth.
11. Feel the rainbow of colors fill you. Feel the peace and balance. Feel the connection with the source as you ground to the earth.
12. When you are ready and it feels right, open your eyes and let your light shine.

All of these techniques will center you in your spiritual roots. They will also help to balance your energetic field, will open the tube down the center of the field to allow the free flow of energy through the body, and ultimately will help to heal you.

Now, let's turn our attention to yet another layer of helping others—specifically, using the hands to heal.

7

❧

Assessing the
Energy Field

When I begin to work with a person, I spend time trying to understand the client's specific issues. I begin by asking the person to fill out an intake questionnaire that describes his or her current symptoms and conditions (see appendix 1). The questionnaire requests information on current health complaints, if any; health history; any herbs or medication being taken; and the person's reasons for seeing me. If the person is not seeing a physician or some other health professional at the time he or she comes to me, I recommend one or another whom I know or whose work I respect. Nothing I do is meant to replace the work of a medical doctor or other appropriate health care professionals. Healing touch is meant to complement the work of a physician, not to compete with it. This is especially important if the person is suffering from a serious illness.

Once the questionnaire has been filled out, I discuss any health, psychological, or interpersonal disharmonies he or she may be experiencing as part of an initial interview. I want to get to know the person I'll be working with in such an intimate and important way. The discussion can involve any aspect of a person's life that is a source of stress or disharmony, ranging from a personal health issue to a marital or financial problem. In addition to getting to know the person, I also try to figure out where in the field the person's problems may be rooted. As I listen to and observe him or her, I try to discern which chakras or areas within the field may be involved in the person's disharmony and where I should begin working.

Once I have some insight into the problem, I assess the energy field. I do this for all my clients, even those whom I have been seeing regularly for some time. I begin by having the person sit on a stool, so that all sides of the field and body are exposed. (If you do not have such a stool, have the person sit in a straight-backed chair so that the chair's back is to his or her immediate left. This will allow you to move your hands through the front and back of the person's field.) Also, I ask my client to take off his or her shoes before I start the session. This allows me to determine whether or not the energy is flowing freely from the feet when I assess that part of the field. I stand behind the seated person, center myself, and as I do, I stand with my left hand raised above my head, with the palm of my hand facing the sky. My right arm is down at my side, slightly away from my body, with the palm facing downward toward the earth (see the photograph 3 on page 225). Now I am receiving the life force from the two poles of life, so to speak, heaven and earth. While in this position, I am saying my prayer.

When I feel deeply centered, I bring my hands together and feel the spongy ball (described in chapter 3)—soft, fluffy, and resilient—between my hands. It's about the size of a basketball, perhaps a little smaller. I feel the ball in front of me at the level of my vibral core. I then move the ball in my hands toward the person's vibral core, at his back, visualizing the connection of my vibral core to the patient through the energy ball. Then I move to my patient's right side and place my hands about a foot over his head. I dissolve the energy ball into his field and "see" it enrich his field with life force. Slowly, I allow my hands to come apart and simultaneously move down the front and back of the patient's field, all the while assessing his energy. My hands are anywhere from six to eighteen inches from the person's body. Meanwhile, I am reciting my prayer to remain centered and empty of distracting thoughts.

"Seeing" and "Listening" with Your Touch

I assess the field with my hands, but in effect I am touching the field with my entire being. I am so attuned to the energy that I am feeling it with a type of perception that is the synthesis of all my physical perceptions and yet is beyond my physical perceptions. It's as if my physical perceptions and those of my higher self all combine to form a singular intelligence, a unified perception, that goes just beyond my everyday senses. Thus, as I touch the field, I am "listening" to it with my hands; I am "seeing" it with my fingers; I am sensing something that might be thought of as smell or taste but goes beyond these as well.

As I conduct my assessment, I move my hands downward from the top of the client's head and down the front and back of the body. I run my hands gently over the field in the area of the heart (right hand) and the back of the lungs (left hand), over the stomach and kidneys, over the lower intestinal tract and lumbar area of the spine, over the front and back of the legs, and down to the feet. Meanwhile, I note any imbalance or deviation from that resilient ball of "cotton candy." I feel how resilient and closed the field feels in most places, as if there is an egg-shaped energy with a specific boundary area. As I move my hands farther along the periphery of the field, I may begin to perceive aberrations.

Perceiving Changes in Temperature and Density

The most common sensation is a very subtle resilience, which dominates most people's fields, or what I referred to in chapter 2 as "cotton candy." Changes in temperature are also common. Some places may feel cool, others cold; some places in the field are warm, and occasionally I encounter significant heat.

In general, you typically do not feel a change in temperature when going over the client's field. However, whenever you do notice a decline in temperature—a relatively cool or cold spot—it can often mean a decrease in energy and may appear over places where there is little life force. Those energy dips may indicate that that part of the body was wounded long ago, causing a diminished flow of blood, lymph, and life force to that area and creating the conditions for a disharmony of some kind. The person may not experience the underlying conditions until the disharmony reaches an acute phase, but long before the physical body experiences the disorder, the underlying energetic causes of disharmony were already present.

Low back injuries are a good example of this phenomenon. It is quite common for people to experience a low back injury simply by bending down and picking up a newspaper—hardly a strenuous task. In fact, the conditions for the injury were there within the back muscles and vertebrae for a long time—sometimes for more than a decade—before these underlying conditions suddenly went from a latent or dormant phase to an acute phase disorder. Picking up the newspaper was simply the proverbial "straw" that served only as the catalyst of the injury. The energy within the back becomes increasingly imbalanced—too much energy in some places, too little in others—until the extremes cause an acute imbalance in the muscles of the back, manifesting as excessive contraction among certain muscles and excessive weakness in others. The spinal vertebrae are kept in alignment by muscle tension that is essentially equal on the left and right sides of the spine. However, muscles on one side usually become too contracted and lose their flexibility; they can no longer expand and contract within their normal ranges. Other muscles become excessively weak and thus can no longer support the vertebrae or other muscles, meaning that one side of the back muscles is pulling harder than the other side. Eventually, the smallest action—such as picking up a newspaper—can cause the contracted muscles to go into spasm and in the process pull the vertebrae to one side of the back. On the other side, the weak muscles give way, allowing the spine to curve unnaturally in the direction of the contracted muscles. This causes the spine to force the vertebrae to pinch nerves and is perceived as an acute injury. Once the condition reaches an acute phase, the area becomes inflamed and hot. Heat is often a sign of increased circulation, inflammation, and sometimes fever—all symptoms of the acute phase.

Stones and Boulders: The Blockages that Bind

To understand the nature of energetic blockages, you must recognize that energy is constantly moving through the field in great channels, like rushing rivers. As long as the energy is circulating through the field and physical body, there is an abundance of life force flowing to organs, tissues, and cells, and thus there is health and harmony within the entire system. Disharmony arises when the energy is blocked. Your job, as a practitioner of healing touch, is to remove those blockages and to send additional life force to areas that have been deprived of energy.

When a river is blocked with a stone or debris, water swirls around the blockage, creating eddies. Also, in front of the stone is an overabundance of water—it builds up and swells high on the rock—while at the other side of the stone the water is low. The side of the stone that faces the oncoming energy is therefore excessive in energy, while the side of the stone that is opposite is deficient. It's the same in the energetic field of the human body. Blockages exist like the stones, or boulders, that create eddies in some areas, excesses in others, and deficiencies in still others. In fact, blockages almost always create excess energy in the foreground and deficiencies in the lee. Boulders tie up life force, or bind it, thus blocking it from flowing abundantly to other areas of the field and body. An example is Wendy, the person I spoke about in chapter 2, who is overcoming MS. Wendy experienced blockages behind the neck, and a deficiency of energy in the limbs.

Deficiencies in the field can be perceived as the absence of energy, and sometimes as a hole, or what I refer to as a leak. Holes or leaks arise not just from blockages elsewhere in the field but also from traumas experienced early in life that inflicted wounds on the energetic body.

Holes in the Field: The Physical Locations of Guilt and Shame

Holes or leaks are energetic patterns within the field that allow energy to escape, causing the person to experience a sudden change in emotions (usually bringing on negative emotions), a loss of energy, and a loss of his or her personal integrity. A common symptom of a leak is a negative emotional pattern that is consistent but usually irrational. Leaks trigger feelings of guilt, shame, anger, low self-esteem, and personal failure.

Leaks in the field, and their corresponding emotional patterns, are established in childhood, when parents or guardians teach children how to react to difficult situations that may involve personal responsibility. They are also caused by physical or psychological abuse. Such abuse injures the field literally, causing a tear or rip or hole. We must remember that verbal or physical abuse is an energetic and vibrational act as well as a physical act. A parent need not strike a child to make the child feel injured; the injury can be accomplished just as effectively—and sometimes even more permanently—with a word or a set of words, especially if those words are shouted in anger or rage. Sometimes, that is the very reason the words are said in the first place, though few people would admit it: They are meant to "wound." The effects of such verbal or vibrational attacks on the field are analogous to striking your arm with your fist. If you strike your arm for a certain amount of time, you will cause the capillaries to be broken and your arm will turn black and blue; if you persist, you will eventually break the skin; and if you persist still longer, you will break the bone. Energetic attacks on one's field are done with the emotional vibration and the intent that is embedded in words and attitudes. This vibration causes an actual wound in the energy field, just as striking your arm causes a physical wound in your flesh. An emotional or psychological wound will leak life energy from the child's—and later the adult's—field until it is healed.

Every human being counts on his or her field to give a clear sense of self, of boundaries, that describes the limits of his or her responsibility in any given situation. To know one's limits is to have control over one's life. When a child's field has a hole in it (or numerous holes, for that matter), the child does not learn a healthy sense of boundaries and has no clear or realistic understanding of personal responsibility. Without such boundaries, the life energy is drawn out of the child's field, the sense of self is weakened, and the child is susceptible to being unhealthfully influenced by other people's values, identities, needs, and desires. The child or adult may come to identify so thoroughly with another human being that he or she adopts that other person's desires as if they were his or her own, living only to please another human being. The child cannot feel any sense of self-worth unless everyone else in his life, including his family members and other key people, are happy and satisfied. This, of course, means that the child can never be happy or centered. He will always try to please others because his life force is constantly extending to and overlapping with others, thus causing him to identify too much with the needs of others. This emotional and energetic pattern determines a child's beliefs about himself, his family, and the world. It affects how a child interprets experience and whether or not he can utilize his own strengths in certain situations.

Even when a child reaches adulthood, he still experiences guilt or shame or anguish whenever he confronts similar situations as those that created the initial hole and energy leak. Once again, he loses his sense of self, of perspective, of boundaries, even of self-protection. In a sense, he doesn't see reality; instead, he feels his pain, or rather, he reexperiences an old, ongoing, and ever-repeating pain. It's the same old drama: Someone close to him isn't happy; he feels he is to blame for that person's pain, so he himself cannot be happy. Thus, he experiences a loss of energy, of integrity, and all the same old feelings of guilt, shame, anger, and injustice. At bottom, he feels he isn't worthy of love or life, especially self-love. In order to compensate for such feelings, he often finds himself doing more than what is actually asked of him, which results in a tremendous expenditure of energy. The resulting praise is often sufficient reward—at least for a time—and can drive a person to high degrees of self-denial. Such a person becomes increasingly self-deprecating. Eventually, his needs begin to surface, however, but because he was trained—and maintained his own training—to deny himself, the result is often anger and even bitterness. This sets up a pattern of ongoing leaks.

To some extent, a hole in the field is always leaking a relatively small amount of energy, even in those situations when the person is not made to feel inferior or shameful. Leaks will continually drain energy, which is why the person who has such leaks closed—even for a short period of time—experiences a sudden increase in energy and overall vitality. This is why I say that closing leaks is one of the most important functions in healing touch.

Guilt: The Wound that Stays Alive by Keeping You Blind to Its Existence

Guilt and shame are the most common emotions to surface whenever leaks in the field are exposed. Guilt makes you feel that you should have done something that you didn't, or that you shouldn't have done something that you did. The implicit belief that gives rise to guilt is that you could have been more than you were, which is a delusion. You cannot be more than you are at any given moment. Each situation arises and you meet it with the physical, psychological, and spiritual resources you have available in that moment. You can be nothing more, nor anything less.

To better understand guilt, we must see the difference between guilt and remorse. Guilt is a chronic feeling, an unhealed wound, that reminds us that we need to be healed. Remorse, on the other hand, is the feeling of deep sorrow for having hurt someone. Deeply felt remorse leads to change. Guilt, conversely, tends to maintain its own patterns. This is the irony of guilt, because you would think that because guilt is so unpleasant, it would prevent us from repeating the same pattern, but it doesn't work that way. *Guilt actually stops us from examining our pain.* Guilt gives rise to a pain that is inarticulate, imprecise, and opaque. Very often, we're not sure why we feel guilty; all we know is that we do. But the underlying belief below the pain is that, somehow, we should have been a different person from the person we were.

Guilt is a wound in the field that leaks energy. Certain energetic patterns in the field and in the person's behavior and thinking may keep that wound from healing. As a consequence, each time one meets a situation that resembles the one that caused the original wound, these same feelings occur.

Guilt and shame, in a subtle yet powerful way, cause all of us to lose our sense of integrity, self-protection, and centeredness. Whoever the person is who has made you feel guilty has managed to open one of these leaky places. Once that happens, you give yourself over to the person's judgment of you, as if he or she had the greater hold on truth. Your own personal integrity has broken down; you feel weaker, more unsure, energetically ill-defined, as if you no longer have a clear sense of who you are, where you begin, and where you end. This loss of clarity is due to the breakdown of your own energetic boundary, a boundary that protects you, identifies you, encloses you within it, and gives you a feeling of integrity, wholeness, and strength.

Looking for the Clues to Guide the Course of Healing

Once I have located an imbalance in the field—no matter what type it is—I note the area, its nearest chakra, and its correspondence to the body. I look for clues that will reveal the source or sources of the imbalance. If the imbalance is over the heart area, for example, I note the possibility of a disharmony in the heart chakra, the possibility of an emotional issue, and perhaps some form of heart disease. If it is over the lower abdomen, I wonder about the health of the large intestine or sex organs; if it is over the solar plexus, I wonder about the liver (particularly if the imbalance is on the right side of the body), or the spleen/pancreas (if it is over the left), or the stomach (if it is directly in the center). An imbalance over the solar plexus, or just below it, might also suggest that the stomach and small intestine are in distress.

I also keep in mind the spiral of energy, which reveals how energy moves through and nourishes the chakras. As you will recall from chapter 4, the order in which the life force moves through the chakras is from the fourth chakra to the third, then to the fifth, to the second, to the sixth, to the first, and then to the seventh. Headaches (a sixth chakra disorder) may be caused by a first or second chakra imbalance. Sore throats (a fifth chakra disorder) may be caused by a third or second chakra imbalance. Whenever I encounter a known symptom, I look for the corresponding chakra imbalance. I also examine the chakras directly above and below the disorder. I am looking for any evidence of excessive or deficient energy that may cause an imbalance in its neighboring chakra. This is particularly true if the condition is chronic and standard medical treatment has been unable to cure it.

Posture: A Window into Imbalance

Both the field and the physical body maintain a dynamic equilibrium. An excess in one place typically creates a deficiency in another. The two extremes work in tandem, often creating visible distortions in the physical body. Posture is an outstanding example of this. The posture will express clearly where excesses and deficiencies lie. When you see a person with a large, expanded upper back and a concave chest, this type of posture creates a distinct S-shaped curve in the body when looked at from the right side, with the shoulder area curved back and the stomach curved in. The upper back seems bigger and fleshier; the chest seems smaller and retracted; the stomach area is pushed forward. Such a posture prevents deep breathing, which means that the breath is most active in the upper lung area and least active in the lower. This means that the upper part of the lungs is expanded and excessive in energy—they are the part doing the most breathing— while the lower lobes of the lung are contracted and deficient of energy. There are probably large blockages of energy over the neck and back, preventing the life force from going deeply into the lungs. Without sufficient life force, the lower part of the lungs will contract, and then atrophy, and eventually manifest a symptom.

Shallow breathing forces the heart to work harder to pump sufficient oxygen to cells; this causes the heart to beat more rapidly. In all likelihood, the heart is tired and overworked, which means that despite its rapid beating—or rather, because of it—the heart is deficient. The small intestine, which is responsible for absorption of nutrients, is probably contracted, meaning that the organ itself has narrowed. The villi, which are fingerlike projections in the organ that absorb nutrients, are coated with bacteria and enmeshed with each other, preventing them from optimally absorbing nutrition. The large intestine, responsible for absorption of water and elimination of waste, is expanded physically and becomes sluggish in its function. The organ is swollen, has lost muscle tone, and can eventually suffer from diverticulosis. The large intestine also lacks life force, or is deficient of energy. Both of these symptoms are revealed by the contraction in the upper stomach area and the swollen abdomen. In short, the person suffers from any of a variety of heart, lung, and digestive disorders, including either constipation or diarrhea. This type of posture invariably causes problems in the second chakra (lower abdomen), the third (solar plexus), the fourth (heart), and the fifth (throat).

Many middle-aged men often present distended stomachs, especially in the area of the solar plexus (third chakra), while the kidney area (second chakra) is curved inward, toward the front of the body. The posture looks like a bow—or one long outward curve from the face to the bottom of the torso. The person does not have to be terribly overweight: The distention and swelling of the stomach varies widely depending on the person and his relative imbalance. Nevertheless, when viewed from the side, the person seems to be all front and no back. This stature is particularly common among businessmen who are constantly struggling to meet deadlines and push through deals. The third chakra is excessive and probably frustrated. The liver is swollen and excessive; the adrenals are overworked, exhausted, and contracted. The life force, housed in the kidneys, is tired, meaning both the kidneys and the second chakra are weak and deficient. For such a person, life is an ongoing struggle for survival among the fittest.

Occasionally you will see a person whose posture is fairly straight and relaxed except for a small paunch around and below the belt and a slightly concave solar plexus. Generally, there are two types of people with this posture: one person is considerably overweight and quite round; the other is tall, thin (except for the paunch in the stomach), and lank. In both types, the second chakra is weak and deficient, which suggests prostate problems (in men) and ovarian problems (in women). It also reveals swollen large intestines and weak elimination. The weak solar plexus area, coupled with the deficient second chakra, suggests a person with a very weak will, but that manifests quite differently in the two different statures, especially among men. The round man is usually jolly, positive, and satisfied with his lot. The tall, lank man is typically dissatisfied but highly repressed. He doesn't think much about his circumstances. It's as if something inside has been turned off. He's surrendered the struggle to grow or succeed. He's getting by; he doesn't enjoy much of anything fully, and he gives the impression of being asleep on some level.

*   *   *

In general, excesses of energy and deficiencies tend to balance each other and work as opposites. Very often, excesses of energy, blockages, and boulders appear in places of acute tension, such as the shoulders, the neck, the head, and the pelvis. Deficiencies are common in the chest, lungs, heart, and sex organs. Sometimes the right side of the body is excessive while the left is deficient, or vice versa. Often, you will find that the liver is excessive (on the right side of the body, just beneath the ribs) while the spleen/pancreas (on the left in the same area) is deficient.

Whenever you see imbalances in the posture, use your hands to explore the field closely. Concentrate and feel the energy with your entire being. Search the field with your hands, heart, and mind to determine where the blockages are and where the deficiencies and holes are located. Feel the tension in the field; feel the temperature changes, the boulders, and the holes. Trust your intuition and sense of touch, but be humble. Gently ask the person whether he or she suffers from digestive problems, if you see the possibility of intestinal imbalances, or heart palpitations, if you see deficiencies or excesses in the heart. When you sense an imbalance in the heart chakra, do not assume that the person has heart disease. Always ask the person if he or she suffers from any symptoms in the areas in which you sense problems, and if so, ask the person to see a physician.

When the Two Become One

During healing touch, you and the person with whom you are working share the same life energy. I have found that this sharing is very much a two-way street and that information passes back and forth between you during your session. This communication occurs in different ways. During the session, you may experience certain symptoms in your body, such as sudden movement, spasm, heat, tingling, prickly sensations, and mild pain. Very often, these symptoms appear in you because you are so attuned to the recipient's body and energetic field that you are reacting to the treatment as he or she is. Changes occurring in the recipient's field and body are reflected in yours, though on a much more reduced and very temporary scale. These experiences can guide you in your work. If you feel it is appropriate, tell the recipient of healing touch what you are feeling and ask if he or she is experiencing similar symptoms. At the same time, do not become attached to the pain or sensation, since it is generally not organic in your system. If you didn't have any similar sensations while you were centering, it is unlikely that they originated in your body. Thank these feelings for guiding you and release them as you exhale. As you become a more seasoned practitioner, you will no longer need to feel such symptoms in your body as a guide.

Another way in which information passes back and forth between you is through images or symbols that appear suddenly in your mind, as they did when I treated Wendy. The mind is not restricted to the brain, but also resides in the field. During healing touch, you are within this person's field; you are touching her mind. Powerful images that have shaped the recipient's life are still stored in her psyche and can pass easily from her field to yours and then suddenly become conscious to you. You might even experience the same thoughts and emotions as the recipient, including sudden feelings of fear, discomfort, or anger.

I cannot stress enough how important it is to center yourself at the outset of every treatment and to remain centered throughout the treatment. Whenever you experience images or emotions during a treatment, redouble your concentration by focusing on your prayer. This will protect you throughout the treatment and afterward.

I avoid discussing any image or emotion that I experience during the session with my client until I feel that we have established a bond of trust. The amount of time it takes to develop such a bond varies widely from person to person, of course, and only you can determine the right time for such a discussion. The essential point is that you should avoid jumping to conclusions after you have experienced this exchange of information. Such interpretations have to be correct, first of all, and shared at a time when the client is prepared to hear and accept such information. Wait for the right moment and then share the experience in a very gentle and unassuming way. The best way is simply to ask the person if the image you saw, or the feeling you experienced, has any resonance with him. You might ask the person: Do you relate at all to this image (or feeling)? If he says no, then file the experience in your memory. He may bring up the subject again when he is prepared to speak about it, or you may have a clearer insight into your experience later on that may be useful in your treatment.

We must remember the axiom I stated in chapter 1: Being a healer makes its greatest demands on the healer and not on the client. Your work as a practitioner of healing touch will force you to grow, and grow rapidly, in part because you will be confronting issues in others that will trigger the same or different issues in you. A person who has a terminal disease will cause you personal fears; the recipient who has undergone traumas that you find abhorrent will move you strongly; the client whom you dislike will make you face old wounds inside yourself. Everyone on whom you practice will present you with a challenge that is entirely your own, because each of those people will make you face yourself. Each person on whom you work becomes your teacher, and should be so revered.

Grounding the Patient by "Opening the Feet"

At the conclusion of the assessment process comes a step I call "opening the feet," or allowing the energy that is flowing down through the body to exit the feet and unify with the earth. This step provides a deep sense of physical, psychological, and spiritual stability to the person on whom you are working. It also allows energy that is backed up and blocked in the upper part of the body to be released. This step alone often harmonizes the entire field and can relieve many painful symptoms in the upper body, especially head-aches, because it draws the energy down from the upper part of the body and field and into the lower parts.

Most people perform more mental labor than physical each day. To support this work, their energy shifts from the lower parts of the physical body to the upper, especially to the head, neck, and shoulders. In addition, stress causes the sympathetic nervous system to shift energy and nerve innervation to the periphery of the body to support the physical reactions associated with the well-known flight-or-fight response. Thus, intellectual work and stress combine to move the energy away from the center of being and into the body's periphery, especially to the brain. This creates energetic imbalances. The upper part of the body, such as the shoulders, neck, and upper arms, can become excessive and stagnant, while organs in the center of the body, such as the liver, stomach, digestive tract, and sex organs, can become deficient and weak. (For more on the kinds of imbalances created by stress, see chapter 9.) Therefore, I try to draw the energy from the upper and peripheral parts of the body to the internal and lower parts by opening the feet. This is how it is done:

Once I have reached the bottoms of the legs in my assessment, I gently massage the muscles and tendons behind the knees, especially the points directly in the center behind the knees—the site of secondary chakras, you will recall. I massage the site in a slow, consistent fashion. This is the first and sometimes the only time I touch the physical body. After a few minutes of gently massaging the back of the knee, I gradually move down the calf and on to the Achilles tendon and then to the bottom of the foot of the same leg, massaging deeply, gently, and rhythmically. (I work on each leg and foot individually.)

While I do this work, I consciously try to pull the energy down from the upper part of the body into the lower legs and feet. You will recall from chapter 3 how we practiced pulling the energy from one part of the body and pushing it to another. Here, I visualize pulling the energy from the head, chest, abdomen, hips, and thighs, and sending it down into the calf muscle, Achilles tendon, and bottom of the foot. This massage and pulling of energy centers the person, balances the energy throughout the body, and stabilizes the patient's field.

I then attempt to "open the feet" by holding the secondary chakras at the arches of the feet. This will allow the energy that I have brought down into the feet to flow out and make its natural link with the earth, thus giving the person a sense of being "grounded," or physically and psychologically stable.

I do this by placing my middle finger on the arch of the foot and massaging gently. At first, I try to sense the subtle energy emerging from the foot. I try to determine if the energy is flowing out of the secondary chakra on the bottom of the foot, as it should, or if it is blocked. You can often feel the stagnation of the energy within the foot because the skin itself feels tight, thick, or hard. Sometimes the bottoms of the feet feel inert, almost wooden, rather than supple and alive. If the energy is blocked, I ask the client to breathe deeply and try to visualize the life force moving into the body with each breath and then down into the feet. On the out breath, the person should visualize the energy moving out of the bottoms of the feet and into the earth. Meanwhile, I hold my hand on the foot, at the arch, and feel myself pulling the energy down into the feet as the patient inhales. I also visualize the secondary chakras at the arch opening and becoming active and revitalized. As the patient exhales, I visualize the energy moving out of the feet and rejoining the earth. I do the same with both feet.

No matter what I sense when I touch the feet, I always try to open the chakras at the feet by gently massaging the arches and pulling the energy down and out of the foot. I then hold the foot at the arch until the energy changes, which can take five to ten minutes.

All of this work has a significant effect on the recipient because, in effect, I have literally directed his consciousness and life force to the areas where I wanted it. Remember, I did not touch the person's physical body until I began massaging the backs of the patient's knees. I then began to work on the calves, tendons, and feet. This pattern of touching the knees, calves, and feet directs the person's awareness first to the backs of the knees and then down to the calves, tendons, and into the feet. By doing that, I am directing his life energy in the same way—downward and ultimately to the secondary chakras at the arches. I am not merely visualizing the movement of energy, but literally directing the patient to move his own energy to the places within the body where I want it. By asking the patient to "breathe into the feet" and visualize the energy moving with the breath, I am also utilizing the person's natural ability to move his own energy. Thus, we are working together to move his consciousness and the life force back into the body and reunite it with the earth.

After I have held one foot for a time and "feel" with my entire being the flow of energy leaving the foot, I perform the same exercise on the other foot, and once again ask the recipient to visualize the energy penetrating deeply into the feet from the rest of the body on the inhalation and out of the feet on the exhalation.

When I am sure that the energy is flowing through the feet, I resume the first position, with my hands over the recipient's head. I then slowly but steadily run my hands over the recipient's field once again to determine how the energy has changed. Each time a healing touch practitioner passes his or her hands through a recipient's field, he or she has changed that energy field.

In the meanwhile, I have forgotten myself entirely in the process. I am thinking of nothing but my prayer, but the prayer allows me to be empty. It gives my mind something to do, something to be occupied with, while my higher self directs my actions. Now I am ready to work on the field.

Associative Ideas

The practice of any traditional healing therapy inevitably leads you into an exploration of other ancient practices, which, you will find, share many underlying themes. Healing touch is consistent with and even shares many of the same principles of other ancient therapies, especially Chinese medicine. The more I study Chinese medicine, the more impressed I am with its insight into the nature of health and disease, the efficacy of its methods of treatment, and its ability to understand the relationship between the body and the mind. It is this latter understanding that can be so helpful to you, particularly when assessing the origin of particular health problems. Nothing within Chinese medicine better articulates the relationship between body and mind better than the Theory of the Five Elements.

More than two thousand years ago, ancient Chinese sages developed a system that has come to be known as the Theory of the Five Elements, which is a complex but powerful healing tool. Among the important aspects of the theory is the association of specific emotions and psychological states within certain parts of the body. The Chinese found that particular types of emotions were grounded in certain individual organs. As the Chinese saw it, the mind was grounded in the body and depended on the health of the body for the proper functioning of the psyche. As long as the organ is healthy, the Chinese sages said, these emotions and psychological states will remain in balance. Hence, the equilibrium of the mind depends upon the health of the body.

After more than fifteen years of practice, I have found that the Chinese were right in their association of organs and emotions. The more imbalanced the liver is, for example, the more a person is prone to anger. The more imbalanced the heart, the less joy and laughter a person experiences. My experience has also given me additional insights into the link between organs and emotional states. Below is a list of organs and their associated psychological conditions; it is based on the Chinese system, my own experience, and research. Use this list as a loose guide in your own practice and, specifically, in your assessment of your client's field. Discover for yourself if these associations are true. I have deliberately kept them short to serve as springboards to your own intuition and creativity. The idea is not to get locked into these associations but to use them as a guide for exploration and study. Also, notice how your recipient's emotional condition changes as his or her health improves.

The list provides the characteristics people experience when the organ is generally balanced and healthy, as well as the characteristics that dominate the personality when the organ is imbalanced and suffers from some disorder. It's important to note that all of us, from time to time, experience the characteristics that are associated with imbalance. What you should be looking for when you do your assessment of a client are the characteristics that dominate the personality and profoundly shape the person's outlook on life.

ORGAN	PERSONALITY CHARACTERISTICS WHEN ORGAN IS BALANCED	EMOTIONS AND PSYCHOLOGY WHEN SIGNIFICANTLY IMBALANCED
LIVER	Strong ability to express strong will; good	Anger, frustration, weak will, inability to express oneself, overly timid
SPLEEN	Good self-esteem, centered personality, lack of worry, compassion and understanding	Worry, anxiety, nervousness
STOMACH	Strong appetite for life, good ability to enjoy a wide variety of people and types of experience	Nervous; poor appetite for life; very picky about food, people, and types of experiences he or she can tolerate

HEART	Can give and feel love, can identify with others, can feel connected to others	Walls self off from love and affection, feels isolated and tends to sustain isolation, may be given to hysteria, depression, low self-esteem
PANCREAS	Good sense of boundaries	Suffers from chronic guilt
GALL-BLADDER	Decisive, good digestion	Indecisive, poor digestion
SMALL INTESTINE	Can determine what is good in experience and what should be discarded	Has trouble finding the good in people, situations, and one's own experience in life
SKIN	Good sense of boundaries, positive sense of self, good self-esteem, good elimination from kidneys and large intestine	Weak sense of boundaries; poor self-esteem and sense of self; poor elimination from kidneys, bladder, and large intestine
LARGE INTESTINE	Able to let go of the past, not overly burdened by sadness or grief	Constipation: holding on to old memories, sadness, and grief; unable to let go of old hurts; trouble letting go of the past Diarrhea: unable to get the most out of experience. Lets go too easily of people and relationships

THYROID	Good self-expression	Hypothyroid: low energy and generally weak self-expression
		Hyperthyroid: racing, unable to deeply appreciate the moment or one's own contributions to an endeavor
SEX ORGANS	Good expression of one's own unique self and creativity	Holding back one's expression and creativity
KIDNEYS	Confident and generally secure personality	Suffers from deep-rooted fears
LUNGS	Good energy and vitality, strong ability to take in and enjoy life	Repressed emotions, low energy (oxygen is the basis for energy), low self-esteem, strong sense of one's own weakness or frailty

Everything Is Searching for Balance

The body, mind, and spirit are always searching for balance in all ways, especially energetically. Whenever you see excessive strength, you will also discover weakness nearby. Always look for the paired opposites. Once you discover the imbalance, you will want to move the energy from the area of excess to the places where it is deficient.

A practitioner of healing touch is always trying to restore balance to the body, mind, and spirit.

If you keep these guidelines in your mind as you are doing your assessment, you will be able to know where the blockages in the field lie, even if you cannot "feel" the energy as yet.

EXERCISE—THREE POINT MEDITATION

As you recall, we have mentioned that it is the whole field that becomes charged with energy from the universal source before the energy work. The healer works as a whole unit. The hands can merely direct and be specific with the energy.

The first part of the following exercise teaches you to use your own field to reach out and "scan" the other person, and the second part teaches you to send healing energy through your field to the other person.

This exercise can be done with two or more people. If there are more than two people, pick the person who is going to be scanned and have him or her sit in the middle with the rest of the group forming a circle around him or her. (See diagram 3-Point Meditation in the color insert.)

1. Start this exercise by using the meditative clearing exercise from chapter 1, choosing one person to guide the imagery. Picture the sun or source over the center of the whole group, not over each one individually. Do this for about five minutes.

    The person who has been chosen to guide this meditation will now guide the rest through the imagery.

    • The person in the center should focus on what he needs to heal within any part of his body, emotion, or mind, while also keeping himself centered in his egg or bubble (see the egg meditation, page 140).
    • The rest of the group should be centered in their individual energy eggs and begin to move their energy from the front of their eggs to gently make contact with the person in the center of the circle in a neutral energy mode. Stay here for

five minutes and just feel or get a sense of what is going on with this person. Note any images you have, any physical sensations, any thoughts, etc.

After five minutes, gently withdraw your energy. Open your eyes and have each person in the group share with the person in the center what each received. The person in the center should also share what he received. Remember that you have been in the center person's sacred space. Not only is this information confidential within the group, but you have been privy to secrets within the person and you should be gentle with how you share the thoughts. Remember that the purpose of healing touch is "to help and to heal" from a nonjudgmental place.

Chat for a short time. Some associations may have *no* relevance at the time. That happens.

2. In the same circle, center yourselves again by breathing. The person in the center should open himself to receive healing energies. The group should bring healing energy from the source through each to the center person through each individual field. Continue this for about five minutes. Your energy is in the "gentle push" stage. At the end of five minutes, consciously feel your energy go into neutral and withdraw your energy from the center person's sacred space.

Each one takes a turn being in the middle, each being supportive of the other.

It is important to remember that when you are in another's sacred space, you know everything about that person. It may not be conscious in you, but on some level there is a great awareness. You must remember not only to be nonjudgmental but to honor this space as you would your own.

8

Working on the Field

Barbara came to me in July 1988 suffering from terrible migraine headaches that kept her in bed about once a week, on average. Sometimes the symptoms that accompanied the headaches—nausea, vomiting, sensitivity to light, and aching shoulders and back—would force her to remain in bed for four or five days. She also endured chronic low back pain, fibroid tumors, ovarian pain (especially at the time of her periods), premenstrual syndrome (PMS), and the early stages of an ulcer that gave her periodic stomach pains. She was in her early thirties, recently married, with no children. One of the things I noticed immediately was Barbara's lack of confidence. She was nervous and distinctly uncomfortable talking about herself. Clearly, she needed help, especially for her migraines, but she seemed reluctant to share her pain with me or, as I would eventually learn, with anyone.

It didn't take me long to realize that Barbara's lack of confidence was central to her physical problems. She grew up as the oldest of five children, her siblings all boys. Her mother relied heavily on Barbara to help raise her brothers. By the time she was ten, she was changing diapers and baby-sitting. Responsibility came early in life for Barbara, and the pattern of focusing on the needs of others rather than her own eventually became a character trait that marked her adult life.

"I didn't think of this as a problem," Barbara recalled many years later. "When I was young, I learned to cook because I wanted to. I wanted to take care of my brothers. I always thought of them as the 'little guys.' I never thought that someone should be taking care of me or that I should be taking care of me. I didn't realize how much this way of thinking was driving me and causing my life to be so imbalanced."

Such a mentality, which is so common today, gives rise to a lifestyle that requires an enormous amount of energy. Barbara was constantly trying to meet the needs of others. Her sense of self-worth and even of her own safety was predicated on removing the discomforts of her husband, her friends, and those with whom she worked. Unconsciously, Barbara felt responsible for making right every situation in which she found herself.

Barbara is a classic example of how holes in the field shape a person's life, and how one compensates for the energy leaks. Her field was so riddled with holes that she had no clear sense of boundaries or identity, and thus she could not discern the needs of others versus her own needs. This identification with others, in fact, is dangerous to one's health, because the person with such a problem is unable to establish any sort of balance in his or her life.

"I was trying to be superwoman," Barbara recalls. "I had to please everyone. I had no sense of my own boundaries or my own limits. I was constantly engulfed by my surroundings. I couldn't block them out."

On the day that Barbara showed up at my office, she was suffering from a dull headache that she was afraid might become a migraine. She also had low backache. After conducting the initial interview with Barbara, I recommended dietary changes—especially a significant reduction in fat and sugar to help reduce the premenstrual symptoms (diets high in fat are associated with more intense PMS due largely to the secretion of estrogen from fat cells; high estrogen levels increase the symptoms of PMS). I also recommended a series of supplements that would support her liver and digestive functions.

Then I began a series of healing touch sessions because I wanted to help her relax and experience her own center. Despite her problems, Barbara responded quickly.

I began the work by doing an assessment. As I passed my hands through her field, I sensed tension, tightness, and a kind of spiky, tingling sensation. "Are you tense?" I asked her. "I'm feeling pretty mad right now," Barbara said. "I just had a run-in with my boss and I can't think straight. I can't talk about it."

Whenever a person is angry and tense, the diaphragm (or third chakra) tends to tighten and cause the breathing to become shallow. Thus, I knew that the first chakra (self-protection and survival issues), second (sex organs), third, and sixth (headaches) were troubled and needed work.

With Barbara, I began by opening the secondary chakras in her feet to drain the backed-up energy in the entire system. After I had gently massaged her arches, I held both of her feet for about five minutes, meanwhile asking her to breathe deeply, slowly, and rhythmically into her feet. Next, I sent healing energy to her second and third chakras. I then worked on the periphery of her field, closing over the holes, thus giving her a greater sense of her own boundary.

Usually opening the feet drains the energy that has been stuck in the upper part of the body and reduces or eliminates headaches. This worked for Barbara, but I noticed during my assessment toward the end of the session that her sixth chakra still felt dull and deficient of life force. To support the energy in the sixth chakra, I placed my left hand over the field at the back of her head (not touching the skin) and my right hand over her forehead area, and then visualized healing energy clearing Barbara's head. I did not send energy through my hands. Headaches are an indication of blocked energy within the body, including the head. You do not want to add to the congestion by sending more energy to the area. Rather, I used my hands to pull stagnation out of the chakra, head, and neck region. Meanwhile, I also envisioned the energy circulating more freely in the chakra, head, and upper body. Usually, this was enough to relieve Barbara's headaches, but if it didn't, I would often return to Barbara's feet and open the secondary chakras again, holding the arches for about five minutes.

"I was amazed at how good I felt after that first session with Deby," Barbara recalled. "I felt as if someone had lifted twenty pounds of weight off my back. I had a great sense of relief."

I did energy work on Barbara regularly, usually once a week or twice a month. Gradually, her symptoms began to diminish, until eventually they disappeared.

"As I started to receive healing touch regularly, I began to realize that this was working. At first, it was some internal knowing, more intuitive than anything, but pretty soon my health was improving. The first sign was that my migraines were not as intense as before. And then I no longer got them as frequently. I went from having a migraine once a week to twice a month. Then I'd go a whole month without a migraine, and that was something."

Besides the diminished migraine symptoms, Barbara had no ovarian pain. Remarkably, after four months of healing touch, doctors could no longer find Barbara's ovarian cysts. Gone, too, were her intense PMS and her digestive distress. It took us more than a year to get the migraines completely under control, but Barbara has not experienced a migraine in two years. Occasionally, she'll experience a tension headache that is quickly relieved by over-the-counter medication. Meanwhile, she's learning how to let go of her tension on her own, as she is becoming increasingly aware of her own energetic patterns.

"Healing touch has helped me to sit down, calm myself, and relax enough to let the tension release," says Barbara. "It lets me experience being in a peaceful internal space, a place where I can leave my family and work outside the door and focus on my own needs. The work is meditative and it's very supportive. The process has really been about getting to know myself. Part of that means knowing how I'm feeling. Now, if I have a headache coming on, I recognize the tension well in advance and I start breathing and allowing my body to relax. I'm learning to let go of my tension."

Improvement in Barbara's physical health has not been the only blessing of healing touch, however. She has undergone a remarkable transformation in her demeanor, attitudes, and self-understanding. As Barbara and I regularly began to work together, she started to see the connection between her low self-esteem and her need to please others. "I was just trying to be loved," she says today. As her energetic field got stronger and her sense of self improved, she naturally began to appreciate herself more and more. "I began to get a glimpse of the person I could be, and that started to feel really good," Barbara said. Much of this, Barbara maintains, has come about because she has learned to turn her focus inward, to the self within.

"Since I began this practice, I have gradually evolved beyond the old mind-set," said Barbara.

In Service to Others, Less Is Often More

After assessing a person's physical and energetic bodies, I start to work on the field, usually at a distance of about eighteen inches, a distance that is traditionally known as the sacred space. Within this area, a person's sensitivity and self-protectiveness are more acute, and consequently you do not want to violate this space, especially during the first few treatments, because you may not yet have established a bond of trust. Even when I work on people I am very familiar with, I still try to remain beyond the eighteen-inch boundary during our first two sessions together. The obvious contradiction to this is my touching of the secondary chakras at the backs of the knees and my massaging the backs of the legs, the tendons in the calves, and the bottoms of the feet. This work, which I call opening the feet, is so important to balancing a person's energy that there simply is no way around it. Nevertheless, I approach the body and these secondary chakras with great respect and appreciation for this person and his willingness to allow me to work with him.

Opening the feet is performed at the conclusion of the assessment. Once that is done, I start at the top of the field and move downward toward the feet. I am aware of the energy flowing to me from the cosmos, above, and the earth, below. I feel the energy passing from my field, to my body, up from my heart, and down to my hands. My hands are flowing with healing energy as I pass them over the patient's field.

The first and most important part of the work is to be an instrument for universal life force. That energy is flowing through me and into the person I am working with. It's that simple. Thus, the very basis of the practice requires very little from me, because the life force flowing from the Universal Healer is doing the healing. I am attempting to direct and facilitate that flow of energy from an infinite source to the person in need of assistance. As I tell my students, once a practitioner recognizes and achieves this standpoint, she is in a position to help a person. Her ego is out of the way and cannot be an obstruction to the process. This is what I mean when I say "less is more."

As I send life force to the field, I am particularly conscious of the places in the field that I had perceived to be imbalanced while doing my assessment, or where a symptom may be manifesting. Of course, I do not have to perceive blockages or holes in the field to recognize and treat a broken arm or a physical wound or some form of disorder. I can treat the imbalance by sending life energy to that part of the body. That is the beauty of healing touch: At bottom, I am sending loving, healing energy. The body and the Great Spirit together know better than I what to do with that energy.

Unblocking the Rivers: Removing Stones and Boulders

In general, all symptoms arise out of imbalance. Either there is too much energy in the area or too little. As a general rule, you are trying to move the excess energy into the places where there is deficiency, as I did in chapter 2, where I reported on my work with Wendy.

Once I discover an imbalance in the energy field, I focus on it and attempt to restore circulation of the life force to that area. If the area is blocked, or stagnant, I try to gently remove the obstruction—often perceived as a large stone, or boulder—from that part of the field. These boulders are perceived as large, dense clumps of energy.

I have found that before you try to remove blockages from the field, it's helpful to ask the person with whom you are working to visualize the energy within her body flowing freely, without obstruction, especially the energy that flows up and down the central tube.

Visualization: Encouraging the Free Flow of Energy Within the Patient

Ask your patient to visualize the following as you are doing your energy work: Picture yourself under a waterfall of the richest, most powerful, life-restoring energy. You can feel the energy wash over and through you, entering your pores, fibers, and cells. Notice that each droplet of energy sparkles light; each droplet is packed with photons of energy; they radiate with all the colors of the rainbow. Notice that your every cell drinks up these droplets of Qi like a thirsty traveler who's been too long in the desert. Breathe in the energy and draw it into every cell and every dark or weakened crevice of your body. Inhale the energy deeply so that it enters the top of your head. All the energy that you need is absorbed fully so that you have an abundance of life force within you. You are fully nourished from an infinite source. All you need is available to you at any moment. As you exhale, visualize all that you don't need being released through the soles of your feet and into the earth to be transformed by the Great Mother.

As the person performs this visualization, begin to remove the blockages in the field.

*   *   *

Whenever you perceive a blockage in the field, visualize it as a big stone in the river of energy that supplies that part of the body with life force. See the eddies, whirlpools, and vortices that manifest in the field around and directly over the injury or disorder in the physical body. Remember that excesses of energy and deficiencies tend to appear in tandem, so that an excess in one part of the body will create a deficiency somewhere else. Excesses of energy, blockages, and boulders appear in places of acute tension, such as the shoulders, the neck, the head, and the pelvis. Deficiencies are common in the chest, lungs, heart, and sex organs.

I try to free the area of a boulder, or chaotic energy (sometimes perceived as static electricity), or stagnant energy (often perceived as dense resistance) by "grasping" and "removing" it with my hands. As I reach into the area of the boulder, I move my hand in a counterclockwise direction and cup my hand to grasp the obstruction. I move my hand out of the field in a clockwise motion. I then release that energy upward into the Light of Love, to be transmuted by the Universal Healer. In places where the energy is turbulent and chaotic, I "smooth" the field, and try to calm it, by giving it healing, even maternal, care. I do this by stroking the field in a calming and loving manner. Wherever I perceive stagnant energy, which is usually excessive energy, I try to move it to a place where the energy is deficient by using the technique of "pulling" the energy, as I described in chapter 3.

To remove blockages from a chakra area, reach into the field at the site of the blockage while moving your hand in a counterclockwise direction. As you move counterclockwise, you are moving healing energy into the area. See your hand grasping the bolus of energy, or stone, from the whirlpool and lifting it from the field. As you retract your hand and pull the stone from the field, turn your hand in a clockwise direction. The clockwise direction facilitates the movement of aberrant energy out of the body.

Once your hand and the stone are free, lift them up to the ceiling and say to yourself: "I release this which she/he no longer needs into the Light of Love." Feel the energy go off your palm and upward, to be transformed. Then say: "I return my hand bringing peace and harmony to my vibral core." You do this so that none of the aberrant energy returns to you. (It is inherent in your treatment and your prayer that you are bringing peace and harmony to the recipient.)

Do the same if you are working with someone whom you perceive to carry a great deal of anger, rage, or intense emotion in the field. When you remove obstructions in the field—which may be accumulations of stagnant emotions—you should release them into the Light of Love. Once that is done, shake off any residual energy from your hands and release that into the Light of Love as well. This will protect you. You will find that even after you have worked on several clients in the same day, you will still feel light and unaffected by their emotional states.

While you are removing disharmonies from the field with your right hand, hold your left on the other side of the patient to maintain balance. Your left hand acts as a stabilizer to his field, while your right removes old or stagnant forms of energy.

Reassess the field and note any changes that have occurred. Repeat the process until all vestiges of stagnation and tension have been eliminated.

If you perceive that the energy is still deficient in the area in which you have worked, move your hand to the nearest chakra and place one hand in front of the chakra and the other behind the patient's back in the general area where the same chakra exits at the spine. Your hands are now opposite each other and the patient is between them. Now build an energy ball between your hands and feel that part of the body expand and become balanced with life energy.

Closing Holes

A vitally important task for the practitioner of healing touch is to close holes, or leaks, in the field. This will allow the person to experience, even for a short time, his or her true wholeness and integrity, an experience that triggers the healing process. Once the patient glimpses his best self, he unconsciously and consciously begins to move out of stasis and stagnation. The more you work on a person, the more you can "repattern" the field to close the leaks permanently, or teach the person to close the leaks whenever he feels vulnerable.

Typically, holes or leaks occur near areas of the field that are loaded with energy, often stuck or blocked from flowing into the hole. The field will try to heal itself of leaks, but blockages may prevent the life force from flowing smoothly to the hole or leak. Leaks are often near those chakras that are related to the kinds of issues the person may be experiencing. (Those issues may well have been discussed during your intake interview or as part of the healing session.) If it's an issue around money, for example, then perhaps the hole is located near the first chakra—responsible for survival issues, or the third chakra—responsible for the will and drive, or the fifth chakra—responsible for self-expression. If the issue involves relationships with the opposite sex, then perhaps it involves the second chakra—responsible for sexuality, or the third chakra—responsible for will and self-empowerment, or the fourth chakra—responsible for the ability to experience love. If the issue involves the discovery of the person's specific work, then perhaps it involves the second chakra—responsible for creativity, or the fourth chakra—responsible for discerning what it is the person truly loves, or the fifth chakra—responsible for self-expression, or the sixth chakra—responsible for one's deep understanding of self.

If the person has come to you complaining of a specific health issue, search the field around the nearest related chakra. If you do not feel a leak or a hole, reassess the field and open the feet. You may need to spend five minutes of the treatment holding the feet and encouraging the person to breathe deeply down into the feet. (Very often, people who are difficult to assess are shallow breathers and, consequently, suffer from stagnant life energy. These imbalances can very often be relieved by asking the person to spend five minutes breathing deeply while you are opening the secondary chakras in their feet.) Be patient with your assessment. It may take several sessions before you understand the person's energetic imbalances. Meanwhile, you are harmonizing the field through your healing touch and by opening the chakras in the feet.

To close off the holes and leaks, I run my hands along boundaries of the field that are healthy and strong and draw the excess energy to the hole or leak. I try to channel additional life force to the hole, filling it with energy, and then close over the wounded area by smoothing my hands over the leak. I give the leak a kind of maternal love; flowing within that love is the healing energy that is flowing through me to the client. I visualize the healing energy flowing into the leak, filling it, and healing the wound. I "see" the wound closing and the integrity of the field being reestablished. I work to balance the energy so that it flows smoothly throughout the region where there was formerly a wound. Once again, the field is closed, strong, resilient, and whole.

The process of closing a leak or hole usually takes several sessions, simply because wounds are usually chronic and the field is patterned to maintain that wound.

When holes or leaks in the field are closed, even if only temporarily, the person experiences a feeling of wholeness. His field is now intact, and energy that was leaking is now flowing within him. This experience may give him a sudden burst of energy or it may make him feel tired, as areas of his body are experiencing energy for the first time in many years. But more important, body, mind, and spirit feel *contained* within one's own boundaries and identity. The effect is profound, because it reminds one on all levels of what it feels like to be whole; it is a glimpse of all that one is and can be. That experience catalyzes the entire being and all the healing forces that exist within. Energies are shaken out of their stasis and awakened to the fact that the field has been wounded and must be healed. In effect, the psyche has been roused and mobilized in a specific direction. The full self-healing of those holes takes place long after the session is over. The person's own field will heal itself. The closing of the holes by the practitioner awakens the healing forces within the field and directs them to those places within the field that must be restored to integrity.

When Someone Complains of Pain

Occasionally, someone will tell you that she or he is experiencing a mild ache or pain after a treatment. If the pain is acute and/or lingers for more than two hours, ask the person to see a physician. In general, you cannot cause any serious side effect—including pain—by administering healing touch. On the other hand, the infusion of the life force can create temporary discomfort, especially in the person who has suffered long-term blockages and stagnation.

The most common pain that may result after a healing touch session occurs after you have cleared an area of obstructions and old energetic patterns begin to break down. Once these blockages are removed, energy, blood, and lymph flow in greater abundance into areas that were previously blocked and deficient of all three elixirs of life. When blood, lymph, and Qi start to move into parts of the field and physical body that were stagnant or blocked, the tissues can be highly sensitive and therefore might experience temporary discomfort or mild pain.

Whenever a client experiences pain—but especially if that pain emerges after a treatment—first open the feet. If there is still pain after opening the feet, place your hands over the site of the pain and send that place soothing, comforting, and healing energy. Visualize the tissues opening, as if they were just now arising after a long sleep, and accepting the increased circulation. Once you have done this, move one hand over the nearest chakra's opening and place the other hand over the back where the chakra exits. Now, create a new energy ball between your hands. See the energy ball fill up the entire area with soft, healing energy and light. See the tissues becoming supple and relaxed. Finally, make sure the energy is flowing freely from the bottoms of the feet.

Balancing the Chakras

After the treatment has been completed, ask the patient to lie down on a table or on a mat on the floor and reassess the field, especially concentrating on what you are feeling when your hands go over the seven chakra areas. Try to balance any disharmonies that may remain. If one or more of the chakras is still weak, you can build the chakra's life force by doing the following. Move to the right side of the client's body. Place your left hand under the client's back, at the exit point of the chakra in question, and your right hand over the front of the same imbalanced chakra. For this treatment, you will have to touch the person on his or her back and/or front at the site of the chakra on which you are working. Visualize the Universal Energy moving through you. See the energy entering your field and your body through the top of your head. Draw in the life force with your breath. As you exhale, see the energy flow up from your heart into your shoulders, arms, and hands. Finally, see the life force building between your hands. You are creating an energy ball, a sphere of life force, between your hands in the chakra that needs healing. As you are filling the chakra with this powerful ball of light, repeat the phrase "To help and to heal" over and over again in your mind. (See Appendix 2 photos.)

One of the signs that the chakra is accepting the energy and being healed is that you will hear gurgling sounds emanating from the stomach and bowels (similar to the growling sounds of a hungry stomach). This indicates that the additional energy being channeled into the field is clearing the stagnation within the chakra and other places in the field and that new additional life force is moving into the body, clearing it of stagnation, and restoring harmony.

Hold the chakra ball for as long as you think is necessary. Intuitively, you will know how long to hold the ball of energy. You will feel the moment when you know the sphere of life force has been accepted into the person's field and body. It usually takes only a few minutes for the body and field to accept the chakra ball.

The purpose of balancing the chakras after the session is completed is to help the energy system accommodate the changes in patterning that have just occurred.

Once you have balanced the chakras, pass your hands through the field and visualize your hands smoothing, straightening, and closing the edges of the energy field. Close any holes or leaks in the field that you may still feel. Finally, groom the field, so to speak. Hold your left palm up at about shoulder height and with your right hand stroke the edges of the field as though you were smoothing all the fibers around that energetic ball of "cotton candy." Move vertically downward in a clockwise direction around the field with each stroke. It usually takes about seven strokes.

When this step is completed, ask the client to lie down for ten minutes. The energy that has been channeled to the client will build on itself over the next twenty-four hours, boosting the immune and healing forces and harmonizing imbalances. Ask the person to assist this process by maintaining a relaxed pace through the next day.

Expanded Integrated Awareness Begins with Remembering

Throughout this book, I have been reporting how people, when they begin healing touch, reintegrate repressed or forgotten parts of their being. I call this "expanded integrated awareness." That experience very often occurs because we hold memories, talents, and awareness in parts of the field that are blocked from our conscious minds. When a practitioner of healing touch begins to work on the disorder, he or she invariably removes many of these repressive barriers, thus freeing these memories and abilities, which are experienced by the person as a gradual awareness of self in a whole new light.

Before that awareness occurs, however, the person with whom you are working may remember and psychologically reexperience an old trauma. In order for the body, mind, and spirit to heal, the person very often revisits the memory of the events that caused the original wound. In fact, this is an essential part of the healing. That experience must be reintegrated into the psyche, especially if it has been repressed and denied for some time. Healing touch greatly assists the person to go back to those painful memories and makes the process of reintegration so much easier because the practitioner of healing touch is sending the client love in the form of healing energy to the very place where the client has been wounded. This place has been deprived of optimal amounts of life force, blood, and lymph for some time. These are the fundamental elements of life. Once these basics are restored, the client feels strong enough to go back to the pain and deal with it in a whole new way. Thus, the person returns to the scene of the crime, so to speak, this time holding the hand of divine love, which is being channeled to the patient from the practitioner.

Here is yet another area where healing touch can greatly assist the work of other health care providers, especially a mental health professional. If a person comes to you with a long-lasting emotional disorder, refer him or her to a psychologist or psychiatrist. Meanwhile, as you work on the field, be sure to keep the treatments short—usually no more than ten to fifteen minutes at each session. You can perform the treatments daily, however. At the same time, strongly urge the person to keep a diary or a journal, especially to write about the painful events in his or her life. Studies have shown that writing about one's life, and particularly about past traumas, has a dramatic healing effect on body, mind, and spirit.

At Southern Methodist University (SMU), James W. Pennebaker, Ph.D., a professor of psychology, has found that writing about traumatic experiences in one's personal journal for twenty minutes a day, for four consecutive days, has a remarkable healing effect both physically and psychologically. Pennebaker and fellow researchers Janice Kecolt-Glaser and Ronald Glaser have discovered that immune response and psychological health are greatly enhanced after confessing traumas to one's journal.

When the scientists compared the immune systems of people

who wrote about their problems to the immune systems of those who didn't, the writers were found to have far more aggressive CD4 cells, the cells that coordinate the immune system's overall response to a disease. In fact, those people whom Pennebaker termed "high disclosers" had the most remarkable improvement in T-cell response of all participants.

Moreover, writing was also shown to dramatically improve psychological health as measured by interviews and psychological testing.

Pennebaker maintains that more than mere catharsis is at work here. He suggests that psychological inhibition—the mechanism by which we keep things secret, even from ourselves—requires a certain degree of psychic and physical energy. As he puts it, inhibition is a demanding form of work, especially when a very painful trauma must be kept secret. Physical symptoms—such as elevations in blood pressure, heart rate, breathing, skin temperature, and perspiration levels—frequently occur as a result of such inhibition. The release that accompanies confession, therefore, occurs on both psychological and physical levels.

Pennebaker points out that one does not necessarily have to write down the event to experience release. Confessing it to someone else will have the same effect, as long as it was a distinct traumatic event that one has kept secret, in whole or in part, to that point.

The rules for writing such confessions are simple enough:

1. Write for twenty minutes, for four consecutive days.
2. Write continuously about the most upsetting experience or trauma of your entire life.
3. Don't worry about grammar, spelling, or the structure of the piece.
4. Write your deepest thoughts and emotions regarding the experience. Write all the details you remember. Write down your insights into the events. In the process, get in touch with your deepest emotions and thoughts.

In any case, revisiting the pain of a trauma is often an essential part of the healing process, and it can be very rewarding for the patient.

One of the most powerful tools for helping a person eliminate unhealthy habits and for reducing psychological pain is clearing the spiritual channel, or the central tube, which is what we'll discuss next.

9

⚜

Clearing Old Patterns

Our lives are made up of a series of experiences that, taken together, can be seen to form patterns that make each of us unique. We all are shaped by patterns of thought, outlooks on life, and our preferences for certain kinds of experiences. A multitude of attitudes and beliefs within each of us combines to form patterns that determine the kinds of people we like, those we love, and those we dislike and of whom we are afraid. Our talents, ambitions, and weaknesses coalesce into patterns that give direction to our lives. Patterns reveal where we are strong and what within us needs to mature and develop. Our appearance is a pattern of physical features. When examined honestly and with insight, our patterns can reveal to us who we are and how we fit in the world.

Some of the forces that shape us are genetic and are therefore either fixed or of limited flexibility. Many of our talents and abilities are genetically determined, for example. Others are created by our experiences and environment. How you relate to authority figures or the opposite sex, your attitudes about money, and your thoughts about yourself and God are patterns that arose, in part, from your conditioning, but they are also ever-changing. They may seem rigid, even to the point of being fixed, yet they are quite mutable and, potentially, subject to enormous transformation.

As everyone who's ever tried to change a negative pattern knows, the work isn't easy, and sometimes it can be downright excruciating. Why is change so difficult? we may ask. Why is it that we can see behavioral problems so clearly at times, and yet succumb to them over and over again? The fact is that change may begin in the mind—it may start with recognition—but the mind alone cannot create change. We all know this to be true because most of the changes that have taken place in our lives have been accomplished without conscious effort and even without recognition. It is true that maturation is painful at times, but it is rarely, if ever, a singularly mental function. If it was, none of us would emerge from puberty, or awaken from adolescence, simply because the mind is not equipped to navigate its way through such troubled waters. Yet, somehow most of us grow beyond these stages. We pass into adulthood and continue to evolve—sometimes consciously, most of the time unconsciously.

What, then, is the driving force behind change, and how does change occur? In Ecclesiastes, the Preacher tells us: "There is an appointed time for everything. And there is a time for every event under heaven . . ." This suggests not only that "to everything . . . there is a season," as the Byrds' 1960s song "Turn! Turn! Turn!" so nicely put it, but that each event has its own purpose according to some larger plan. Change comes at its appointed time, says the Preacher, and is ordained by God. Why, then, is change so difficult?

When we examine nature, we find that change is occurring all the time. Many of the most profound changes are both smooth and orderly—so orderly, in fact, that we even set our calendars by them. In temperate climates, for example, nature makes four dramatic transformations annually, each according to its time. Insofar as we know, the tree does not think that it is now autumn and therefore time to let go of its leaves; or summer and therefore time to let out its fruit. Something else takes place that permits the tree to undergo such a remarkable transformation. That something is a change in the energy of the tree. In the fall, the life force of a tree turns downward and brings with it the sap, causing the leaves to fall off their limbs for lack of energy to support their lives. In winter, the energy stays below ground; it waits for the moment when the rising energy of spring will cause the life force of the tree to rise. Then the sun returns and the life energy rises through the trunk and flows into the branches and sprouts blossoms and leaves. In summer, the periphery of the tree is bursting with energy; all of nature is exploding with the life force, and so there are flowers and fruit.

Humans change in similar ways, and each of the changes we experience has its own season. Still, we have the power to alter the energy flowing through us with our thoughts, emotions, food, and behavior. We can promote the life force, or we can cause it to be blocked and stagnate. Most of the time, we do this without realizing it. Yet, no change takes place inside of us—no matter how hard we try—until there has been a dramatic energetic shift within. Once the energy in the field has changed—just as the energy within a tree has changed—our lives make some dramatic shift on every level of our being—physically, emotionally, psychologically, and spiritually. We grow into the next stage of our evolution and it happens almost effortlessly. Examples of this phenomenon appear regularly in our world today.

Suddenly, a talent for the piano emerges in a woman at the age of forty, who previously had no experience with the instrument. With regular practice and proper instruction, she is playing beautifully in a year. Another woman who has endured many years of abusive relationships suddenly frees herself from that pattern and finds dignity, self-love, and a healthy, rewarding relationship. A drug addict kicks his habit; an alcoholic overcomes his addiction; a person who has been seriously ill spontaneously is cured. We all know such people and have heard such stories many times over. The common thread implicit in all these experiences is that the transformation is made without extreme effort and, in every event, not by willpower alone. Conversely, there are many people in the very same circumstances who struggle valiantly but do not pick up the instrument, or kick the habit, or overcome the pattern of abuse. What separates those who change from those who do not? What makes one set of people different from the other? In many cases, it is not effort. Indeed, those who struggle in vain often struggle harder than those who change.

Such profound transformations are made possible by a remarkable shift in the energetic patterns within the person's field. Something changed the field; we do not know who and we may not know how, but the field was changed and the person made some remarkable step that was previously believed to be impossible. This is not to say that such a change was without its emotional pain or suffering. Indeed, there is always some pain around letting go of an old pattern. But people who make these dramatic shifts invariably say that while they fought their addiction for decades, or struggled against their illness for years, the actual step was quite mysterious and remarkably easier than they had ever dreamed possible. No one can explain it, we say. It's a mystery, a miracle. Anyone who has witnessed the remarkable changes that occur in people when they release an old pattern from the field recognizes the process as miraculous.

Conversely, blockages in the energy field can restrict a person from making a step in evolution, even if the person wants desperately to make such a step and is doing everything he or she can think of to change.

Energetic Patterns and the False Self

Before I discuss how to make additional changes in the field, beyond those I discussed in chapter 8, let me talk about the kinds of patterns we have within us and which ones we need to release. All of the patterns that make up your life—whether they are genetic or environmental—can be grouped into two categories. The first set emerges from your true self, the inner being that you long to fully experience and express in the world. The second set makes up the false personality, which, when it is expressed, can sometimes give certain short-term pleasures but usually blocks the expression of your deeper self, and consequently leads into dark alleys, dead ends, and disappointments. You are the only person who can discern the difference between your true self and your false self, and the patterns each gives rise to. However, there is one test that can help you determine the source of a particular pattern: Behavior patterns that permit you to love yourself and others, promote self-expression, and give you deep connection to the source of life come from the true self and provide the deepest sense of happiness and satisfaction. Behavior patterns that arise out of chronic fears, anger, hostility, hatred, and feelings of dependency all emerge from delusion and the false self.

The false self prevents you from becoming happy and fulfilled because it does the two things that guarantee unhappiness. First, it prevents you from expressing your true nature, and second, at the same time, it blocks you from experiencing a deep and loving relationship with God, however you perceive Him/Her/It.

Patterns that obstruct the true self arise from one and only one cause: the training that love is conditional. To varying degrees all of us were raised on conditional love, meaning that we were loved or not loved according to our ability and willingness to conform to certain behaviors. Since our survival depended on that love, its tenuousness caused many of us to be shaken at the very roots of our being. Those who were raised on such an unstable love learned that reality always contains an implicit threat, and therefore requires a certain degree of conformity, adaptation, and sacrifice. The biggest sacrifice of all, of course, is the sacrifice of one's true nature, or simply one's true self.

People sacrifice that which they truly want to express because they believe that they cannot be themselves and at the same time be loved. Therefore, they must develop a way of being, a persona, that satisfies the people they depend on for love. That persona becomes the barrier that blocks us from experiencing the true self within. The persona is made up of many negative beliefs about ourselves, beliefs that can become powerful prisons.

A gifted dancer who believes she has insufficient ability, or none at all, may never realize her true talents and potential as a human being. That belief may well corrupt her life and cause endless suffering and sickness. Beliefs actually combine to form our personality—they describe how we think we should behave in given situations. They tell us what is possible and what isn't.

Such false or negative beliefs combine to form an outer personality that, like an ill-fitting costume, creates obstructions and energetic restrictions within this field. Negative beliefs are maintained in a vicious cycle, beginning with the repetition of that belief by the mind. Such statements as "I am no good" create wounds in the energetic field. Those wounds can become holes, or leaks, or they can be covered over by a kind of energetic scar tissue that forms blockages or boulders, thus blocking the flow of life force through your energy field. This creates eddies in one place, weak spots or tightnesses in others. Those blockages prevent the life force from flowing optimally to your cells, tissues, and organs. Leaks, blockages, and wounds in the field maintain negative thinking patterns and beliefs because they prevent fresh ideas from emerging in the field. In effect, the field is not as supple, changeable, and growing as it once was, and thus the life of old beliefs is sustained, which in turn sustains the wounds in the field.

Energetic Patterns Can Be the Cause of Disease

Once these energetic restrictions are imposed on your field, they manifest in the body as stress, muscle tension, restricted respiration, hormonal imbalances, and blocked blood and lymph flows. These energetic and physical conditions can become your accepted way of being. Gradually, they can affect your heartbeat and respiration, the amount of oxygen your tissues receive, the amount of carbon dioxide your body releases, the relative strength of your immune system, your posture, the way you move, the way you feel, and how you interact with others. In short, they can mold you into someone other than your true self, and in the process can make you ill.

Healing occurs when we break the circle by healing the wounds in the field and thus changing the energetic, physical, and psychological patterns. By removing the blockages in the energetic field, the life force flows abundantly to cells, organs, and even to the mind. Soon we feel better and see things differently. Old and negative beliefs are shed because we now begin to realize how capable and powerful we truly are.

Growing into health and maturity is, in effect, shedding those restrictive ideas that have been imposed on us. In a sense, it is an expansion of what we currently believe to be possible. It is a widening of consciousness or "expanded integrated awareness," which means that you expand your view of yourself so that those qualities that are implicit within you can emerge and express themselves.

As your innate qualities and talents emerge, you become aware of who you truly are. Your true nature steps out of the shadow of your unconscious and into the light of consciousness. Now you can begin to integrate your underlying abilities by creating a new, expanded picture of yourself. That's what I mean by expanded integrated awareness: It is the perception of the larger and truer you. Healing touch removes the barricades and opens the doors to your true self. Let me give an example.

Sam: Releasing Old Patterns

Sam is a thirty-eight-year-old man in a high-level, high-pressure, executive position. He came to me complaining of intense stress and stomach trouble. His day, he said, was essentially a race against time. He had too many appointments to make, too many deadlines to meet. He was very ambitious, but at the same time delicate: Anything and everything that went wrong in his world was perceived by Sam as evidence of his inadequacy or as a personal failure. He berated himself harshly. Yet, despite the fact that he was extremely hard on himself, or perhaps because of it, he continually strived to achieve more.

The physical side effects of such behavior were severe: chronic anxiety in the pit of his stomach, causing pain in his stomach and solar plexus, especially when he was under pressure. He also experienced pain whenever he missed a meal. Yet, he complained of chronic indigestion and took a lot of antacids. At the same time, he suffered from digestive problems, alternating between diarrhea and constipation. Stress impacts the human body in numerous ways, but I suspected that Sam might well have a congenital weakness in the gastrointestinal system, which is why his symptoms manifested there.

Sam's energetic patterning was clearly revealed by his nervous system's response to stress. The so-called flight-or-fight response is governed by the sympathetic nervous system, which shunts nerve innervation to the muscles and nerves in the heart, lungs, and periphery of the body whenever the body is under stress. This sends energy away from the digestive tract to the extremities so that the body can respond rapidly and aggressively in the face of danger.

Digestion, on the other hand, is conducted by the parasympathetic system, which directs nerve energy to the small and large intestines. Yet, Sam was continually under stress, and therefore under sympathetic dominance, which means that energy was continually being taken away from his digestive tract and channeled to his arms, legs, and cardiovascular system. Meanwhile, his stomach and third chakra would tighten, causing constriction of energy within the chakra and tightening of tissues and blood vessels within the organs. Sam often ate when he was stressed, which means that he was taking in food when there was insufficient nerve innervation and life force within the digestive tract. This causes digestion to be weakened and results in dyspepsia, bloating, gas, and putrefied food matter in the gut.

At the same time, stress tightens the diaphragm, causing the breathing to become shallow and emotional. Studies have shown that shallow breathing is associated with poorly oxygenated blood and cells, fatigue, weakness, and emotional instability. Not only did Sam suffer from all of these problems, but the chronic stress had brought on depression. He simply couldn't see himself carrying the burden any longer. Needless to say, Sam hated going to work in the morning.

After Sam told me of these issues, I immediately urged him to see a gastrointestinal specialist to determine if he suffered from an ulcer. In addition, I made numerous dietary recommendations, which Sam adopted, to support his stomach and digestive function.

Then I went to work on his field, focusing initially on the first, third, and fourth chakras. I tried to strengthen his first chakra in order to give him a stronger hold on the physical world and his own physical existence. Sam needed to feel grounded and centered, which the first chakra would give him. The third chakra needed to be strengthened to boost Sam's will, which had grown tired, weak, and frustrated. I channeled healing energy to the fourth chakra to boost his morale and overall emotional condition.

Clear the Spiritual Channel, or Central Tube, and Restore the Connection Between Heaven and Earth

In the last chapter, I showed how we can heal leaks and chakras to change the patterns within the field. Here, we want to take another step in changing patterns by removing blockages from the central tube, which is something I worked on with Sam.

As I pointed out in chapter 4, the central tube is a flow of energy that originates from a cosmic or heavenly source and runs from the top of the head to the base of the spine. It exits out of the spine and moves down into the earth. At the midpoint of this tube is the vibral core, and located along the tube are the seven chakras. The central tube is a shaft of energy, often referred to in other disciplines as the "spiritual channel," that is the energetic connection between the two great polarities of life: the infinite and the finite, heaven and earth. As such, the tube serves as the matrix around which the material body coalesces, and this is the channel through which life energy flows from the top of the body to the bottom.

The central tube can become clogged with old emotional debris, thus blocking one's sense of connection to the universe and the earth. The person with a blocked spiritual channel cannot feel an intuitive connection with the source of life, nor with Mother Earth. Without this feeling of connectedness, a person cannot draw inspiration from above or sustenance from below. One is neither a child of heaven nor a natural inhabitant of the earth. This is the ultimate experience of aloneness and isolation, and with such feelings comes a host of other negative emotions and attitudes toward life.

We can reestablish that sense of connection by clearing the central tube of obstructions. Once those obstructions are eliminated, a person begins to feel more relaxed in life. He feels more connected to his heavenly source, and therefore has greater faith in the forces that sustain him every day he exists. He can be inspired with ideas, creativity, and the power of the life energy that is streaming down upon each of us every instant of our lives. Not only that, but his connection with the earth is also improved, thus giving him a clearer sense of what must be done to secure his place on the earth. The physical, psychological, and spiritual effects of clearing the tube are profound and myriad, but they all add up to the same two great blessings: They improve our connection with the true self, and they reestablish our connection with the source of life.

Moving Old Energetic Waste Out of the Channel

Very often, when I am working with people like Sam, I finish my treatment by clearing the central tube. I do this form of treatment only after I have established a strong bond of trust because it requires the practitioner to touch the client's head, shoulders, and back. I have found that clearing the tube is highly effective at eliminating old emotional wounds, memories, and attachments to old relationships that limit the person's outlook and growth—even when the person doesn't even realize that he still holds on to such memories or relationships. It is also a powerful way to raise the life force. Keep in mind that clearing the tube is usually done at the end of a treatment. That means that by the time you clear the tube, you have centered, done your assessment, and finished your energy work. Here are the steps that you can use to clear your patient's central tube.

1. Move to the back of your patient and gently place your hands on the back of his neck with your thumbs gently pressing against the muscles on each side of the vertebrae at the base of the head. Massage these points ever so gently so that the muscles relax.

2. Slowly move your thumbs down the left and right sides of each vertebra, pausing at each vertebra to massage the muscles on each side of the spine. Do not stop until you reach the base of the spine.

3. Your intention in this first phase of the clearing is to loosen the muscles and gain the body's trust. The client may well trust you intellectually, but you must now convince his body that it can release its armor and allow you to probe its soft and vulnerable interior. Massage gently and firmly. You want your client to feel good, to relax, and to put down his armor so that you can go deeper with each step of the clearing.

4. Repeat the procedure again, moving from the top of the spine to its base, with the same loving, healing hands.

5. Do the procedure a third time. As you move down the spine this time, go a little deeper. Try to wake up the spinal nerves so that energy is released into the system.

6. Begin again from the top vertebra, only this time move your own life force beyond your hands, so that your "etheric hands" move deeply into the client's inner field and directly into the central tube running through the center of the body. Your energetic hands are now deep within the tube and you can sense where the blockages in the tube are located. Merely

loosen the blockages that you sense and then keep moving downward through the tube. Allow yourself to perceive any information your client's field may be communicating to you about these blockages, but more important, stay focused on your work, stay centered, and keep reciting your prayer (if that is the tool you use to keep yourself centered).

7.   When you reach the base of the spine, keep your thumbs at the base and rest your hands on the sides of each buttock. Between your hands, create an energy ball. Visualize the energy forming and becoming stronger and more vital at the base of the client's spine. You are now strengthening the client's Qi, or life force. Take a few minutes and allow the energy ball to grow and become strong.

8.   When you feel the ball is strong enough and of very good quality Qi, slowly begin to move your thumbs up on either side of the vertebrae while visualizing the energy gently moving with your hands. As the energy moves upward, it serves as a vacuum cleaner, gathering all the old blockages and debris from the tube.

9.   As you reach the back of the client's heart chakra, pause and ask the client to take a deep breath. With his inhalation, continue moving up the spine to the base of the head. Try to visualize and "feel" the ball growing ever more powerful as you move up the spine.

10. At the base of the neck, gently place your hands and palms on either side of the client's head. Ask him to exhale and to visualize the release of all he no longer needs out of the top of his head. At the same time, gently squeeze his head between your hands and pull the ball of energy and debris that it holds out of the top of his central tube at the top of his head.

11. As you raise your hands high above your client's head, release the debris into the Light of Love, to be transformed by the Great Healer.

     If the client feels congestion in his neck, repeat the process from step 6 to the end.

Many people describe the feeling upon being released from central tube debris as an "energy rush." Others feel lighter, and still others feel tired and need to rest for a while.

Using Energy to Change—Sam's Story Continues

Sam continued to see me once a week or twice a month for about six months as I worked on his central tube. During this period, we made gradual but steady progress. The central issue, as far as my practice was concerned, was getting Sam to see life in different terms, which is to say, to see life in a more positive light. Sam believed too strongly in the delusion that he had to be responsible for every little detail in his personal and professional life. He was assuming way too much responsibility in every situation. Underlying this attitude was his hidden belief that everything goes wrong in life, that the universe is an unfriendly and even a hostile place, and that every weak link in the chain of life will be broken. It was up to Sam to make the links strong, he secretly contended. This belief was very strong in him. It didn't matter to Sam when I told him that every link in the chain of life is weak and that every day is filled with millions of tenuous dramas that were all going in his favor even though he was unwilling or unable to see these positive events. It didn't matter when I said that each and every time he experienced a difficult day at work, or believed that a project was about to fail, he had, in fact, had a successful day and the project he was working on would succeed. It didn't matter a bit to him when I told him that he was a successful man and that he was high up in the corporate world in which he lived. All of this only served to reinforce his belief that he had to go on struggling to succeed. "Sam, you are where you are in spite of your struggle," I said.

These words, of course, were meaningless against the powerful energetic pattern that existed within him. Sam and I could have gone back into his past and analyzed all the details of his childhood. That may or may not have changed things. Given the fact that so many people undergo therapy today, and so few actually emerge from their patterns, I suspected that therapy alone would not be adequate to change Sam. (Although it is my experience that psychotherapy works very well in conjunction with healing touch.) What existed at the bottom of his belief system was, in all likelihood, a very powerful energetic pattern comprised of emotional scar tissue and blockages that prevented the transformative energy of heaven and earth from changing his life. He could not get adequate life force to evolve, to change, and to let go of the energetic debris that was holding him back. And in order to do that, we would have to eliminate the blockages in his field and his tube.

I tried to do this every time we got together. I especially concentrated on Sam's tube. I perceived that Sam's tube was heavily scarred. As I removed the scar tissue and blockages from Sam's field and central tube, Sam began to have insights about his relationship with his father, who regularly undermined him as a child and prevented him from ever feeling truly safe in his family. Sam realized that the central power in his life, his father, was hostile to him, which had conditioned him to believe that the power in life was negative. When he began to consider all the ramifications of this conditioning, Sam began to refer to his father's behavior as a kind of "emotional and spiritual abuse."

Meanwhile, Sam began to realize that his adult life was remarkably successful, despite the problems of his childhood. This stood in stark contrast to his childhood, which triggered another round of revelations in Sam about the possible nature of reality and about his relationship with God. Many things were going right in his life, Sam realized, though in the past he had been afraid to acknowledge them. He had prevented himself from appreciating his blessings, he said, because he feared exposing them to the hostile universe, which he believed would wipe out the good in his life if that good was ever exposed by Sam's open appreciation. This caused Sam to focus exclusively on his problems, which gave him an internal life of strife and, in turn, began to destroy his health.

The miracle of Sam's transformation was that while he

changed no lights flashed on and no fireworks went off. One day, he confessed to me: "I'm starting to feel better about things. I'm actually enjoying my work more," he said. "I think I'm changing." Gradually, Sam's outlook on life did change, and with this change his stomach and digestive disorders disappeared. I would say that healing touch helped Sam to accept life; it also helped him open up to the reality that he was being supported a lot more than he had previously believed or was willing to admit. He became a much more positive person, especially in his feelings toward himself, yet there was no one instance or single moment that he could point to and say, That's when I changed for the better.

After many of my sessions with Sam, I would lead him through a visualization I call the rainbow meditation, which is designed to help us overcome whatever beliefs may be holding us back or keeping us in fear, scarcity, and old patterns.

EXERCISE: RAINBOW MEDITATION FOR PLENTY

1. Visualize above your head a disk of utterly beautiful and vibrant rainbow light. This rainbow disk represents the opening into "the spiritual field of plenty." It is a ring of energy, an opening into the abundance that has been provided for your soul in this life. Within this ring, all that you need is available to you. Visualize the disk open and available to you now.

2. Reach up with your hands and see yourself pulling down from this spiritual realm all that you need, no matter whether that need be material, psychological, or spiritual—or all three (see diagram 10).

3. This visualization can be done at any time, but the intention may vary depending on when it is done. If you do this exercise upon awakening, try to visualize bringing down through your whole body all that you need to promote healing on the physical, emotional, mental, and spiritual levels. Also, visualize receiving through the disk of rainbow light whatever help you need that day.

DIAGRAM 10. RAINBOW DISK

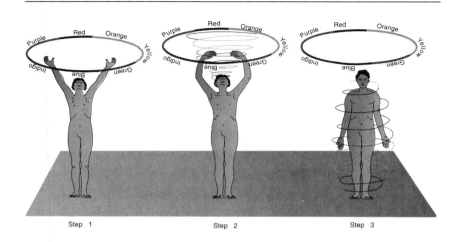

Step 1   Step 2   Step 3

If you are performing the meditation to help you serve a patient better, do it silently after you center yourself and before you do your prayer. In this case, visualize yourself bringing down through the circle of light all that the recipient needs to be healed. Do the meditation as you stand behind the recipient, very close to her back.

If you are leading a friend, loved one, or client through the meditation, do it at the conclusion of the session and ask the person to silently visualize herself receiving all that she needs through the circle of rainbow light. Before you do the meditation, go to the back of the person and stand close to it. Visualize the disk above the recipient's head. See the recipient reach up into the disk to bring down with her hands all that she needs for her complete healing. And always end this session with a prayer of thanksgiving for all that is being healed.

Healing Yourself to Know Yourself

Knowing the true self is perhaps our greatest goal, for in coming to know ourselves we come to understand our relationship to the universe at large. In that knowing is the realization that each of us is loved—indeed, that we are loved far more than we can conceive of. This invariably is the perception people experience when they go beyond their conditioning. Reaching beyond our conditioning isn't easy, however. Very often it feels as if we are hitting a wall, and indeed we are—it is a wall of energy that must be healed. For the practitioner of healing touch, psychological conditioning is not some abstract term that is applied to behavior patterns but is an energetic fact, a blockage, that prevents change from occurring smoothly and relatively painlessly. Energetic patterns and blockages cause us pain, and that pain is real. The reason is simple: Change is a constant; the universe demands evolution and transformation. This is both the fact and the fabric of life. But if we are blocked, we cannot move with the universal rhythms, and therefore we cannot see the light toward which we all are traveling.

A Healer's Checklist

Here is a step-by-step snapshot of your healing session—a checklist, so to speak. Use this list as an overview to help guide you through a session.

1. Have the patient sit on a stool or a straight-backed chair with the back and front and right sides exposed.
2. Ask the patient to do the "flowing water" visualization, along with deep breathing into the bottom of the stomach.
3. Assume your position behind the patient, with your left hand raised (palm up) and your right hand lowered (palm facing the earth). Center yourself.
4. Begin saying your prayer.
5. "Turn on your hands" by rubbing them vigorously and then creating the energy ball between your hands. Pass the energy ball into the person's field.
6. Do your initial assessment.

7. Open the feet so that the life force flows through to the earth.
8. Clear the field and chakras of restrictions, tension, blockages, and boulders.
9. Close the holes in the field.
10. Balance the excessive and deficient areas.
11. Release all energy that you remove from the field into the Light of Love.
12. Do a second assessment.
13. Check the feet again to assure that the energy is flowing out from them.
14. Clear the tube by moving the energy up the spine and pulling it off the top of the head.
15. When the main part of the treatment is finished, return to your standing position, with your hands over your solar plexus, restoring yourself to peace and harmony.
16. Have the patient lie down.
17. Balance the chakras.
18. Allow the patient ten minutes to rest and integrate the treatment.

10

Working with Specific Illnesses and Serious Disease

Healing touch can be used in conjunction with all other therapies to treat any illness. No matter what the disease, your primary focus is to restore the optimal flow of life energy through the field. You will be doing this by clearing away blockages in the field, closing the holes and leaks, moving excessive energy to the areas of the field that are deficient, channeling additional life force to places that are weak, clearing and balancing the chakras, and clearing the central tube. While you are doing this, you remain centered. Whenever necessary, you enhance the flow of energy within the client, and between the two of you, by using the meditations and guided images I have provided. This is your work, no matter what the disharmony with which your client may be working.

Nevertheless, it's essential that you tailor your treatment to the specific imbalances you may be facing. Following is a set of guidelines for dealing with specific illnesses that you may face in your practice. These recommendations can be used by anyone who wishes to use healing touch to help a friend or family member. As I said in chapter 3, treatment time varies according to the severity of the illness. There are times when very short sessions are all that should be done, and there are other times when you can take a longer period to work on the client's field.

How do you decide the correct work? Let's go through some examples.

Colds and Flu

Healing touch is very helpful in the treatment of acute illnesses such as the common cold and flu. It helps to alleviate many of the symptoms by decongesting and clearing the energy field. It also speeds the healing process.

The traditional view of the common cold is very different from the one we typically hold in the modern, Western culture. Traditionally, colds were considered the body's method of housecleaning—that is, of eliminating accumulating waste, toxins, bacteria, viruses, and stagnant energy. Sneezing, coughing, runny nose, diarrhea, and frequent urination are all the body's attempts to discharge these toxins rapidly and efficiently. As the study of immunology has proven, fever is a deliberate act of the immune system (namely, CD4 cells and macrophages) to create a hostile environment against pathogens. In other words, it is all part of the body's attempt to heal itself. In this view, the symptoms of the cold actually serve a very positive purpose and should be allowed to do their work. Suppressing the symptoms of a cold with various pharmaceuticals—the customary approach to colds in our modern culture—prevents the body from cleansing itself.

But cleansing is only one aspect of the cold's job. Traditional healers have viewed the cold and flu as the body's demand for rest. Many healers also view a cold as a release of old and unexpressed emotions, especially sadness and grief. In other words, it can be thought of as a safety valve, a long cry, particularly when we have neglected our emotional lives.

Whenever you work on a person with a cold or flu, work on the sixth chakra (sinuses), the fifth chakra (the throat and ears), the fourth chakra (the heart, especially to strengthen one's emotional life and assist in the release of emotions), and the second chakra (to promote elimination through the intestines).

Do your assessment in all of these areas. Usually, you will discover feelings of "thickness" and/or "heat" in one or more of these areas, indicating congestion and increased blood flow. Generally, you will spiral the energy out of the second, fourth, fifth, and sixth chakra areas. To do this, enter the chakra by moving your hand slowly in a counterclockwise direction, cup your hand, and lift stagnant energy out of the chakra. Do this for all the chakras that are involved in the cold symptoms. Pay particular attention to the chakras that are congested, such as the sinuses (sixth chakra), or the bowels (second chakra), if the client is constipated. Once that is done, open the secondary chakras on the feet. This will allow excess energy to be discharged from the body and new, healing earth's energy to enter the body. Again, it is better to begin at the bottom of the tube and work your way up.

Healing touch will boost the healing forces within the body and speed up the elimination and healing process, thus helping the client avoid an unnecessarily long cold. Keep the treatment short: no more than ten minutes.

If you perform the work for a longer period, it could trigger an even bigger discharge and cause a very intense discharge over a twenty-four- to forty-eight-hour period.

A friend of mine worked on one of the doctors in our office who had just begun to experience mild cold symptoms. In her attempt to do a good and thorough energy treatment, she spent about twenty minutes doing healing touch. When the doctor got home that night, he developed a fever of 103 degrees and was in bed with severe symptoms for two straight days. My friend might well have done him a great service, because this forced him to rest and allowed his body to eliminate a lot of accumulated waste, but the suffering was excessive, as far as he was concerned, and could have been avoided had she worked on him consistently for shorter periods of time. This would have allowed the elimination to be gradual and painless, while she strengthened the healing energies in his field.

Usually, seven to ten minutes of healing touch are all you need to help alleviate the symptoms of a cold and enhance the body's own healing forces.

Remember, the physical body is the densest part of the field. Disharmony occurs in the energetic body before it manifests in the physical. The physical body is the final discharge point in a process that begins in the field and finally manifests in the body. All energetic disturbances start the disease process by affecting the body on a cellular level. If the cell wall is compromised, there can then be bacterial or viral invasion of the cell, creating a virulent cold. However, if blockages, stagnation, and destabilizing energy can be eliminated from the field, the cells can be protected and the virus or bacteria cannot gain a foothold in the system. By reducing the disturbance in the field, you will reduce the harmful energetic forces and thus reduce the symptoms of the illness. Even if a virus or bacteria is taken in, the symptoms may only be mild, such as a little nasal discharge, but no significant disease process will develop.

In addition to energy work, the patient should get plenty of rest and take in adequate fluids, especially if there is fever. If the symptoms worsen considerably or persist longer than one week, you may need to encourage him or her to see a medical doctor.

When Treating Fever, Reduce the Energy

A fever occurs when tissues are injured from one or another of several possible causes, among them: some type of invasive event such as surgery or a blow to the body; a vascular accident, such as a heart attack; an infection caused by a virus, bacteria, or protozoa; diseases that trigger an autoimmune response such as arthritis; or certain types of cancers.

Once tissues are injured, the immune system sends out a signal to raise the body's temperature to prevent bacteria or viruses from gaining a foothold in the injured tissues. The fever itself is triggered by CD4 cells, the commander or general of the immune system. These cells send out orders to the rest of the immune system by producing powerful chemical messengers, collectively known as cytokines. These cytokines, in turn, trigger a battery of changes in your body, including a rise in the body's temperature, creating inflammation (which increases heat and blood flow to the affected area), and signals to your brain to make you sleepy. Once you're resting, your immune system can direct your body's energy to fight the injury or pathogen.

Thus, fever is part of the body's healing mechanism. In general, most physicians will tell a person not to treat a fever unless it gets beyond 104 degrees Fahrenheit.

Unlike pharmaceuticals, which will suppress the fever and thus deprive the body of its good work, healing touch strengthens the healing forces within the body and thus reduces the need for a high fever. Healing touch will also bring down a fever by reducing the destabilizing energies within the field.

One of the many ironies of the body's healing mechanisms is that while inflammation is produced by the body in its efforts to heal, the swelling that accompanies inflammation gets in the way of healing by blocking blood flow. Sometimes the swelling is so severe that the flows of energy and blood are blocked or severely restricted. There is also a heat reaction throughout the body as a result of the injury. Invariably, you will feel heat and congested energy in the field over areas of inflammation.

Treat fever and inflammation by removing the heat and congested energy from the field with your hands. Then build an energy ball within the vibral core and visualize the area surrounded by the color dark blue. The dark blue color cools the body and has an antiinflammatory effect. Your hands may become very hot. This means you are removing the heat from the body.

As the temperature begins to decrease in your hands, visualize the color of the light in the energy ball becoming green, which has a balancing effect on the area.

Do not send life force into the body initially. This will serve to further inflame the condition. Do this only as the patient becomes stronger. The treatment time should be one to five minutes initially and gradually increase to ten to twelve minutes.

Unblocking the Field to Alleviate Headaches

In general, headaches are caused by congestion or constricted energy in the lower chakras, which block life force from flowing out of the feet. Instead, the energy backs up into the head and causes a headache.

These treatments can last anywhere from five to fifteen minutes and consist mainly of opening the root chakra and the secondary chakras at the bottoms of the feet so that the backed-up energy in the head can drain. In cases like this, we move to the opposite end of the pain.

The primary work is to open the feet and clear the constriction most often found in the area of the solar plexus. The feet may have to be held for up to five minutes at a time. Ask the client to take deep breaths into the bottoms of her feet as you conduct the work. The deep breathing will help release the diaphragm and open the solar plexus area as well.

Also, remove blockages in the chakra at the solar plexus. Clear the shoulders of any tension and gently massage the neck and shoulders to loosen the throat chakra area. The massage here is similar to the massaging of the legs and feet required for opening the feet. With a headache there is usually tension in the shoulder and a palpable tightness. A gentle massage here will stimulate energy flow. You can then proceed with the regular energy work around the body. If the headache is of a sinus nature, clear any congestion found in the second chakra (sacral) as well (see the section on the chakra energy spiral in chapter 5).

The headache will usually ease, if not disappear completely, during the treatment. Encourage the client to go home and rest for an hour or so. If the headache is not gone at the end of the treatment, resting afterward will probably take care of the headache completely.

The life energy can be boosted if the shoulders relax during treatment and if the headache is not severe. If the life energy is raised during a severe headache with very tight shoulder muscles, it will only exacerbate the headache. Severe headaches (especially migraines) need supportive, gentle treatment, especially in the early sessions with your client.

Catastrophic Disease: Make the Treatments Short

In general, when treating catastrophic illnesses such as cancer or AIDS, less is more. The sicker the patient, the less you treat. Very sick patients can be treated for short periods (up to five minutes) every day. The treatment consists of clearing and balancing the energy field. My experience is that very sick clients are extremely appreciative of healing touch because of its effects on fatigue and because it calms and often balances the chaotic, destabilizing, and destructive influences within the field. These energies cause the rapid progression of the disease and create a sense of instability within the client. Practitioners have also noted that clients experience better rest and often require less pain medication with regular healing touch treatments.

When the patient is very ill and is unable to sit up, do not raise the life energy. Since catastrophic illness depletes the Qi, trying to raise it in the very ill patient can cause more pain and most certainly more energy depletion.

When treating people with cancer, *do not send energy to the area of the tumor.* This will only serve to strengthen the disease and make it more virulent. Instead, the work should focus on supporting healthy tissue and maintaining its health and integrity. The stronger and healthier the unaffected tissue, the less likely it will be to be invaded by the disease. Focus your energy work on the healthy

tissue to make it so strong that it can resist the assault of the unhealthy cells, and thus prevent the illness from spreading.

Julie's Story

Julie began seeing me in July 1988 at age forty. Eight and a half
years earlier, she had been diagnosed with ovarian cancer and had
a radical hysterectomy. She also underwent radiation treatment,
chemotherapy and another pelvic operation that resulted in a colostomy. Her presenting complaints at the time of her first visit
were incomplete digestion and difficulty in wearing her colostomy
appliance without developing irritation and polyps around the
opening, or stoma. She had also developed a considerable amount
of scar tissue in the abdominal area. Scar tissue impairs energy flow
within the field and the physical body.

Since I am also a nutritionist, my initial work with Julie was to
give her dietary advice. The digestive system and stoma had to be
stabilized before she could trust me to give her energy work. As
Julie put it, "I felt my body wasn't receptive to anything until I
could receive food."

Nine months after we began working on the physical body, or
the "root" of the energy field, she was digesting her food well, feeling more energetic for activities of daily living, and was less depressed. She also was wearing her colostomy appliance for three
days between changes with no irritation around the stoma.

We began energy work with a meditation to make her sensitive to the way energy moves in the body. The guided imagery
helped Julie reconnect to the organs that she had lost to surgery, but
were still there as energetic organs in the etheric field (see chapter 4
to refresh your knowledge of the etheric field). We then started
healing touch, initially focusing on integrating and releasing the
emotions related to the loss of her female organs. We did energy
work for nine months, during which time Julie made remarkable
progress in integrating very difficult emotions and restoring her
sense of femininity.

After this period, Julie and I began to work on the scar tissue within her stoma and intestinal tract. We were joined in this work by an acupuncturist whose specialty is eliminating scar tissue. The three of us worked together for the next two years. At one point, her surgeon, who examined Julie periodically, reported how amazed he was that the scar tissue in her abdomen had decreased so markedly. In fact, Julie had made so much healing progress that her surgeon said that he would consider reversing the colostomy in the future if she continued to make such progress.

Julie's critique of her four-year process of energy work is as follows:

"Energy work lightens up the physical body. It seems to release physical blocks to feelings. As the parts of my body released, I felt more available to spirit. I began to be more able to trust the movement and changes in life. Initially, I saw myself as having very separate parts. My mind was very separate from my heart, which was very separate from my stomach and intestines and other organs. Energy work has helped me see and feel myself as a whole being—an integration of body, mind, and spirit.

"It has also helped me gain a trust of living.

"As I've become more conscious of having to breathe during energy work, I feel more empowered and in control. I feel like I am participating in the healing effort, which also makes me feel less of a victim. As I have surrendered to the process, I am owning more of my intuitive and spiritual self."

Working with Terminal Illness: Giving Peace and Comfort in Life's Most Challenging Hour

Facing death is hard enough, but facing it alone is a tragedy beyond words. When working with a client who is clearly terminal, your work is intended to assist the spirit as it prepares to leave the physical form. You are there to make the transition easier and to contribute to the loving, spiritual, and gentle forces that are now at work in the client's life. Healing touch offers the gentle power of love, and that is what a person needs most when making life's most frightening transition. The practice can help relax the client's body and clarify his mind, open his chakras, and assist his birth process into the next world. The healing energy you give to the client will assist him in many ways—physically, emotionally, psychologically, and spiritually. But the very fact that this is energetic healing, that you are addressing the spirit and not the body, is crucial to the person who is dying. Your presence and your work are a statement of love and faith: There is more to this life than the body you are about to leave.

The actual energy work usually lasts for only five minutes.

During the dying process, as the spirit prepares to vacate the earthly body, the lower three chakras begin to lose their integrity. The spirit, or soul, is no longer firmly rooted in the body. The patient is not always coherent and may appear to lie talking with someone who is not physically in the room. When this is occurring, one does not try to "ground" the patient by holding his feet and directing energy downward. Instead, calm and smooth the field; groom it, so to speak, by running your hands slowly and gently over the front of the body (if the client is in bed and lying on his back) or the sides of the body, whichever is available to you. Try to remove any blockages that may be holding the spirit back or causing pain or suffering. When you've done this, open the crown chakra. To do that, hold your hands just above the head at the seventh chakra and send gentle energy upward. This chakra is actually a great circle of energy above the head. It is now drawing the life energy out of the body and collecting it unto itself as it prepares to return to its natural home, the world of spirit. Visualize the chakra opening and the spirit being able to release itself from the body whenever it chooses to do so. You are only assisting in the process that the spiritual world has well in hand.

The energy work helps calm and relax the patient and allows for an easier transition. It is important to remember that healing touch cannot cause or speed death. Death is a private process between the individual and the Creator.

Crystal's Story

Crystal, a forty-two-year-old woman suffering from acute myelocytic leukemia, wanted me to do energy work with her in preparation for a bone marrow transplant. She had been diagnosed with leukemia two years earlier and had since tried some nontraditional approaches. This alternative treatment had kept her in remission for two years, but the leukemia had become active again. Since she had a bone marrow donor, she decided to go the more orthodox route while incorporating healing touch.

I worked with Crystal every two to three days over a two-month period. During this time, Crystal fought a life-threatening fungal sinus infection and underwent intensive chemotherapy and antibiotic therapy in preparation for the bone marrow transplant.

During the eight weeks, my focus with Crystal was to help her center herself and strengthen her own inherent healing abilities. She showed remarkable courage and stamina in dealing with the side effects of chemotherapy and the disappointment that her body was not able to handle the treatments that would prepare her for the transplant. If she could not respond to the chemotherapy there could be no transplant.

Often I would work on her liver. After smoothing her field and attempting to balance her central tube, I would hold my hands over her liver (front and back) and build a healing ball of energy between them, concentrating on the liver. I did this to support her liver as it tried to deal with the toxic pharmaceuticals being introduced into her body. These treatments would last seven to ten minutes.

Many of the nurses and doctors were very skeptical of healing touch at first, and some were openly critical. They argued that she was going to die and she should not have tried nonorthodox approaches in the first place. Meanwhile, Crystal was improving. She felt better and had significantly more vitality after I conducted each treatment. Her physicians and nurses could not help but notice, and they were remarkably forthcoming with me in their support. "I don't know what you're doing, but she feels better and is less agitated after you've worked with her," one doctor told me. "Keep doing it." They also reported that she rested easier and was not as nauseous after the treatments.

It soon became apparent, however, that all I could do was make her comfortable. She was losing her battle against the leukemia, and the highly toxic drugs she was being given were far too powerful. She returned to her home to be with her family. I visited her a couple of times very near to the end of her life. The healing touch took on a very different tenor at this stage. The treatments were three to four minutes in length and consisted of smoothing the field, clearing any debris in the lower three chakras, opening the crown chakra, and preparing the path for the spirit to exit the body. Although Crystal died, she made her passing gently and with great dignity.

Her husband shared his perception of the healing touch process as he watched it unfold:

"Healing touch helped Crystal focus her own innate healing powers. While it is easy for someone to say that Crystal died, and therefore all treatment was a failure, that was not the case. She came back against astronomical odds to beat a deadly fungal infection. While we will never know exactly how she came back, in my own mind, it was some blend of her astounding will, the intravenous medicine, and the energy work.

"Into the insane, hectic medical model of a cancer hospital setting, the healer and energy work brought a sense of safe space and trusting. Crystal believed in this work and resonated with it. There was a magical sense when you [Deby] came into her room. I would shut the door and protect the room from intrusion. Then you and Crystal would do your work.

"There was a deep consistency in the work, although it varied according to Crystal's physical condition, her mental condition, and the healer's inner sense of what was appropriate. Crystal always felt safe and that it helped her."

A Dynamic Treatment Plan

A good treatment plan always begins with a good initial interview. The healer should take a complete health history of the client as well as the presenting complaints. An extended family history should be obtained, along with information on any medicines, herbs, or vitamins or dietary supplements the patient is currently taking. It is also imperative that the healer have a working knowledge of the disease or disharmony the patient wants to work on. Invest in a few good textbooks on internal medicine, such as a *Merck Manual, Taber's Cyclopedic Medical Dictionary,* or *Harrison's Principles of Internal Medicine*.

Once you have established what the client sees as a problem, a care plan can be developed to guide both you and the patient through the treatment.

There is a five-step process that takes into consideration the patient's medical diagnosis and leads the healer to develop a plan of action to enhance the healing of the patient. The steps are as follows:

1. Assessment: This includes all information obtained in the initial interview.
2. Analysis: This includes analysis of the patient's problems.
3. Plan: In healing touch, the plan is the energy work, based on prioritizing the problems and establishing patient-centered goals, along with the specific intervention and rationale. This also includes the networking and the list of other professionals involved on the care team. The plan of energy work remains the same. What changes each week are the symptoms the patient arrives with and the changes that have occurred in the field as a result of the past week's work. Part of the plan is to talk with the patient and help him recognize the changes and evaluate the effect the work is having on him.
4. Implementation: This is putting the care plan into action to fulfill the patient-centered goals.

5. Evaluation: This includes determining the value and results of the treatment plan and evaluating the patient's progress. The evaluation comes from the patient, the family, other health care professionals involved (psychotherapist, massage therapist, chiropractor, family doctor, other nurse practitioners, etc.), and most important, from the healer observing the patient's response to the therapeutic touch process.

When a patient comes to you for healing touch, it is very important that he or she has had a recent physical examination by a doctor and that you are aware of any physical problems or limitations the patient may have.

For example, it was imperative that Sam (chapter 9) see a gastrointestinal specialist to rule out any type of ulcerative condition. If Sam had developed a bleeding ulcer, the first step in the care plan would be to stop the bleeding, not to do energy work on his solar plexus! Energy work may be appropriate, as are counseling on stress reduction and proper diet, but only after the life-threatening condition is identified and stabilized.

With certain conditions and illnesses, alternative health care methods work very well. However, if the patient finds himself facing a life-threatening situation, such as bleeding ulcers, extreme labile blood pressure, certain advanced stages of cancer, even broken bones, it is necessary to seek allopathic or orthodox medical treatment—in addition to doing healing touch. This brings us to the planning stages of our treatment phase, which includes the use of other caregivers in the healing process. If your client faces acute emotional issues and you are not qualified to handle them in a proper manner, your responsibility is to encourage the client to find a psychotherapist or therapeutic group situation to help him deal with the issues the two of you are uncovering with energy work.

Keeping in mind the importance of proper referral for physical and emotional needs, know that there are many other methods of healing that may enhance the treatment. For example, acupuncture and Chinese medicine may be helpful for the patient. They also enhance the energy work. Other good compatible modalities include massage, physical therapy, chiropractic, homeopathy, and nutritional counseling. Sometimes combining therapies helps move the patient toward health at a faster, more comfortable rate.

Five minutes of healing touch before any kind of massage or body work can make the body work session much more healing. By the same token, five minutes of energy work prior to a psychotherapy session can also enhance the work and productivity of the session.

Although treatment plans or care plans have been traditionally used in nursing, they can be modified for psychotherapy and body work.

The treatment plan is dynamic and does not remain static. It changes and expands as the energy needs of the patient change. The energy work creates the need for the dynamic treatment plan. The therapeutic touch and energy work usually help the patient to move and release at a faster but still safe pace. Therefore, each week you may find that different areas in the central tube need attention and support based on the healing that resulted from the work you and the patient did the prior week. Dynamic treatment comes with the healer's ability to implement treatment based on the growth and changes occurring within the patient.

Conclusion: Recognizing Spirit as the Healer

We are living in a time when the old duality that separates body and mind, energy and matter, is giving way. Quantum physics is teaching us that at the molecular level, scientists cannot determine whether matter is composed of particles or waves of energy. In fact, physicists tell us that the central factor that determines the essential nature of reality—that is, whether matter is made up of tiny bits of substance or waves of energy—is the mind. Look at the material world one way and you see particles as the basis of life; look at the matter in another way and you see waves. The only conclusion to be drawn is that reality is composed of both matter and energy, particles *and* waves.

We practitioners of healing touch couldn't agree more. We wish to point out, however, that for too long our society has stressed the material aspects of life, while it has undervalued the energetic or spiritual part of our being. Each of us is matter and energy, body and soul.

Science is now making the most tenuous of forays into the realm of energy and is coming up with many surprising discoveries that support the age-old view of human existence. Naturally, this frightens many people. It shakes our worldview at its very foundation. To think that you could affect someone at a distance with your thoughts, or that you could use your hands to send healing energy to someone you care about—these ideas run counter to many of our society's most fundamental beliefs. We take it for granted that, while we might have been raised in a very religious home, we base our belief system on materialistic ideas. The materialistic view of life maintains that you are your body and that's all you are. Not only is that a sad and frightening idea, but it is so limiting. Those who embrace this materialistic worldview ultimately discover that it leads to a very dark and lonely dead end.

Fortunately for all of us—including the disbelievers—we are much more than matter. We are energy, too. What we have only begun to discover—or, I should say, rediscover—is that there is tremendous power in the realization that we are luminous beings, living spheres of energy, who possess the ability to share that living energy with one another. For practitioners of healing touch, that means utilizing this practice as a tool against all types of disharmonies, including those that threaten life.

For those just starting out as practitioners, that means walking into difficult situations and employing the work even before you have sufficient experience to know as a certainty how powerful the practice really is—even before you know in your heart that matter is composed of both particles and waves and that you can transmit those waves of energy to another human being to make a profound difference in his or her life. Those of us who have been around a while and who have had that experience, have the joy and the comforting knowledge that there is more to life than merely the particles that make up the body.

In the end, healing touch is a challenge to the most fundamental beliefs of our society, to our modern world, and to each of us. Yet, it is the most liberating of practices and among the most powerful because it puts you in harmony with a greater reality, one that has sustained the world from the very beginning and will go on sustaining it forever.

Appendix 1

Intake Questionnaire

DATE   /   / _____

PATIENT _____

HOME ADDRESS _____

CITY _____ STATE _____ ZIP _____

HOME PHONE _____ WORK PHONE _____

OCCUPATION _____

MARITAL STATUS _____ AGE _____ BIRTHDATE _____

REFFERED BY _____

PRESENT AILMENT/SYMPTOMS _____

_____

_____

_____

_____

FAMILY HISTORY: FATHER: _____

MOTHER: _____ SIBLINGS: _____

FAMILY HEALTH HISTORY: ARITHITIS _____ CANCER _____

HIGH BLOOD PRESSURE _____ DIABETES _____ TB _____

ASTHMA _____ GOITER _____ MENTAL _____

HEART DISEASE _____ GOUT _____ OBESITY _____

KIDNEY   EPILEPSY   ALLERGIES
_____

OTHER
_____

PERSONAL HEALTH HISTORY: TB   SCARLET FEVER   PNEUMONIA
_____

INFECTIOUS DISEASES (i.e. measles, chicken pox, mumps)
_____

TONSILLITIS   HEART DISEASE   HYPERTENSION
_____

VENEREAL DISEASE
_____

OTHER
_____

_____

_____

_____

_____

LIST ALL SURGERIES:
_____

_____

_____

_____

HABITS: LIST NORMAL BREAKFAST, LUNCH, DINNER FOR YOURSELF
_____

BREAKFAST
_____

LUNCH
_____

DINNER
_____

HOW MUCH/HOW OFTEN?
_____

ALCOHOL   TOBACCO   DRUGS   COFFEE   TEA
_____

WATER   SLEEP   BOWEL HABITS   EXERCISE
_____

LIST ALL MEDICATIONS, VITAMINS, OR HERBS YOU ARE CURRENTLY TAKING

FEMALE MENSTRUAL HISTORY: CYCLE ONSET   PERIODICITY

DURATION   TYPE OF FLOW: HEAVY   MEDIUM   LIGHT   PAIN

COLOR: BRIGHT RED   DARK RED   CLOTS   MOOD SWINGS

BREAST TENDERNESS   WATER RETENTION   LAST MENSTRUAL PERIOD

OTHER

PREGNANCIES: CHILDREN   MISCARRIAGES   ABORTIONS

BIRTH CONTROL   D&C

COMMENTS YOU WISH TO MAKE:

SIGNED:

Appendix 2

Energy Work Treatment with the Patient in the Sitting Position

1

2

1-2: Practitioner opening Rainbow Disk and pulling energy down to herself.

3

4

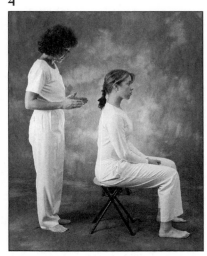

3: Practitioner collecting energy for the energy ball.

4: Practitioner forming the energy ball.

5

6

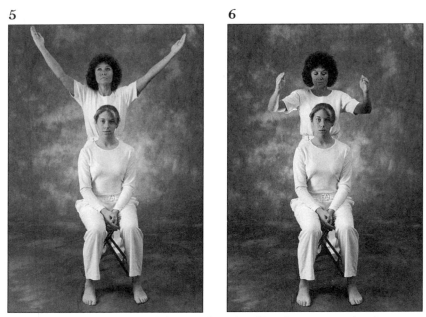

5-6: Practitioner opening Rainbow Disk and pulling down energy for the patient.

7

8

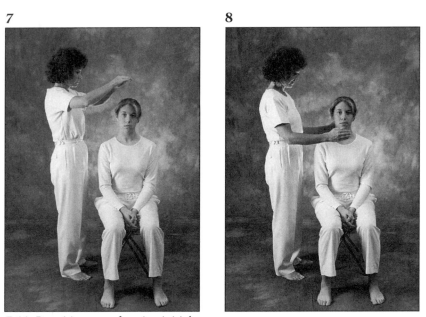

7-11: Practitioner performing initial assessment.

9

10

11

12   13

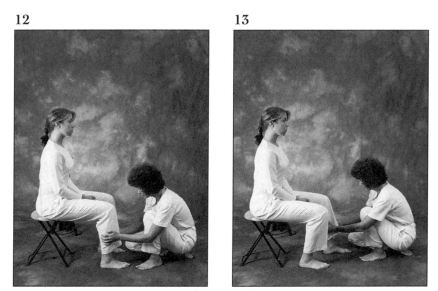

12-13: Practitioner pulling energy down each leg.

14

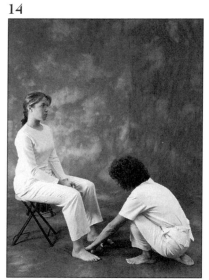

14: Practitioner opening the patient's feet and balancing the energy flow.

15

16

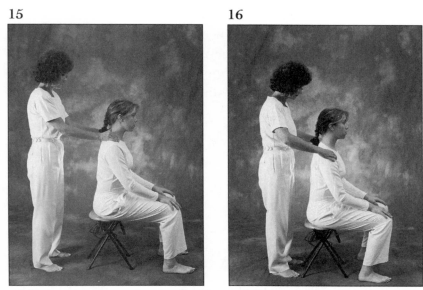

15-18: Practitioner opening the shoulders and directing energy flow down each arm (same procedure as opening the feet).

17

18

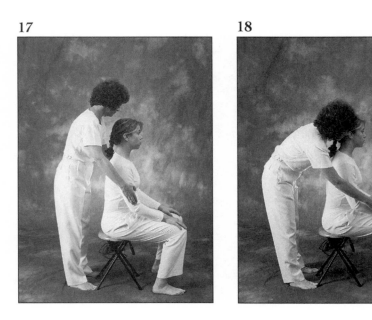

At this point in the treatment, the practitioner needs to perform another assessment, which can be done by repeating steps 7-11, and any appropriate intervention as described in chapter 7. The practitioner should also periodically check the patient's feet (step 14) to make sure they are open.

19

19: Practitioner gently moving down the patient's spine.

20

20: Practitioner building the energy ball to raise the life force, or Qi.

21

22

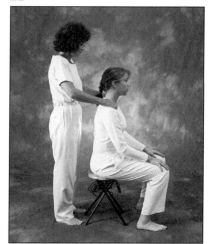

21-22: Practitioner slowly moving up the patient's spine while visualizing the energy ball, clearing the central tube, and raising the patient's energy.

23

24

23-26: Practitioner releasing energy.

25

26

27

27: Practitioner returning light and love to the patient's vibral core.

28

29

28-32: Practitioner grooming the field in a clockwise direction at the patient's left side.

30

31

32

Balancing the Chakras with the Patient in a Supine or Lying-Down Position.

Complete treatment may also be given this way.

1

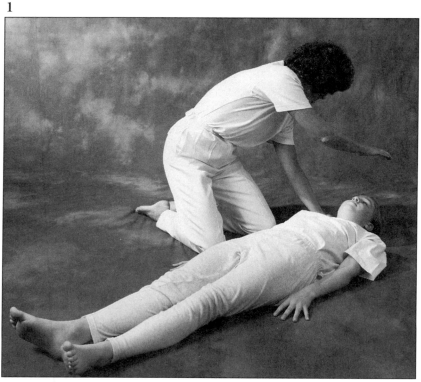

1-3: Initial assessment with the practitioner's left hand supporting the patient at the back of the neck.

2

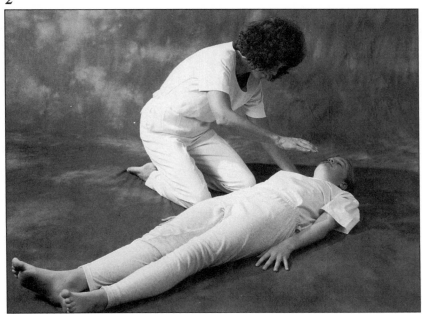

3

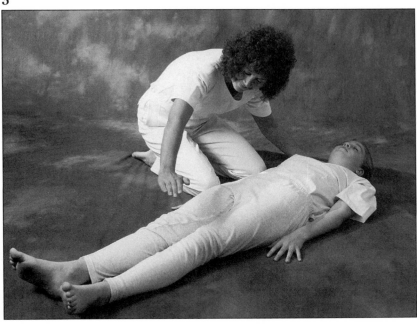

4

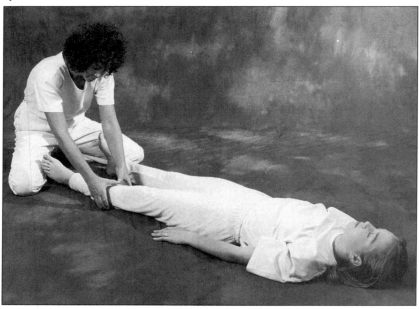

4-6: Practitioner pulling energy down both legs.

5

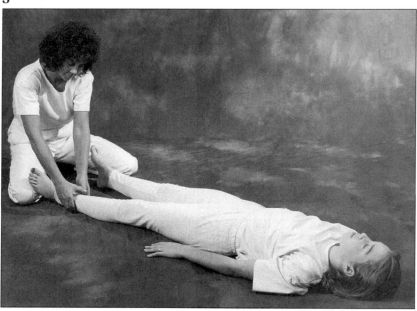

6

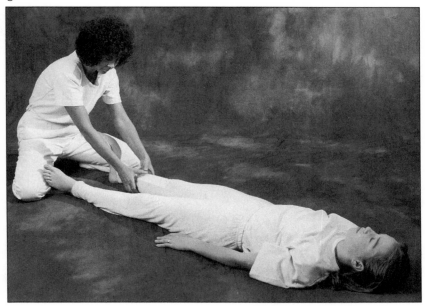

7

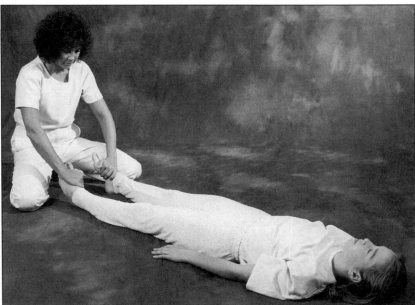

7: Practitioner opening the feet.

8

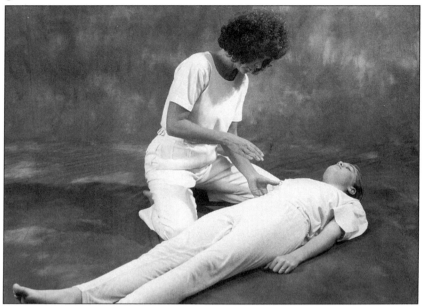

8-9: Practitioner placing hands around the patient's solar plexus.

9

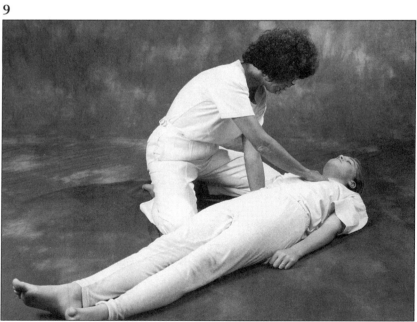

10

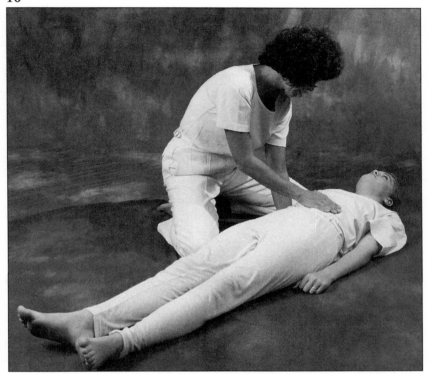

10: Practitioner visualizing the energy ball between her hands to balance the Chakra.

NOTE: The pictures depict only the solar plexus, but steps 8-10 may be done for any of the Chakras.

References

Angelo, Jack. *Your Healing Power: A Comprehensive Guide to Channelling Your Healing Energies.* Piatkus Books, 1994.

Berger, Ruth. *The Secret Is in the Rainbow.* York Beach, Maine: Samuel Weiser, Inc., 1979.

Berkow, Robert, M.D., ed. *Merck Manual of Diagnosis and Therapy.* 14th ed. Rahway, N.J.: Merck, Sharp, and Dohme Research Labs, 1982.

Besant, Annie, and Leadbeater, C. W. *Human Thought Forms.* Wheaton, Ill.: Theosophical Publishing House, 1969.

Brennan, Barbara A. *Hands of Light: A Healing Guide Through the Human Energy Field.* London: Bantam Books, 1988.

Chia, Mantah. *Awaken Healing Energy Through the Tao.* Santa Fe, N.M.: Aurora Press, 1983.

Chopra, Deepak, M.D. *Quantum Healing: Exploring the Frontiers of Mind/Body Medicine.* New York: Bantam Books, 1989.

Clark, P. E., and Clark, M. J. "Therapeutic Touch: Is There a Scientific Basis for the Practice?" *Nursing Research* 33(1) (1984):37–41.

Cooke, Ivan. *Healing by the Spirit.* White Eagle, 1985.

Earl, Jonathan. "Cerebral Laterality and Meditation: A Review of the Literature." *Journal of Transpersonal Psychology* 13 (1981):155–73.

Fanslow, Cathleen A., R.N., M.A. "Therapeutic Touch: A Healing Modality Throughout Life." *Topics in Clinical Nursing* 5(2) (1983):72–79.

Fastwolf, Oh Shinnah. Various lectures on healing with crystals.

Gerber, Richard, M.D. *Vibrational Medicine.* Santa Fe, N.M.: Bear and Company, 1988.

Grad, Bernard. "The Influence of an Unorthodox Method of Wound Healing in Mice." *International Journal of Parapsychology,* Spring 1961, pp. 5–24.

———. "Some Biological Effects of 'Laying On of Hands': A Review of Experiments with Animals and Plants." *Journal of the American Society for Psychical Research* 59(2) (1965):95–127.

Heidt, Patricia, Ph.D., R.N. "Effect of Therapeutic Touch on Anxiety Level of Hospitalized Patients." *Nursing Research* 30(1) (1981):32–37.

Johari, Harish. *Chakras.* Rochester, Vt.: Destiny Books, 1987.

Judith, Anodea. *Wheels of Life.* St. Paul, Minn.: Llewellyn Publications, 1990.

Kaptchuk, Ted J. *The Web That Has No Weaver.* Rider, London, 1983.

Karagulla, Shafica, M.D., and van Gelder Kunz, Dora. *The Chakras.* Wheaton, Ill.: Theosophical Publishing House, 1989.

Kilner, Walter J. *The Human Aura.* Secaucus, N.J.: Citadel Press, 1965.

Krieger, Dolores, Ph.D., R.N. *Living the Therapeutic Touch: Healing as a Lifestyle.* New York: Dodd, Mead and Company, 1987.

———. "Therapeutic Touch: The Imprimatur of Nursing." *American Journal of Nursing* 5 (1975):784–87.

Krieger, Dolores, Ph.D., R.N., et. al. "Therapeutic Touch: Searching for Evidence of Physiological Change." *American Journal of Nursing,* April 1979, pp. 660–62.

Kunz, Dora, comp. *Spiritual Aspects of the Healing Arts.* Wheaton, Ill.: Theosophical Publishing House, 1985.

Landsdowne, Zachary, Ph.D. *The Chakras and Esoteric Healing.* York Beach, Maine: Samuel Weiser, Inc., 1986.

Laurie, Sanders G., and Tucker, Melvin J. *Centering: A Guide to Inner Growth.* Rochester, Vt.: Destiny Books, 1983.

Leadbetter, C. W. *The Chakras*. Wheaton, Ill.: Theosophical Publishing House, 1987.

Macrae, Janet. *Therapeutic Touch: A Practical Guide*. Penguin Books, 1990.

———. "Therapeutic Touch in Practice." *American Journal of Nursing,* April 1979, pp. 664–65.

Miller, Lynn A. "An Explanation of Therapeutic Touch: Using the Science of Unitary Man." *Nursing Forum* 18(3) (1979):278–87.

Mitchell, Edgar D. *Psychic Exploration: A Challenge for Science.* New York: G. P. Putnam and Sons, 1974.

Nitsch, Twylah. Various lectures on healing.

O'Connor, John, and Bensky, Dan, trans. and eds. *Acupuncture: A Comprehensive Text.* Chicago: Eastland Press, 1981.

Pellitier, K. R. *Mind as Healer, Mind as Slayer.* New York: Dell Publishing, 1977.

Quinn, Janet, Ph.D., R.N. "One Nurse's Evolution as a Healer." *American Journal of Nursing,* April 1979, pp. 662–64.

Randolph, Gretchen L., Ph.D., R.N. "Therapeutic and Physical Touch: Physiological Response to Stressful Stimuli." *Nursing Research* 33(1) (1984):33–36.

Rea, John D. *Patterns of the Whole.* Vol. 1. Healing and Quartz Crystals. Boulder, Colo.: Two Trees Publishing, 1986.

———. *Voluntary Controls.* New York: E. P. Dutton, 1978.

Stein, Diane. *All Women Are Healers.* Calif.: Crossing Press, 1990.

———. *The Woman's Book of Healing.* St. Paul, Minn.: Llewellyn Publications, 1987.

Taber, Clarence Wilbur. *Taber's Cyclopedic Medical Dictionary.* 11th ed. Philadelphia: F. A. Davis Company, 1969.

White, Ruth. *Working With Your Chakras.* Piatkus Books, 1993.

Williams III, Gurney. "The Lowest-Tech Medicine Ever." *Longevity,* January 1992, pp. 60–69.

Wilson, Jean D., M.D., et al., eds. *Harrison's Principles of Internal Medicine*. 12th ed. New York: McGraw-Hill, Inc., 1991.

In case of difficulty in obtaining any of these books, please contact:

Compendium Books
234 Camden High Street
London NW1
Tel: 0171-267-1525

Watkins
19–21 Cecil Court
London WC2N 4EZ
Tel: 0171-836-2182

Resources Note

There is no national source list specifically for energy workers or therapeutic touch therapists. However, further information can be obtained from the following organisations:

The Institute for Complementary Medicine (ICM)
PO Box 194
London
SE16 1QZ
Tel: 0171-2375165

The National Federation of Spiritual Healers (NFSH)
Old Manor Farm Studio
Church Street
Sunbury-on-Thames
Middlesex
TW16 6RG
Tel: 01932 783164

The Confederation of Healing Organisations
Suite J, Second Floor
The Red and White House
113 High Street
Berkhamsted
Herts
HP4 2DJ
Tel: 01442 870660

Index

About the Author

Deborah Cowens is a nurse practitioner in women's health and a clinical specialist in psychiatry. For the past sixteen years she has had her own private practice, providing clients with physical exams, blood chemistry readings, nutritional supplement recommendations with dietary consultations, therapeutic touch, and guided imagery. She also worked with a gynecologist in Brookline, Massachusetts, doing annual exams, menopausal counseling, and colposcopic exams.

Cowens was also on the faculty at Regis College in Weston, Massachusetts, for six years. She has taught seminars at Interface, a holistic teaching center in Cambridge, Massachusetts, and has spoken before numerous organizations on topics ranging from nutrition to stress management. She also conducts a self-designed, ten-week course to teach nurses and other health care workers how to use therapeutic touch and energy work.

She currently resides in San Antonio, Texas, with her husband and two daughters.

Dr Sarah Brewer MA, MB, BChir

CANDIDA ALBICANS

KU-678-744

Thorsons
An Imprint of HarperCollinsPublishers

Thorsons
An Imprint of HarperCollins*Publishers*
77–85 Fulham Palace Road,
Hammersmith, London W6 8JB
1160 Battery Street,
San Francisco, California 94111–1213
Published by Thorsons 1997

10 9 8 7 6 5 4 3 2

A catalogue record for this book
is available from the British Library

ISBN 0 7225 3391 8

Printed in Great Britain by
Caledonian International Book Manufacturing, Glasgow

To Richard and Saxon

CONTENTS

PREFACE: THE ESSENTIAL GUIDE SERIES

This series offers up-to-date, in-depth information on common health problems. These books contain detailed, medically accurate information in a user-friendly, easy to read style.

Each book covers:

- What the condition is
- How common it is
- Who is affected by it
- Normal body functions and how each condition affects them
- Symptoms
- Causes
- Risk factors
- How the condition is diagnosed – blood tests, investigations, etc.
- Other similar conditions that need to be ruled out
- The drugs used to treat it – including side-effects and who shouldn't take them
- Surgical treatments that can help
- Complementary treatments
- Self-help tips
- Dietary changes that may prove helpful
- Latest research findings
- Addresses of support groups and sources of further information

This invaluable series will answer all your questions and help you to make the best decisions regarding your own health care.

Chapter One

AN INTRODUCTION TO CANDIDA

Not all yeast cells are as accommodating as those that produce the finest vintage champagne. Unlike its cousins, yeasts used in brewing and baking, the yeast known generally as Candida can cause a number of human diseases ranging from nappy rash to lethal meningitis in people with lowered immunity.

At the beginning of the 20th century, infection with Candida was rare. It now seems to be a significant problem for a great number of people. Many researchers believe this is due to wide-spread use of broad-spectrum antibiotics, which disrupt the normal balance of healthy micro-organisms in the body as well as killing disease-causing pathogens. It is also partly because modern medical treatments allow people with serious illnesses and lowered resistance to live longer so they become suscep-tible to yeast 'super-infections'.

Many apparently healthy people are plagued with recurrent Candida infections despite being otherwise well. Not only is the Candida yeast changing – and perhaps becoming more virulent – but modern lifestyles are also partly to blame. Hormonal methods of contraception, raised stress levels, low-temperature washing machine cycles and a diet of highly processed food are all playing a role. It is also thought that Candida can produce an allergic-type reaction (Candida hypersensitivity syndrome) linked to a number of common conditions such as Irritable Bowel Syndrome and constant fatigue.

WHAT IT IS

Candida is the name for a group of yeast-like fungi that live quite happily in or on the body of just about everyone. They exist in balance with other micro-organisms (commensals) – on the skin, in the intestines and sometimes in the mouth or genital tract – usually without causing any obvious harm.

Altogether, around 80 different species of Candida exist, but only a quarter of these can cause disease in humans. Of these, the most important is *Candida albicans* – or white fungus. It is named after the white plaques that form on mucous membranes in a well-established infection. The common name for Candida infection is thrush.

Candida belong to a large group (division) of fungi that are described as imperfect (*fungi imperfecti*) because they have mostly lost the art of sexual reproduction. Most increase in numbers by growing and putting out little buds that break off and form new daughter cells.

When Candida are viewed under the microscope, they take on several different forms, some of which look like classic yeasts, while others resemble fungi:

- large, round, thick-walled inactive resting spores (chlamydioconidia)
- active yeast cells that may be round, slipper- or pear-shaped
- asexually reproducing yeast cells with budding daughter cells (blastoconidia) projecting from their surface to resemble knobbly Jerusalem artichokes
- a collection of elongated buds and threads that have remained attached to one another rather than breaking off (pseudohyphae)
- long thread-like structures (germ tubes or hyphae)
- a network of interwoven threads (mycelium).

The simple-cell forms of Candida remain superficial and are seen when Candida yeasts colonize the skin, mouth, gut or lower reproductive tract without causing symptoms. The thread forms (hyphae and psudohyphae), however, can burrow down between human cells to literally invade the tissues and cause symptoms of Candida overgrowth.

If Candida proliferates in large numbers or starts to invade the tissues, it produces varying symptoms depending on the part of the body affected and how mild or severe the infection is. These symptoms include:

- itching
- discharge
- soreness
- redness
- painful swelling
- swollen glands
- skin rash
- brittle nails
- difficulty swallowing
- painful intercourse
- cystitis
- weight loss
- lack of energy.

Recurrent Candida infection makes life a misery for countless numbers of people.

Candida infection is also known as:
- Candidiasis
- Candidosis
- Moniliasis
- Thrush

WHERE IT COMES FROM

Candida yeast cells are found just about everywhere on Earth. Because they can enter a resting state similar to suspended animation (spores) they exist even in inhospitable places – including surviving a relatively low-temperature (40°C) cycle in your washing machine. Candida have been recovered from soil, food and also from the air. Most of us carry around our own unique strains of Candida, which cause no problems until our natural immunity is lowered, as during illness (such as a cold) or through taking antibiotics.

HOW COMMON IS IT?

Candida albicans is so common that it lives in or on the body of just about every member of the population. Altogether, it accounts for up to 75 per cent of yeasts recovered from sites of infection. It can also be isolated from normal, healthy individuals with no signs of disease, and is found in:

- the mouths of up to 50 per cent of healthy people
- the oesophagus of 11 per cent of healthy people
- rectal swabs of 30 per cent of healthy people
- vaginal swabs of up to 55 per cent of apparently well women
- the faeces of 80 per cent of healthy people
- the skin creases of up to 80 per cent of healthy people
- the hands of 12 per cent of doctors and nurses
- the mouths of 76 per cent of hospital patients.

Three out of four women experience vaginal thrush at least once in their life; some are plagued with never-ending recurrences.

WHAT TRIGGERS CANDIDA OVERGROWTH?

Candida yeast cells usually live in a happy balance with healthy bacteria and cause no harm. It is only when conditions change, encouraging the overgrowth of yeast cells, that they can invade your tissues and cause symptoms. Its favourite conditions for optimum survival are a warm, moist place with an acid pH (2.5 –7.5) and a temperature of 20 to 38°C – the usual conditions found in the vagina and some parts of the gut. Even when conditions are not ideal, the yeast can still proliferate. In general, a symptomatic Candida infection is most likely to develop if:

- a particularly virulent strain of Candida is present
- local conditions such as temperature, humidity or acid levels

change enough to encourage Candida growth (as after vigorous exercise, after using a vaginal douche, when taking antacids)

- circulating hormones (especially oestrogens) activate yeast cells (for example, at certain times in the female menstrual cycle and during pregnancy)
- there is an imbalance of other micro-organisms which usually keep yeast cells in check (for example in the gut or vagina after taking antibiotics)
- local carbohydrate levels (glycogen or glucose) are increased, providing ideal growing conditions for fungal cells (as in people with diabetes, or in vaginal secretions at certain times of the menstrual cycle)
- physical or mental stress (for example work stress, surgery, accidents) has lowered a person's natural immunity
- immune cells are temporarily less efficient at fighting fungal infections (for example because of another illness such as a viral cold, or because of a deficiency of certain vitamins or minerals)
- natural immunity has been lowered by taking certain drugs (for example steroids, chemotherapy, immune suppressants)
- immune cells are less efficient at fighting fungal infections because of a serious illness such as cancer or AIDS.

Candida albicans can infect different parts of the body, including:
- joints (Candidal arthritis) (see Chapter 3)
- skin (see Chapter 4)
- ears (see Chapter 4)
- nappy area (see Chapter 4)
- nails (see Chapter 4)
- bladder (cystitis) (see Chapter 5)
- vulva (see Chapter 5)
- vagina (see Chapter 5)
- mouth (see Chapter 6)
- oesophagus (gullet) (see Chapter 6)
- gut (enteritis) (see Chapter 6)
- lungs (fungus ball pneumonitis) (see Chapter 7)
- lining of the heart (endocarditis) (see Chapter 7)
- lining of the brain (meningitis) (see Chapter 7)

- brain (Candidal abscess) *(see Chapter 7)*
- kidneys (pyelonephritis) *(see Chapter 7)*
- blood (septicaemia) *(see Chapter 7)*

The more serious infections only affect patients whose immune system is seriously impaired, for example patients undergoing organ transplants, or those with terminal cancer or AIDS.

Chapter Two

THE NORMAL IMMUNE SYSTEM

To understand how the symptoms of Candida infection develop, it's worth looking at the function of the normal immune system and how it usually fights off infections such as yeasts.

The immune system is made up of millions of armed cells that patrol the body and protect it against disease. These cells can recognize and help to repel:

- foreign invaders such as bacteria, viruses or yeasts
- foreign proteins such as poisons
- infected or cancerous cells
- transplanted foreign tissues.

In order to perform these functions, immune cells have to identify normal components of the body and leave them alone, while at the same time recognizing cells that shouldn't be there. To add to the complexity of their task, they also have to pick out and destroy body cells that have changed in some way – either through infection or another disease process such as cancer.

Each body cell bears surface identity tags that brand it as part of the self. Immune cells learn to recognize these early, during fetal development, and generally leave them alone.

Foreign cells such as bacteria, viruses or Candida cells bear very different cell markers – usually in the form of sugar-protein complexes (glycoproteins) sticking out from their cell walls or membranes. Usually, immune cells instantly recognize these markers (antigens) as foreign and activate the full brunt of their arsenal to engulf or destroy the invaders.

As well as displaying self-markers, body cells continually process and break down internal proteins, fragments of which are transported to the cell membrane and displayed on their surface. This allows each body cell to communicate its internal conditions to circulating immune cells. As soon as an infected or cancerous cell is encountered that bears both a self-hallmark plus foreign markers (for example cells belonging to a virus, or tumour protein), the cell is recognized as undesirable and destroyed.

CELLS INVOLVED IN THE IMMUNE RESPONSE

All the cells involved in your immune responses are derived from common stem cells which develop in the bone marrow or the thymus gland. In general, cells known as B cells are derived from bone marrow, while those referred to as T cells are pro- grammed in the thymus. The thymus is a gland found in the upper part of the chest, behind the sternum. It is relatively large in infancy but starts to shrink at puberty and has virtually dis- appeared by adulthood, although remnants are often present until middle age.

Immune cells communicate with each other by secreting chemical alarm signals called cytokines. Cytokines are soluble factors that quickly attract other patrolling immune cells into an area and super-stimulate them for a swift immune response. The main cells involved in the immune response are macrophages, neutrophils and lymphocytes.

Macrophages

Macrophage literally means 'big eater'. These are long-lived scavenger cells that patrol all parts of the body. They start their early training in the bloodstream where they have a round, compact shape and are usually referred to as monocytes. When a monocyte encounters signs of trouble, it quickly sticks to the blood vessel wall, contorts itself into a long thin shape and squeezes between the cells in the blood vessel wall to take up residence in the body tissues. It then moves around the body by putting out cell elongations known as pseudopodia, or 'false feet'. It hunts down and envelops unwanted tissue debris, dead or dying cells and foreign invaders. Once it has identified a bacterium, virus, yeast or infected body cell, it secretes a chemical 'siren' in the form of cytokines which quickly attract other immune cells into the area. At the same time, the macrophage absorbs foreign proteins (antigens) from the unwanted cell on to its surface and presents these to the circulating lymphocytes to super-stimulate them. Macrophages are particularly concentrated in the liver, spleen and in the lymph nodes dotted throughout the lymphatic system. They even take up residence in tissues such as the brain, where they are known as microglial cells, and inside calcified bone, where they are known as osteoclasts and help to dissolve and remodel old bone tissue.

Neutrophils

Neutrophils make up around 60 per cent of circulating white blood cells and are more commonly known as pus cells. These only live for 6–20 hours but play a vital role against infection and disease – their absence usually proves fatal. They are attracted into areas of infection and inflammation by cytokines. Once there, they literally eat invading micro-organisms such as bacteria by enveloping them and pulling them inside their cell membrane (phagocytosis). A lethal bag of chemicals (containing toxic hydrogen peroxide among others) is then quickly emptied onto the invader to kill it. Neutrophils also have special receptors on their cell surface that can interact with antibodies or special protein bombs (complement – *see below*) to speed up the process of destruction. With larger invaders such as Candida yeast cells, neutrophils can stick to them and release chemicals that damage the cells sufficiently to put them out of action. Neutrophils carry around their own energy stores in the form of a starchy glycogen. This means they can penetrate inhospitable areas (for example the middle of an abscess) and still survive long enough to do damage despite lack of other nutrients or oxygen.

Lymphocytes

Lymphocytes make up around 40 per cent of circulating white blood cells. There are three different types which are recognized by their different surface markers and different patterns of activity:

1. Natural Killer (NK) cells (10 per cent of total lymphocytes)
2. B lymphocytes (20 per cent of total; derived from the bone marrow)
3. T lymphocytes (70 per cent of total; derived from the thymus).

Natural Killer Cells

These are mainly concerned with killing abnormal body cells which are infected with a virus or which have turned cancerous. They are super-stimulated by tissue macrophages and provide an important first line of defence while the more specific T and B lymphocytes power themselves into action. Rather like a kamikaze pilot, the NK cell usually dies during its attack.

B Lymphocytes

These make antibodies. You inherit many different families or lines of B cells, each of which makes one – and only one – specific antibody aimed against a particular foreign protein (antigen). A number of these identical antibodies stick out from the surface of the B lymphocyte rather like the weapons on a Dalek. Until it is activated, a B lymphocyte patrols the body in low numbers, in an armed but inactive form known as a B memory cell. When a foreign antigen enters the body, it encounters a dazzling array of different B lymphocytes, only one or two of which bear the right antibodies to recognize and react to its foreign proteins. As soon as the B lymphocyte encounters the foreign protein against which its antibody is directed, it powers up and starts to produce large numbers of its single, specific antibody. These active, bristling lymphocytes are known as B plasma cells. Their activity is regulated by various T lymphocytes, which act like administrators to control, encourage or inhibit their various activities. During activation, the B plasma cell divides repeatedly to build up a sub-population of cells producing a particular type of antibody. Once the invasion is over, there will be many more B lymphocyte memory cells for this particular type patrolling your body. If the same invader is encountered again, your immune response will be that much quicker and angrier, making it less easy for the organism to gain a foothold.

T lymphocytes

These exist in several different forms, some of which interact with B lymphocytes to regulate antibody production:

- T helper cells – help to power up B memory cells and stimulate them into making antibody
- T suppresser cells – bring antibody production to a halt (as when an infection has been beaten)
- T cytotoxic (killer) cells – more sophisticated versions of the natural killer cells which tend to survive their attacks and go on to assassinate other targets.
- T delayed hypersensitivity cells – involved in some hypersensitivity (allergic) reactions.

Antibodies

Antibodies, or immunoglobulins, are soluble glycoproteins (made from sugar and protein molecules) present throughout body fluids. They are produced by activated B lymphocytes, each of which produces only one type of antibody.

An antibody is made up of four protein chains: two identical heavy (long) chains and two identical light (short) chains, that link together to form a Y-shaped molecule.

When an antibody encounters a foreign antigen (for example a surface marker on a yeast cell) that it is directed against, the open end of the Y-shaped antibody clamps on to the antigen, making the cellular equivalent of a citizen's arrest. The antibody's tail chain sticks out behind and waits for help to arrive in the form of a macrophage, neutrophil, natural killer cell, cytotoxic T lymphocyte or a protein bomb (complement – *see page 12*). This extra help homes in on the antibody-antigen complex and quickly destroys it.

Antibodies are divided into five different classes depending on the type of heavy chain they contain:

1. IgA – a double antibody made of two identical antibodies joined tail to tail; mainly secreted into fluids on body linings and surfaces, for example into sweat, tears, saliva, intestinal juices, vaginal secretions; one of its main functions is to interfere with the binding of organisms such as Candida to body cells, so preventing them from invading the body
2. IgD – seems to play a role in controlling the activation and powering down of B lymphocytes
3. IgE – involved in triggering inflammation to produce a rapid immune response – unfortunately, this often misfires and produces an allergic response, for example the release of histamine when pollen grains land in the nose or eyes
4. IgG – the main type of circulating, protective antibody which neutralizes toxins and helps to wipe out invaders
5. IgM – a complex made of five antibodies joined together to form a star shape; they are largely confined to the bloodstream and are highly affective at trapping and immobilizing invaders.

Complement

The complement system is a series of around 20 circulating proteins that stick to antigen-antibody complexes in a specific sequence. As the different proteins link up, like part of a jigsaw, they eventually form a powerful enzyme. This acts rather like a protein bomb to blow up and destroy an antibody–antigen complex or an invading organism – complement can literally blow holes in the side of a bacterium or yeast cell to kill it.

The Lymph System

The body contains an extensive network of lymph vessels which drain every tissue in the body. Fluid that passes out of the blood bathes the cells and forms what is known as the internal sea. This fluid provides your cells with nutrients and flushes away wastes resulting from cell metabolism. The fluid also contains salts and dissolved immune chemicals such as antibodies, cytokines and complement, and is patrolled by billions of immune cells. Fluids from the internal sea are drained away through lymph vessels which filter it through a series of lymph nodes (sometimes known as glands) before returning it to your veins. Each lymph node varies from 1–20 mm in diameter and contains a series of channels packed full of macrophages plus lymphocytes armed with antibodies. Any debris or infection (for example yeast cells) present in the fluid drained from your tissues is filtered out by the sieve-like action of the lymph nodes and promptly attacked and destroyed by the immune cells present.

WHEN CANDIDA STRIKES

In order to cause symptoms, Candida must first get a hold in part of the body and evade the normal immune defences.

Sticking

The first step in an attack of Candida occurs when yeast cells stick to the mucous membrane cells, for example in the mouth, gut, vulva or vagina. They do this by using special receptors on their outer cell wall (the so-called fuzzy coat) which act rather like suckers or NASA landing equipment. Some species of Candida (for example *Candida albicans*, *C. tropicalis*) stick to epithelial (lining) cells more easily than others and are therefore more likely to cause disease. The ability to stick also depends on local conditions, such as temperature and acidity levels.

Growing

Once the yeast cells have obtained an anchorage on the host cell they start to develop germ tubes (hyphae) which coat the surface of the host cells. As the Candida yeast cells bud, increase in numbers and put out hyphae, they may form a raised white plaque resembling a curd of cottage cheese.

Dissolving

The next stage in causing an attack comes when the hyphae start to secrete enzymes that can break down protein (such as collagen) and fats. The enzymes loosen and dissolve connections between the host cell membranes and let the hyphae burrow their way down between layers of cells to penetrate quite deeply. The hyphae can actually penetrate inside your cells, from which they steal nutrients and energy. The main body of the yeast may remain attached to the epithelial surface (the lining of the gut, vagina etc.) or it may slip inside one of your cells. This is thought to be one way in which some yeast infections manage to evade your immune defences, hide from anti-fungal drugs and pop up again and again to cause infection. The species of Candida that produce the most enzymes (such as *C. albicans*) are the ones most likely to produce symptoms and signs of infection. This enzyme activity is also responsible for some of the soreness and inflammation that accompanies an attack of thrush.

Switching

Smooth colonies of Candida yeast cells growing in cell cultures can switch to producing colonies with an uneven, rough surface when exposed to low doses of ultraviolet light. The switched (rough) colonies produce different patterns of germ tube threads (hyphae), and seem to:

- stick to body lining cells more easily
- proliferate more readily
- secrete more enzymes that break down proteins, fats and cell walls
- be more invasive
- escape from detection by immune cells more easily
- be less susceptible to anti-fungal treatments.

Translocation

The gut is the main site from which Candida yeasts enter the body. This is known as translocation (moving across). Live yeast cells can enter the circulation from anywhere in the bowel, but the most likely source seems to be a part of the small intestine called the jejunum. When only a small number of yeast cells are involved, these are usually quickly mopped up by macrophage scavenger cells – it is only when large numbers of Candida cells are involved, or where the immune system is seriously weakened, that Candida can invade deeper body tissues. Candida can also enter the circulation from the lungs, though this is thought to account for less than 3 per cent of systemic Candida infections.

Invasion

Occasionally, if the immune system is very weak Candida can set up colonies deep in body tissues to form micro-abscesses. This causes serious, even potentially lethal problems (for example Candidal brain abscess, meningitis, fungus ball pneumonia, etc.) and is known as systemic Candidiasis.

HOW THE IMMUNE SYSTEM FIGHTS CANDIDA INFECTIONS

Most yeast infections are kept at bay by a fine balance between the strength of your immune system and the virulence (ability to cause disease) of the strains of Candida living in and on your body. In the majority of cases, Candida benignly colonizes your body without causing harm. It is only when there is a breakdown in your normal defences that Candida strikes, acting as a disease-causing organism (opportunistic pathogen).

Your Skin

Your outer layer of skin forms a hardened (cornified) physical barrier. It is made up of dead skin cells that have been transformed into armoured plates of the tough protein, keratin. These plates are regularly sloughed and replaced, so that any yeast cells sticking to them are lost from the outer surface of the body. Fats (lipids) present in skin sweat and oils also seem to inhibit the growth of Candida cells. The usual cause of a Candida infection taking hold on the skin is a breach in skin integrity, for example a wound, burn, exposure to excessive moisture (maceration) or the presence of another disease such as eczema. This is one reason why Candida infections are likely to infect skin folds (for example in the nappy region) – a build-up of warmth, moisture and chemicals in sweat makes the skin boggy so that Candida can take hold. For a similar reason, Candida infection of the hand may occur in people whose hands are often wet (for example dishwashers) and in children who regularly suck their thumb.

Your Mucous Membranes

The mucous membranes lining your mouth, gut, respiratory and genito-urinary tracts are less well defended than your outer skin and are therefore more susceptible to Candida infection. These body surfaces are warm, moist places – exactly the sort of sites where Candida loves to stick and grow. Subtle changes in the local environment can tip the balance so that symptoms of infection occur.

In the mouth, some protection is provided by the continual flushing with saliva that contains enzymes, chemicals and antibodies, mainly of the double antibody type IgA which inhibit Candida growth. Factors which increase the risk of mouth yeast infections include having mouth ulcers, smoking cigarettes, wearing dentures, using inhaled steroid preparations (as to treat asthma) and having raised blood sugar levels in diabetes. Experiments also show that sheer numbers of Candida cells can cause infection – a volunteer who drank a solution containing 1,000,000,000,000 Candida cells developed Candidosis of the gut; live yeast cells were later isolated from his bloodstream and urine.

Secretions in the oesophagus (gullet) and intestines also contain enzymes, antibodies (mainly antibody type IgA) and infection-fighting cells (macrophages, neutrophils, lymphocytes). Taking oral corticosteroid tablets, antibiotics or treatments to suppress stomach acid production (for example when peptic ulcers are present) can all increase the chance of Candida taking hold and causing problems in some people. Similarly, those using inhaled steroids are also more likely to develop oesophageal Candidiasis.

Tissue Fluids

After your skin or mucous membrane barriers have been breached by Candidal cells, your next line of defence consists of the immune factors present in your tissue fluids (the internal sea). These include complement and antibodies. These factors coat invading yeast cells and hasten their destruction by immune cells. The presence of too much antibody may coat the yeast cells so well that they are hidden from attacking immune cells, however, and paradoxically this may help to keep the infection going. Some people also develop an allergic response if they have made antibody of the IgE type, which can make symptoms of Candidiasis worse.

Immune Cells

Your most important final line of defence against Candidiasis is made up of the pus cells (neutrophils) and scavenger cells (macrophages in the tissues and monocytes in the blood) that roam your body and attack invaders. Lack of neutrophils – for example in some people with leukaemia – or a default in neutrophil function (present in some people with inherited enzyme defects) makes the risk of widespread Candidiasis much higher. Dying neutrophils that have been overwhelmed by an infection also release chemicals which either damage yeast cells or interfere with their function by mopping up the mineral zinc ions which the yeast cell needs for its metabolism.

Inflammation

Most of the symptoms associated with an attack of thrush are due to the inflammatory reactions set up as part of your body's natural immune defences. Macrophages patrolling your tissues come across fungal hyphae and instantly recognize something is wrong. They start trying to eat the invaders and send out chemical alarm signals (cytokines) which quickly attract other macrophages, neutrophils and lymphocytes into the area. Circulating antibodies may also bind to the hyphae and attract immune cells and complement proteins, making the immune response more effective.

As a result of tissue damage by thrush cells, and the chemicals released by the body to fight off the infection, local blood vessels (capillaries) dilate and leak clear blood fluids (plasma) into the area. This brings in extra complement protein and extra antibodies, and makes it easier for immune cells to slip through the blood vessel walls. This dilation of blood vessels results in the increased warmth, redness and swelling that accompanies inflammation. The chemicals also irritate nerve-endings to cause pain. This is why a thrush infection of the mouth, vagina or vulva, for example, can be so uncomfortable.

Altering Your Defences

There is evidence that chemicals made by yeasts can alter the normal immune response which keeps infection at bay. Substances released by the hyphae and pseudohyphae of *Candida albicans*, and present in their cell walls, have been found to increase susceptibility to certain bacterial infections (for example Staphylococci and Streptococci). These substances damp down the activity of neutrophils (pus cells) so that they:

- are less likely to be attracted into the area
- move more sluggishly
- are less able to engulf and absorb fungal cells
- are less able to bombard absorbed fungal products with a bag of toxic chemicals.

Other fungal products seem to impair activity of T lymphocytes so that they don't react to the presence of Candida cells, in which case a long-term (chronic) infection is more likely to occur.

Allergic Reactions

Some people are particularly sensitive to Candida infections as they have circulating antibodies of the IgE type which respond to Candida proteins. IgE can trigger release of histamine and other allergy chemicals from cells. They may also have T lymphocytes sensitized against yeast cells. These trigger an over-reaction and keep inflammatory reactions powered up to cause excessive redness, pain and swelling. They may also be associated with chronic inflammatory reactions which can lead to feelings of tiredness all the time and lack of energy (*see* Candida Hypersensitivity Syndrome, *pages 22 and 91*).

Predisposing Factors for a Single Attack of Candida

- antibiotics
- stress
- hormone levels – periods, pregnancy

Predisposing Factors for Recurrent Candida

- low ferritin levels (*see page 57*)
- high blood sugar levels in diabetes
- nutritional deficiencies: lack of vitamins and minerals

Factors that May Increase Your Risk of Candidiasis

- exposure to large numbers of Candida cells
- being overtired, run-down, physically unfit or under another form of stress
- having another infection that ties up your immune system and weakens it (for example influenza)
- taking treatments that suppress stomach acid production (for example antacids)
- using inhaled corticosteroids (for example for asthma), which damp down immune reactions in the mouth and respiratory tract
- taking oral corticosteroid therapy, which damps down immune reactions throughout the body
- having a serious illness that weakens the immune system (for example cancer)
- having treatment that damps down the immune system (for example chemotherapy, radiotherapy)
- poor nutrition and weight loss
- tissue damage (for example cuts, burns, ulcers, tooth extraction)
- smoking cigarettes
- wearing dentures

Chapter Three

SYMPTOMS AND SIGNS OF CANDIDA INFECTION

So many symptoms seem to be triggered by Candida – either through an overgrowth of the yeasts or as a result of hypersensitivity to them – that it is easy for sufferers to be dismissed by their doctor, family and colleagues as suffering from hypochondria or a neurotic problem. This is especially true if symptoms come and go or change, as they often do. While some people will only suffer mild nuisance symptoms which do not interfere unduly with their life, others are debilitated by constant tiredness and non-specific feelings of being unwell. This interferes with concentration, quality and quantity of work output and can make you so irritable and depressed that it jeopardizes relationships at home and at work.

The symptoms you might experience depend on where the Candida infection has struck. You may only develop a few of the symptoms listed here, or may suffer from the lot:

Skin	itchiness/soreness/redness/scaly rash/flakiness/acne-like spots
Skin folds	itchiness/soreness/redness/maceration (moist breakdown of skin)/weeping sores/build-up of white clots
Nappy area	generalized redness involving skin creases/soreness/weeping areas/red spots (satellite lesions) outside main affected area/possible build-up of white clots

Nails	unsightly ridges/brittleness, flaking, splitting/ discoloration of nail plate/soreness around edge of nails (paronychia)
Mouth	coated tongue/bad breath (halitosis)/itching (for example on the roof of the mouth, beneath dentures)/redness/soreness/dryness (xerostomia)/pain on eating or drinking/ white plaques on inside of mouth/ulceration cracks at corners of mouth
Oesophagus	difficulty or pain on swallowing/pain behind the breastbone (retrosternal)/nausea, vomiting/bringing up blood (haematemesis)/ sometimes fever
Intestinal tract	sensitivity to certain foods/pain on swallowing/heartburn, indigestion, flatulence, bloating/diarrhoea/constipation
Anal area	intense itching/soreness/moist discharge/ weeping sores/difficulty or pain on opening the bowels/worsening of symptoms due to piles
Female reproductive tract (vaginitis/vulvitis)	itching/redness/soreness/dryness/a white, cottage-cheese-like discharge/pain on intercourse/cystitis-like pain on passing urine (dysuria)/frequency of urination/enlarged lymph nodes (glands) in the groin
Male reproductive tract (balanitis)	mild itching on end of penis/soreness of end of penis/red spots/white plaques/build-up of white material under the foreskin/pain on passing urine (dysuria)/enlarged lymph nodes (glands) in the groin

CAUSES

When Candida cells change from their simple cell form to the activated form, threads of fungal material (germ tubes, or hyphae) burrow down between mucous membrane cells lining your mouth, gut, vagina, end of the penis or around the anus. This causes small areas of ulceration and fissuring which exposes tiny, sensitive nerve-endings.

Some of the threads also puncture straight through your cells, releasing powerful intra-cellular enzymes into surrounding tissues. This starts up the inflammatory response which attracts immune cells into the area. Yet more chemicals are released into the inflamed tissues as blood vessels dilate, so the area swells and becomes sore. These chemicals irritate the already raw nerve-endings and you may experience pain and throbbing sensations depending on how bad the infection is and where it has struck.

This inflammation due to your normal immune response to infection causes symptoms of redness, swelling, tenderness and throbbing pain. Local lymph nodes (glands) may also be swollen.

As well as specific symptoms linked to the site of infection, you may also develop non-specific symptoms linked with Candida Hypersensitivity Syndrome:

- fatigue
- tiredness all the time
- lethargy and disinterest
- malaise
- dizziness
- irritability
- anxiety
- depression
- insomnia
- difficulty concentrating
- headache
- joint and muscle pain
- poor appetite
- cravings for sugar and carbohydrate

- recurrent cystitis where no evidence of infection is found
- Irritable Bowel Syndrome
- alcohol intolerance
- problems after taking antibiotics.

Chapter Four

FUNGAL INFECTIONS OF THE SKIN

Fungal skin infections vary from widespread dry rashes to single scaly patches or moist, boggy areas. Single lesions are often known as ringworm, as they can form rings with a raised edge that spread outwards as the centre clears and returns to normal. There is no worm involved, however, only a fungus of which three types are the main culprits:

1. Candida yeasts
2. Pityrosporum yeasts
3. Dermatophytes.

Symptoms vary and can include:

- itchiness
- diffuse redness in skin folds, usually with a distinct edge
- beefy, red, slightly raised areas of swelling in skin folds
- white thrush-like plaques
- discrete ring-like red lesions (ringworm)
- small satellite lesions spreading away from the main area of infection
- scaling
- enlarging red lesions with a raised, irregular edge
- widespread inflammation of hair follicles (folliculitis)
- burning soreness
- painful cracking
- oozing sores
- loss of skin (desquamation)
- pink-brown patches

- depigmented white areas
- patches of hair loss.

Other skin conditions can be mistaken for fungal infections, and vice versa. These include eczema, psoriasis, and even some forms of skin cancer (for example squamous cell carcinoma). If you think you have a fungal skin infection which has not responded to treatment within a couple of weeks, or which seems to be getting worse rather than better, it is important to seek medical advice.

CANDIDA SKIN INFECTIONS

Candida skin infections only usually occur if the skin is damaged by a build-up of moistness (for example in skin folds, within your shoes), by burns or friction or where there is an existing skin problem such as eczema. It is more common in people with diabetes, those taking antibiotics and where the immune system is weakened by another disease. When Candida infection does strike, it frequently affects skin folds such as those in:

- the groin
- the armpits
- under the breasts
- between the toes or fingers (Athlete's foot)
- in the groin (tinea cruris)
- around the scrotum or penis (balanitis)
- around the vaginal entrance (vulvo-vaginitis)
- under rolls of fat, for example on the abdomen
- between the buttocks in adults
- the nappy area in babies.

These areas are warm, moist places where yeast cells thrive quite happily. In 8 out of 10 cases, *Candida albicans* is responsible as this type of yeast seems to stick to the outer, toughened skin scales (keratinocytes) more easily than other Candida species. The infection usually stays confined to the upper skin layers, but where the immune system is weakened, or damage to the skin has penetrated into deep layers, it may penetrate further into tissues to cause more severe symptoms.

Careful hygiene is needed – especially in warm summer months – to prevent a build-up of acid, sweaty skin secretions which can damage the skin (maceration) and allow Candida or other skin fungi to take hold. Classic lesions have the appearance of white clots on a bright red background.

Candida can also cause inflammation of hair follicles (folliculitis) with small raised red pimples/pustules surrounding tiny hairs on the skin. This usually occurs under occlusive dressings that have become wet with sweat (for example plaster casts, bandages) and can also be triggered by shaving near infected areas. This condition is known as *Candida miliaria* or 'heat rash', and is also linked with profuse sweating. The yeast infection may be mistaken for similar symptoms caused by bacteria or inflammation (for example pustular eczema) and may get worse if the wrong treatment (for example antibiotics) is given.

PITYROSPORUM YEAST INFECTIONS

Pityrosporum yeasts are similar to Candida yeasts, but are normally found only on the scalp. Like Candida, they usually live on the skin quite happily as commensal organisms without causing problems. If they proliferate excessively, however, they can trigger skin flaking, dandruff and – in babies – cradle cap (*see page 32*). These conditions are known medically as seborrhoeic capitis, which literally means greasy inflammation of the head. If the infection is left untreated it may spread onto the face, skin flexures or chest to produce a more inflamed skin reaction known as seborrhoeic dermatitis.

On the face, the red, scaly rash commonly affects the eyebrows and forehead, with greasy scaling of the skin folds running between the nose and lips. In people with depressed immunity this may lead to a severe, widespread inflammation of the hair follicles (folliculitis) producing small, itchy, raised lumps (papules).

Under certain circumstances, especially hot, sweaty conditions, Pityrosporum yeasts (especially *Pityrosporum orbiculare*) change to produce fungal-like hyphae similar to those produced by Candida yeasts. This form of the yeast is known as *Malassezia furfur* and causes a characteristic skin rash known as *Pityriasis versicolor*.

The word *pityriasis* comes from the Greek for *bran*, while *versicolor* means of *variable colour*. This fungal infection produces fine, bran-like scales on the skin surface. These cover numerous round or oval patches which are initially pale pink or brown in colour. They gradually become depigmented, to leave white areas that may only show up after exposure to sun, when surrounding uninfected skin becomes tanned. Pityriasis versicolor is often widespread and may be distressing in people with dark skins. The lesions may persist for some time after successful treatment.

DERMATOPHYTES

Dermatophytes are fungal organisms that constantly produce a network of thread-like growths (hyphae). In comparison, yeasts living happily on the skin as commensals usually exist as simple budding cells and only put out germ cell tubes (hyphae) when actively invading your tissues. The dermatophyte hyphae can invade the thickened, outer superficial (keratinized) layers of your hair, skin and nails, but generally only produce mild symptoms. In people suffering from a severely weakened immune system – either as a result of serious illness or some drug treatments – the hyphae can penetrate more deeply into the body.

Three main species of fungus produce dermatophyte infections in humans:

1. Trichophyton rubrum – by far the commonest
2. Trichophyton interdigitalae
3. Epidermophyton floccosum

These dermatophytes affect different parts of the body to produce lesions that are named after the site on which they occur, for example:

- tinea capitis (fungal infection of the scalp)
- tinea pedis (fungal infection of the foot/athlete's foot)
- tinea corporis (fungal infection of the trunk)
- tinea cruris (fungal infection of the groin)
- tinea manuum (fungal infection of the hands)
- onychomycosis (fungal infection of the nails)

The term *tinea* just refers to a fungal infection. Skin fungal infections can also be caught from animals (zoophilic infections). These include fungus spread from cats and dogs (for example *Microsporum canis*), from cattle (for example *Trichophyton verrucusum*) and rodents (such as *Trichophyton mentagrophytes*). These zoophilic infections tend to produce either:

- dry skin infections such as scaling patches of hair loss (alopecia) on the scalp or ring-like scaly lesions (ringworm) on the trunk or limbs
- moist, inflamed, boggy, pustular swellings usually due to cattle ringworm and known as kerions.

Investigation

If you think you have ringworm, it is important to consult your doctor as several other skin problems can cause similar symptoms. Ideally, skin fungal infections need to be confirmed from skin scrapings, as several skin conditions can mimic fungal infection. Skin scrapings, nail clippings or plucked hairs are collected, placed in a fold of black paper and sent to a laboratory for analysis. Examination under a microscope will confirm a dermatophyte or yeast infection. If identification of a particular dermatophyte is important (for example if it may be an infection caught from an animal), the fungus has to be cultured to produce vegetative spores (conidia), as each species has spores of a distinctive shape.

In folliculitis (infection of hair follicles) a Candida or a bacterial infection are told apart by opening and swabbing a fresh pustule, examining it under a microscope for fungi or bacteria and by growing organisms in the laboratory.

Treatment

Localized areas of skin infection can be treated by applying an anti-fungal cream. If the area is very moist (for example under the armpit or breasts), an anti-fungal powder can be used separately, or applied after the cream.

- Clotrimazole cream/powder: applied 2 or 3 times a day and continued for 2 weeks after symptoms have gone
- Miconazole cream/spray/powder: twice a day and continued for 10 days after healing
- Econazole cream: 2 or 3 times a day and continued for 10 days after healing
- Tolnaftate cream/powder/aerosol: twice a day
- Sulconazole cream (prescription only): massaged in twice a day and continued for 2–3 weeks after healing
- Terbinafine cream (prescription only): massaged in once or twice a day for 2–4 weeks.
- Amorolfine cream (prescription only): once daily in the evening for 2–3 weeks, continued for 3–5 days after healing
- Nystatin cream/ointment/gel (prescription only): 2–4 times a day until 1 week after healing

Combined anti-fungal and anti-bacterial treatments may be used where a mixed infection is suspected, for example:

- polynoxylin cream
- nystatin/chlorhexidine cream.

If an underlying inflammatory skin problem such as eczema is suspected, then a combined anti-fungal and anti-inflammatory (corticosteroid) cream may be needed. These are usually only available on prescription (for example clotrimazole and 1 per cent hydrocortisone cream, or the stronger clotrimazole and betamethasone cream) – although preparations containing some of the drug separately (for example 1 per cent clotrimazole or 1 per cent hydrocortisone) are available over the counter.

If a fungal skin infection is mistaken for eczema, and only a plain steroid cream used to treat it (for example 1 per cent hydrocortisone or betamethasone) a condition known as *tinea incognita* (hidden fungal infection) occurs. The steroid cream damps down redness, scaling and itching so that the lesions feel better, but the underlying fungal infection continues to thrive so that skin lesions persist and grow larger – sometimes quite quickly. As soon as treatment is stopped, the infection will return with a vengeance. It is only when an anti-fungal agent is used that the skin infection will get better.

Treating Pityriasis Versicolor

Mild cases of the skin infection pityriasis versicolor, can be treated by using a selenium sulphide shampoo on the skin every day while showering or bathing.

It may take a while for the skin colour change to clear, especially if you are tanned. More advanced cases will usually respond to topical anti-fungal creams or – if widespread – to an anti-fungal drug taken by mouth:

■ Ketoconazole cream (prescription only; available at NHS expense for people with seborrhoeic dermatitis or pityriasis versicolor). All areas of the body from the neck down to the elbows and knees should be treated. Used once or twice a day.
■ Itraconazole capsules: 2 capsules once a day for 7 days. If treating a fungal skin infection other than pityriasis, it may be prescribed at a dose of 1 capsule a day for 15–30 days.
■ Terbinafine tablets: 1 a day for 4 weeks
■ Griseofulvin tablets: 1–4 times a day for varying lengths of time depending on response – absorption is improved if taken after a fatty meal.

Prevention

■ Take steps to prevent excessive sweating, for example by using an aluminium chloride hexahydrate anti-perspirant (*see page 31*).
■ Wash, shower or bathe every day to remove acidic, sweaty secretions from skin folds.

- Dry your skin thoroughly after washing.
- Wear loose-fitting clothes made from natural rather than man-made fibres.
- Spray an anti-fungal powder spray in skin folds prone to excessive sweating.
- Don't share towels, flannels or bath sponges.

Excessive Sweating

Everyone has around 3 million sweat glands, of which there are two different types:

1. Eccrine glands, which open directly onto the skin surface
2. Apocrine glands, which open into hair follicles rather than the skin.

Eccrine glands are found all over the skin, but are concentrated on the palms and the soles of the feet. They mainly secrete water and salts during overheating and exercise. This sweat is designed to cool the body down, although high humidity (for example hot, sticky summer weather, conditions inside the average pair of trainers) will interfere with evaporation of sweat and lead to stickiness, embarrassing wetness and an increased tendency to fungal skin infections.

Apocrine glands only develop at puberty and are found in the armpits and groin. As well as secreting water and salts, they also produce fatty acids which are broken down by bacteria to cause the unpleasant smells characteristic of body odour.

Some people suffer from excessive sweating all year round – a condition known as hyperhydrosis. This is due to overactivity of nerve-endings and can also be brought on by anxiety or stress. The main areas to be affected are the armpits, groin, palms, soles of the feet or forehead.

If you suffer from problem perspiration, a 20 per cent solution of aluminium chloride hexahydrate can now be bought over the counter. Until recently this was only available on prescription. When applied to problem areas it enters the sweat glands to form a gel matrix which reduces, then stops the flow of water. The solution should be applied to clean, dry skin at night – when sweat glands are inactive – and washed off the next morning. As excessive sweating comes under control, you will only need to use it once or twice a week.

CANDIDA EAR INFECTIONS

The external ear canal and behind the ear flap are common sites for Candida skin infections, especially in babies. This can produce symptoms of:

- itching
- flaking skin
- soreness
- weeping behind the ears
- discharge from the ear which often smells unpleasant
- white clots seen inside the ear canal.

Once the diagnosis is made, a Candida ear infection can usually be quickly treated with ear drops containing anti-fungal drugs such as clioquinol (stains skin and clothing) or clotrimazole. Drops should be applied two to three times a day and continued until at least 14 days after symptoms have disappeared.

SCALP YEAST INFECTIONS

Scalp yeast infections affect everyone at some time in life – either as a baby or later, when dandruff can cause great social embarrassment.

Cradle Cap

Mottling and redness of the scalp are common in infants during the first few days and weeks of life. This results from changes in the baby's circulation once he or she adapts to independent life. At the same time, the baby's skin – which was sterile inside the womb – is getting used to being colonized by relatively harmless organisms including skin bacteria and Candida yeasts. This may trigger a mild inflammatory reaction, with redness, dryness and flakiness. Hair follicles may also become more pronounced and pimply.

The skin on the scalp is often affected as bacteria and yeasts take up residence. In most cases only a few flakes develop which quickly fall away. In severe cases, a thick circle of yellow, waxy deposits or crusts builds up, resembling a crocheted hat. This is commonly known as cradle cap and usually appears after the age of 1 month.

Cradle cap is harmless but is a common cause of distress for new mothers. It is a form of seborrhoeic dermatitis whose exact cause is unknown, although it is thought to be a reaction to an overgrowth of the yeast *Pityrosporum ovale*. As well as affecting the scalp, it can also appear on the face, neck, behind the ears and in the nappy area. The skin in these areas may also look red and inflamed.

Sometimes, patches of cradlecap become super-infected by other skin organisms such as Candida or the bacteria Streptococcus or Staphylococcus.

Treatment

Cradle cap is a self-limiting condition and will eventually go away on its own, without treatment, within a few months. This process can be speeded up by a few simple measures:

- Loosen the scales by gently rubbing the scalp with a simple baby shampoo, cetrimide solution, baby oil, olive oil or arachis oil to encourage early sloughing.
- Olive oil or arachis oil can be rubbed into the affected area, left overnight, and then washed off the following day along with the loosened crusts.
- After several days of treatment, most scales should have fallen away. Brushing the hair with a clean soft-bristled brush will help.
- It is important to avoid scratching or picking at affected skin or exposing it to irritants such as detergents. This can lead to inflammation or infection.
- Adding drops of Evening Primrose Oil (EPO) to your baby's feed – or rubbing directly onto affected areas – often results in dramatic improvement. EPO contains an essential fatty

acid – gammalinolenic acid – needed as a building-block for skin cell membranes (*see page 139*). Paediatric capsules with elongated, snippable tops are available, as is a dropper bottle containing pure Evening Primrose Oil.

If the cradle cap is widespread with red inflamed skin that spreads to the armpits, behind the neck and in the nappy area, the baby will need to be checked by a doctor and prescribed the correct treatment for seborrhoeic dermatitis: emollients (skin-softening agents) plus 1 per cent hydrocortisone cream (a mild anti-inflammatory steroid) to reduce any inflammation and redness.

If the skin looks very angry or starts to weep, swabs will need to be sent off for analysis. Anti-Candida creams (for example clotrimazole) or antibiotics may also be needed. If your baby becomes unwell and shows signs of a temperature, goes off his or her food, or seems in any way unwell, obtain medical advice immediately.

Adult Dandruff

Dandruff – dry, flaky skin on the scalp – is a common and annoying problem that affects over 40 per cent of people at some time in their life. It tends to start in adolescence and, unfortunately, once established may be persistent and return once treatment is stopped.

The skin on the scalp is made of normal skin cells that are continually replacing themselves, like skin elsewhere on the body. Dead cells that fall off are usually washed or brushed away without any problem. If the cells are replaced at a faster rate than normal, or if the scalp is excessively dry or greasy, dead cells may clump together to form larger, visible flakes.

The usual cause is a condition known as seborrhoeic dermatitis which produces an itchy, scaly rash on the scalp. Sometimes other areas such as the eyebrows, beard, chest, back and even the groin are affected too, and the skin in these areas may look red and inflamed. Dry or greasy scales may form around the hairline, and in severe cases, a yellowish-red crust appears.

Both mild dandruff and seborrhoeic dermatitis are thought to be triggered by hypersensitivity to the Candida-like yeast,

Pityrosporum. Everyone has small quantities of this yeast on their skin, but in people with scaly scalp problems it may be present in large numbers.

Other conditions that can trigger dandruff include neurodermatitis (stress-related skin scaling), contact dermatitis (for example due to an allergy to ingredients in a shampoo), eczema, psoriasis and sunburn. If your dandruff doesn't clear up within 2 weeks of using an anti-fungal shampoo, don't be embarrassed to consult your doctor as you may have a skin problem needing treatment that is only available on prescription.

Treatment

For mild dandruff, regular shampooing with a gentle product designed for daily use may be enough to clear the condition.

Anti-fungal ingredients reduce flaking and help to control the number of yeast cells present. There are a wide range of shampoos available; different ones work best on different people – experiment until you find one that controls your problem. Shampoos that can clear moderate dandruff contain different active ingredients such as coal tar, zinc pyrithione and selenium sulphide. For more severe problems, a more powerful anti-fungal agent such as ketoconazole will usually work rapidly – until recently this was only available on prescription, but it can now be bought from pharmacies.

If over-the-counter treatments do not clear symptoms within a week or two, or if they are more widespread, consult your doctor as stronger products are available on prescription. Occasionally, dandruff is due to another skin problem such as psoriasis or ringworm, which needs to be properly diagnosed and treated.

Prevention

Wash hair regularly, at least twice a week, to help prevent a build-up of yeast cells and grease.

Use an anti-fungal treatment shampoo once a week, using normal shampoos in between.

Lack of the following nutrients has been linked with adult scaly skin problems:

- vitamin A
- vitamin B$_2$
- vitamin B$_3$
- biotin
- vitamin C
- iodine
- manganese
- selenium
- zinc

For information on which foods are good sources of these nutrients, *see Chapter 10.*

NAPPY RASH

Nappy rash is common and affects many babies at some time in infancy.

There are four main causes, and it is important to tell them apart so that the right treatment is given:

1. chemical irritation from soiled nappies
2. Candida fungal infection (thrush)
3. bacterial infection
4. allergy to creams, detergents or wipes.

The commonest cause of nappy rash is chemical irritation from soiled nappies and the baby's own waste products. Ammonia forms when bacteria in the faeces break down a chemical, urea, found in the urine. Ammonia is a powerful scouring agent that can easily burn if left on delicate skin for any length of time. Strong intestinal enzymes designed to digest food are also present in baby's bowel motions, as are organic acids made from bacteria fermentation of dietary fibre in the colon. These chemicals can all digest delicate skin in the nappy region, causing soreness, redness and rawness (napkin dermatitis). A nappy rash due to this type of chemical burn usually leaves skin creases unaffected, as chemicals tend not to seep into skin folds. This is a useful way of telling a chemical rash from an infective

(Candida or bacterial) rash. Nappy rashes due to infection tend to involve the skin creases as well, because yeasts and bacteria like creeping into the protection of warm, moist skin folds.

Yeast cells are present on the skin of most young babies and – as the baby's immune system is still immature – will quickly invade the skin if it becomes broken or inflamed. This commonly happens in the nappy area or in skin folds (for example behind the ears, in the armpits).

Thrush causes a red rash with a well-defined edge. The skin tends to be moist and bright red, with scattered spots of infection further away from the main area. These are known as satellite lesions. Unlike the chemical nappy rash, skin folds in the area are usually involved in a thrush rash, too.

Bacterial nappy rashes can be difficult to tell from Candida ones. They are also bright red, may seem to centre around the cleft between the baby's buttocks, and may cause small collections of pus. The baby may seem unwell and may have a fever, in which case you must contact your doctor straightaway. You should also seek immediate medical advice if the nappy rash has open sores, yellow crusts or spots.

SYMPTOMS OF CANDIDA NAPPY RASH

- multiple small red spots in nappy area (these spots may join up to form a more generalized redness of nappy area)
- the rash will involve skin creases, for example at the top of the legs, as well
- red spots (satellite lesions) spread outside the main affected area
- soreness
- blistering and weeping areas
- possibly a build-up of white clots and, occasionally, pustules.

Investigation

If a baby with nappy rash shows signs of being unwell (for example if he has a temperature, is off his feeds or is snuffly or shows other symptoms) it is important to seek medical advice in case a bacterial infection is present. Swabs can be sent for analysis to confirm a yeast infection and rule out a bacterial rash.

Treatment

The treatment of a simple chemical nappy rash is relatively simple:

- Change nappies frequently, as soon as they are soiled.
- If using washable nappies, use an enzyme-free powder and make sure nappies are thoroughly rinsed to remove all traces of detergent.
- Cleanse the nappy area every time you change a nappy – use oil, petroleum jelly or plenty of water, but no soap. Make sure you remove all cream from the previous nappy change to avoid a build-up of waste products and cream.
- Dry the area thoroughly with a tissue or a hair-dryer set on gentle heat.
- Whenever possible, leave the baby's bottom exposed to the air – let your baby lie *on* the nappy rather than *in* it as much as possible, even if only for an hour or two.
- Before putting the baby's nappy on, use large quantities of a barrier cream containing zinc oxide, titanium dioxide, silicone or castor oil. This protects the skin from chemical irritation. Don't use a barrier cream when baby's bottom is exposed to the air, however, as this will prevent the air getting to the skin – only use it when applying a nappy.
- During the night, use a good quality disposable nappy. Choose one that has a one-way layer next to the baby's skin and a built-in plastic backing to help keep skin comfortable and dry.
- If using cloth nappies at any time, use a good quality one-way nappy liner with them.
- Don't use plastic overpants with nappies, as these keep the skin hot and moist.
- If the rash doesn't clear up quickly, ask your doctor or health visitor for advice; an anti-fungal cream or other treatment may be needed.

Treatment of a Candidal nappy rash also involves keeping the affected area clean, dry and exposed to the air as much as possible. You will also need to apply an anti-Candidal cream such as clotrimazole to affected skin 3 times a day. If the skin is very inflamed and raw, a cream combining the anti-fungal with an anti-inflammatory agent (for example 1 per cent hydrocortisone) is often prescribed. Continue using the cream for at least a week after the rash seems to have cleared up, to prevent a recurrence.

A bacterial nappy rash needs urgent treatment with antibiotics to prevent the infection spreading and the baby becoming unwell – if in doubt, consult your health visitor, practice nurse or GP.

Prevention

- Check your baby's nappies frequently so they can be changed as soon as they are soiled.
- Cleanse the skin thoroughly with oil, cream or water (not soap) after each dirty nappy
- Dry thoroughly and apply a protective barrier cream.
- Use a barrier cream before re-applying a nappy.
- If using non-disposable nappies, use a good one-way nappy liner with them.
- Occasionally, a recurrent nappy rash is due to an allergy to chemicals in baby creams, detergents or wipes (for example lanolin, chlorhexidine). If a rash does not respond to normal treatment, or keeps coming back, it is worth trying to avoid perfumed baby products containing plain zinc and castor oil to see if this helps.

ATHLETE'S FOOT

Athlete's foot, or *tinea pedis*, is the most common fungal skin infection affecting as many as 10–15 per cent of the population at any one time. It is highly contagious and is often picked up at communal changing rooms and showers. Fungal spores are also in the air and often lurk in shoes, ready to strike whenever conditions are ripe. It may be triggered by inadequate drying of the spaces between the toes after washing or when skin is rubbed and blistered. Although the toewebs – especially that between the two smallest toes – are usually the first sites to be infected, or ignored and left untreated, the infection can spread to involve the soles and back of the foot as well as the toe- or fingernails themselves. Athlete's foot can be caused by Candida yeasts or dermatophyte infections.

Symptoms

- redness
- build-up of white, dead skin with peeling of skin between the toes (erosio interdigitalis blastomycetica)
- moistness
- itching
- soreness
- formation of painful cracks
- a spreading, dry scaling rash across the surface of the foot
- cracking, brittleness and discoloration of nails.

If an unpleasant smell occurs, this usually means the damaged skin has also become super-infected with bacteria.

Investigation

Investigations are not usually needed for athlete's foot confined to the toeweb unless a secondary bacterial infection is also suspected. Swabs will help to identify the cause. If the nails are affected, nail clippings and skin parings may be sent for analysis to culture and identify the type of fungus present.

Treatment

Don't ignore athlete's foot, as the infection can rapidly spread to involve the nails. Once embedded there treatment will take months and the fungus can be difficult to eradicate. You can also spread infection to elsewhere on your body, for example the hands and nails, through scratching – this can cause the so-called 'Right hand, Left foot' syndrome in right-handed people. Always continue treatment for at least 10 days after symptoms seem to have disappeared, to prevent a recurrence.

If the affected skin area is intact, an anti-fungal powder spray is the easiest treatment to use. This should not be used on broken skin, however, so if cracking has occurred use an anti-fungal cream instead. An anti-fungal powder can also be dusted over the cream and on the foot to keep the skin dry during treatment.

- Benzoyl peroxide/potassium hydroxyquinolone sulphate cream: applied sparingly night and morning
- Clotrimazole cream/powder: 2 or 3 times a day and continued for 2 weeks after symptoms have gone
- Miconazole cream/spray/powder: twice a day and continued for 10 days after healing
- Econazole cream: 2 or 3 times a day and continued for 10 days after healing
- Tolnaftate cream/powder/aerosol: twice a day
- Sulconazole cream (prescription only): massaged in twice a day and used for 2–3 weeks after healing
- Terbinafine cream (prescription only): massaged in once or twice a day for 2–4 weeks
- Amorolfine cream (prescription only): once daily in the evening for 2–3 weeks, continued for 3–5 days after healing
- Nystatin cream/ointment/gel (prescription only): 2–4 times a day until 1 week after healing.

If athlete's foot has spread to the soles of the feet, it will usually only respond to treatment taken by mouth. The skin layer here is much thicker than anywhere else on the body, and it is difficult for treatment creams to penetrate down to the deepest layers. Terbinafine tablets, taken daily for 2 weeks, or itraconazole capsules taken daily for 4 weeks may be prescribed by your doctor.

Prevention

- Take steps to prevent excessive sweating, for example by using an aluminium hexahydrate anti-perspirant (*see page 31*).

- Wash feet every day to remove acidic, sweaty secretions.
- Dry feet thoroughly, especially between the toes – use tissue paper or a hair-dryer set on gentle heat.
- Change socks, stockings or tights at least daily.
- Wear open-toed shoes/sandals as often as possible – avoid wearing synthetic nylon trainers for prolonged periods of time.
- Spray inside shoes and socks with an anti-fungal powder spray, or dust with powder before wearing.
- Discard shoes such as trainers which have developed an unpleasant rotted smell.
- Don't share towels or bath mats.

FUNGAL NAIL INFECTIONS

The nails are specialized skin structures made of a tough protein, keratin. This is secreted by cells at the base and sides of each nail in the matrix. Nails help to strengthen the tips of fingers and toes, protect them from damage and splint the end of the fingers so that the fingertips are more sensitive to touch. The average fingernail grows at a rate of up to 5 mm per month, while the toenails grow 3 times more slowly. It takes around 6 months for a fingernail to grow from base to tip. Nail growth is slower in the non-dominant hand (the left hand if you are right-handed) and slows with increasing age.

Fungal nail infections are known as *tinea unguum* or *onychomycosis*. If the problem is severe with breakdown and distortion of the nail plate, you may be told you have *onycholysis*, in which the nail starts to lift off from its underlying bed. Fungal nail infections are thought to affect up to 3 per cent of the population at any one time. Unfortunately, the condition is often ignored – especially if it only affects hidden toenails – or is disguised by nail varnish. This is not a good idea, as the nails will become riddled with fungal/yeast cells and act as a source of infection that can spread elsewhere on the body, for example to skin folds, the groin, etc. You can also pass the infection on to other members of your family.

Infection of the skin around a nail (*paronychia*) often occurs in people whose work involves repeated wetting of their hands, for example housewives, bar staff, nurses, etc. This leads to redness and swelling of the skin and often a brownish discoloration of one side of the nail. The usual cause of a single infected nail is a bacterial infection, while if many nails are affected (chronic paronychia) the usual cause is a combined *Candida albicans* yeast plus a bacterial infection.

Symptoms

Early symptoms may start as soreness around the edge of the nail (*paronychia*), which spreads to cause:

- thickening of nail folds
- loss of cuticles
- unsightly ridges on the nail
- brittle, flaking, split nails
- dingy discoloration of the nail plate due to infection of the matrix cells which secrete the nail plate
- white patches on the nails (*leukonychia*) – although most white markings are due to mild trauma to the nail bed
- lifting of the nail from its bed (*onycholysis*)
- thickened, distorted nails (*onychogryphosis*).

Investigation

The nails are affected by many illnesses and may develop ridges, pits or discoloration that resemble a fungal infection. For example, a serious illness can produce multiple horizontal ridges, psoriasis can cause roughness and pits, while iron deficiency causes splitting, brittleness, pallor and, if severe, a spoon-like curvature (*koilonychia*). If you develop a nail problem it is important to consult a doctor for a proper diagnosis. If a fungal infection is suspected, nail clippings may be sent for analysis.

Treatment

Paronychia (infection of skin around the nail)
Use a nystatin cream 2–4 times daily. A course of oral antibiotics may be needed if a bacterial infection is also present.

Onychomycosis (infection of the nail itself)

Simple infections can be treated by applying anti-fungal creams or an anti-fungal nail lacquer that hardens to protect the nail as it treats the infection. Alternatively, tablets may be taken by mouth, but prolonged courses are needed.

The damage to the old nail cannot be repaired, and it is difficult to kill the fungal infection riddling it. The aim of treatment is to protect the new nail growing through – so that as your new nail plate develops, it looks pink and healthy compared to the scarred, discoloured nail slowly moving further away from your nail bed.

Treatment should be continued until all the old infected nail has grown through and has been cut and discarded. If treatment is stopped, fungus/yeasts will usually grow down into the new nail from the old infected one and treatment has to be started all over again.

- Amorolfine nail lacquer: applied once or twice a week for 3–6 months
- Tioconazole nail solution: twice a day for 6–12 months
- Terbinafine tablets (prescription only): once a day for 6 weeks – toenail infections require therapy for 3 months
- Itraconazole capsules: once a day for 6 weeks – toenail infections require therapy for 3 months
- Griseofulvin tablets (prescription only): 1–4 times a day. Works well over 6 months' duration for treating fingernail disease, but has a cure rate of only 30–40 per cent for toenail infections, even when treatment is prolonged for 1 year.

Prevention

- Keep nails as dry as possible.
- Use cotton gloves inside rubber ones when washing up or having to put your hands into water.
- Avoid manicures, which can damage cuticles and nail folds – if you wish to have one, make sure it is performed professionally and not by an amateur.
- Avoid using artificial nails.
- Avoid using nail varnish.
- Don't bite or suck your nails.

Chapter Five

CANDIDA INFECTION OF THE GENITALS

MALE GENITALS

Candida infection of the male genitals is common. The groin is a warm, moist, sweaty area that harbours a variety of bacteria and yeasts. In hot conditions – in summer, on holiday abroad or after exercise – Candida yeasts may overgrow to cause symptoms.

Balanitis

Candida yeast infection is the most common problem to affect the tip of the penis. This is known as balanitis and affects up to 5 per cent of young boys, usually striking before school age. Older males can also be affected. Inflammation around the foreskin is called posthitis, and when both occur together – which they frequently do – the result is known as balano-posthitis.

Mild Candidal balanitis may result just in mottled red spots, slight soreness and itching of the tip of the penis. There may also be a build-up of yeasty smegma under the foreskin. If the condition is left untreated and becomes worse, the skin may break down to leave weeping areas, a sticky discharge and painful swelling of the foreskin. This may lead to difficulty passing urine.

Symptoms
- itching on end of penis
- soreness of end of penis
- red spots
- white plaques

- build-up of white material under the foreskin
- pain on passing urine (dysuria).

Other causes of balanitis include infection with common skin bacteria, sexually transmittable diseases, allergic reactions to soap or bath additives and chemical irritation (for example nappy rash in babies).

Investigation
Swabs may be sent for examination to see whether the infection is due to yeasts, bacteria or both. Urinalysis to check for glucose is important to rule out sugar diabetes, in which balanitis is often one of the first signs in men.

Treatment
A study among 43 men with mild balanitis showed that by just washing the penis with water alone, almost all symptoms disappeared without the need for further treatment. It is important not to use soap as this will cause irritation and change skin acidity, making the inflammation and infection worse.

Moderate to severe balanitis due to Candida will need medical assessment to exclude a bacterial infection or overtight foreskin. If a yeast infection is confirmed, treatment is with a topical anti-fungal agent. A cream or gel is less greasy than an ointment and will feel more comfortable. If you are very sore, however, an ointment will provide a barrier that protects skin from contact with urine and stale sweat. You may also find it helpful to use an anti-fungal powder spray around the groin, scrotum and tops of the legs to keep the area clean, dry and prevent the infection spreading under cover of the warmth and humidity of your underpants.

- Clotrimazole cream/spray/powder: applied 2 or 3 times a day and ideally continued for 2 weeks after symptoms have gone, to prevent a recurrence
- Miconazole cream/spray/powder: twice a day and continued for 10 days after healing
- Econazole cream: 2 or 3 times a day and continued for 10 days after healing

- Sulconazole cream (prescription only): massaged in twice a day and used for 2–3 weeks after healing
- Terbinafine cream (prescription only): massaged in once or twice a day for 2–4 weeks
- Amorolfine cream (prescription only): apply once daily in the evening for 2–3 weeks, continuing for 3–5 days after healing
- Nystatin cream/ointment/gel (prescription only): 2–4 times a day until 1 week after healing.

If balanitis is severe, with gross swelling of the foreskin, or if it is recurrent, circumcision may be necessary.

Although Candida is not necessarily sexually transmitted, it is a sexually transmittable disease. It is important to avoid intercourse until symptoms have disappeared, as it is easy to pass the infection on to your partner. Alternatively – assuming your symptoms aren't too unpleasant – you should use a condom together with the spermicide nonoxynol-9, which has some anti-fungal action.

Prevention

Balanitis can largely be prevented by proper hygiene and frequent washing under the foreskin. In mild cases, simple bathing with salt water (saline) twice per day will quickly help symptoms to resolve. Some cases of balanitis are also due to detergent allergy or irritation.

When washing baby boys, the foreskin should never be forcibly retracted – in 96 per cent of babies the foreskin is still attached to the front of the glans penis; forcing it open can cause tissue damage, bleeding and scarring. The natural adhesions break down over the first few years of life – except for the normal attachment underneath, the frenulum – until by the age of 3, 90 per cent of foreskins are partially separated. Tissue remnants may remain up until the age of 17, however.

Males over the age of 7 years who have not been circumcised and whose foreskin can be gently retracted should be taught how to wash underneath the foreskin and should then do so at least once a day – and preferably after every urination. After washing, it is important to make sure the foreskin is pulled forward again to cover the tip of the penis. If it is left back, its blood supply may become restricted leading to swelling (paraphimosis).

Jock-Strap Itch or Dhobie Itch

Candida yeast cells live in the skin creases of up to 80 per cent of the population. They commonly overgrow when conditions are right (that is, warm, moist) to produce an infection around the male groin, scrotum and top of the thighs. This part of your body is often encased in warm, tight-fitting synthetic underwear, tight trousers or sports cloths, which keep conditions hot and humid – ideal for Candida overgrowth.

Other fungi may also be involved and the condition is usually referred to as *tinea cruris* (literally fungal infection of the groin). The first symptom is often itching, followed by the appearance of a dry, red rash with a sharply defined edge. Small pustules may form around hair follicles. If you are prone to heavy sweating in this area, the skin may break down (macerate) to leave raw, weeping areas, especially if you are overweight. The sores ooze a straw-coloured fluid which may harden to form a pale brown crust.

Symptoms
- itching around the scrotum and tops of the legs
- soreness in skin folds
- yeasty, stale-smelling sweat
- red/brown rash with a distinct advancing edge
- sometimes small pustules around hair follicles
- sometimes white plaques
- moist skin breakdown with oozing
- sometimes formation of pale brown crusts
- dark pigmentation of skin
- pain on walking (from the friction of clothes).

Investigation
Swabs may be sent for examination to see whether the infection is due to yeasts, other skin fungi or bacteria. Urinalysis to check for glucose is important to rule out sugar diabetes.

Treatment

Scrupulous hygiene is important to get on top of the infection. You will need to bathe the area regularly with warm water or saline (salt) solution.

Try to keep the area as dry as possible. After washing, pat skin dry with tissue paper or blow dry with a hair-dryer set on gentle heat. Where possible, expose the affected skin to the air as often as possible – for example, wear a long, loose T-shirt with no underpants or trousers when you are home on your own. If this is not possible, wear clothes that are loose and allow air to circulate.

Treatment creams in a vanishing base are less greasy and messy to use during the day when wearing clothes. An ointment will protect sore, weeping areas from crusting and sticking to clothes. An anti-fungal powder spray will help to keep the groin dry.

Treatment preparations are the same as those for treating balanitis (*see page 46*).

Prevention

- Wash the groin area regularly, especially in hot weather and after exercise.
- Dry skin thoroughly after washing.
- Wear loose clothes that allow air to circulate – avoid tight jeans, cycling shorts, etc.
- Wear loose underpants and trousers made from natural fibres rather than man-made ones.
- Choose boxer shorts made from cotton, rather than tight jockey-style briefs.
- After an attack, continue using a dry powder anti-fungal spray to prevent a recurrence.
- Don't share bath towels.

FEMALE GENITALS

The Normal Vulva and Vagina

The vulva is the name for the visible, external female genitalia. It is made up of the clitoris, two outer fleshy folds of skin (labia majora, or large lips) and two smaller, thinner inner folds (labia minora, or small lips). The most common problem affecting this area is itchiness (*pruritis vulvae*). This is usually accompanied by vaginal itching, as well. Vulval itching may be accompanied by redness and soreness, in which case it is known as vulvitis (inflammation of the vulva).

The vagina normally measures around 8 cm (3.25 inches) in length. The corrugated front and back walls are in contact and form an H-shape in cross-section which expands during intercourse and childbirth. During sexual arousal, vaginal tissues become increasingly engorged, changing in colour from rosy pink to purplish red and producing lots more discharge as fluid is forced out of engorged blood vessels under pressure.

Normal Vaginal Discharge

Because the vagina is the most efficient self-cleansing organ in the body, a certain amount of vaginal discharge is both natural and inevitable. A healthy discharge is characterized by being:

- relatively light rather than profuse
- non-irritant
- white or buff in colour
- slightly acidic with a fresh smell that is not offensive.

Your vaginal discharge has a number of important functions, including:

- flushing the vagina clean
- protecting the vaginal lining (epithelial) cells from drying out
- protecting against infection
- preventing chaffing

- providing lubrication during intercourse
- acting as a sexual attractant.

Vaginal discharge contains:
- watery secretions made up of mucus (a glycoprotein made from sugar and protein) and fluid
- sloughed cells from the cervix and vaginal lining (epithelial cells)
- infection-fighting pus cells – these are usually scant but may be profuse when infection is present
- antibodies that help to fight infection
- normal, healthy (commensal) bacteria such as *Lactobacillus*
- potential disease-causing organisms (pathogens) that are normally kept in check by the healthy commensal bacteria
- menstrual debris (blood and endometrial lining cells) during a period
- semen and sperm for a short time after making love without a condom.

How Your Vaginal Discharge Changes throughout the Month

If you are not using a hormonal method of contraception your vaginal discharge will change naturally throughout each monthly cycle. In the first 2 weeks of your cycle (day 1 is the first day of your last period) cervical mucus is mainly under the influence of the female hormone, oestrogen. This keeps it fluid and slippery so that it can be drawn between two fingers to a length of several centimetres. It has an appearance and consistency similar to raw egg white. This thin cervical mucus is sperm-friendly. Its molecules are all lined up in a similar direction and sperm can swim through it easily and survive in it for a relatively long time.

Immediately after ovulation, cervical mucus comes under the influence of progesterone hormone and suddenly changes virtually overnight to become scant, thick and sticky. Its molecules become entangled, rather like barbed wire, so that the mucus becomes hostile to sperm – they cannot swim through easily and perish quickly. These changes in the quantity, fluidity, glossiness, transparency and elasticity of vaginal secretions are monitored regularly by women using the natural, fertility awareness method of contraception.

Vulvo-Vaginal Candidiasis

Candida infection is the most common cause of inflammation of the vagina (vaginitis) and the outer surrounding area (vulvitis). If it affects both sites simultaneously, it is known as vulvo-vaginitis.

Candida is found normally as a harmless (commensal) organism in the vagina of many women without causing symptoms. When vaginal swabs are taken and grown in special cultures which encourage the overgrowth of Candida cells, yeasts are detected in 10–55 per cent of apparently well women (the average seems to be 1 in 5, or 20 per cent) who have no symptoms of thrush infection at all. In these cases, yeast cells are either present in an inactive state (as resting spores) or surviving quite happily in low numbers, kept in check by other healthy bacteria such as *Lactobacillus acidophilus*. During the symptomless phase, active yeasts are present as simple cells (non-filamentous forms) in relatively small numbers rather than in the filamentous form with hyphae (yeast cell germ tubes – *see page 2*).

Whether the yeast cells come and go or are present all the time is not really known. Studies suggest that Candida remains in the vagina for at least several months, and possibly for years at a time without causing obvious harm. If the natural balance is tipped, however – due to changing levels of hormones, acidity, sugar content or the numbers and types of bacteria present – Candida cells may suddenly proliferate to cause symptoms which may include:

- itching
- redness
- soreness
- vaginal dryness
- a white, cottage-cheese-like discharge
- a yeasty smell
- pain on intercourse
- cystitis-like pain on passing urine (dysuria)
- increased frequency of urination
- enlarged, tender lymph nodes (glands) in the groin.

The amount of discharge does not necessarily relate to the severity of symptoms, and some women find that vaginal dryness makes their other symptoms worse.

Other causes of itching and soreness which may be confused with Candida include:

- other infections, such as anaerobic vaginosis, Herpes simplex (cold sore) virus, Human papilloma (wart) virus
- allergy to chemicals in deodorants, spermicides, creams, douches, bath products, soaps, lubricants and, rarely, to sperm and semen themselves
- lack of oestrogen after the menopause (atrophic vulvo-vaginitis)
- skin changes linked with ageing (vulval dystrophies)
- chemical irritation due to urinary leakage (as caused, for example, by stress incontinence).

Simple itching may also be caused by infections such as pubic lice and scabies, or skin problems such as eczema or psoriasis which can affect this area as well as other parts of the body.

Vaginal Acidity and Candida

The acidity of vaginal secretions changes throughout your menstrual cycle. For most of the month, secretions are acidic. This partly results from acids secreted by your own vaginal cells, but most are made by friendly bacteria such as *Lactobacillus acidophilus* as a by-product of their metabolism. These 'gold-standard' bacteria thrive in acid conditions and usually keep Candida infections at bay by competing with them for micronutrients, food (glycogen/glucose) and binding sites which both organisms (Lactobacilli and Candida) use to stick to the epithelial cells in your vaginal walls.

As your period approaches, natural hormone changes mean that your vaginal discharge becomes less acidic. Blood itself is slightly alkaline, and during menstruation this makes the vaginal environment much less acid again. This affects the friendly bacteria present in your vagina. They struggle due to lack of acidity, which means it is easier for Candida to take over and proliferate.

When conditions are acidic, Candida tends to stay in its less invasive form as simple yeasts cells. When conditions become less acid and near neutral, Candida tends to produce threads (germ tubes, or hyphae) which are more invasive and likely to trigger symptoms. This switch from a simple-celled form to the thread form occurs at around pH 6 (just below neutral) and can happen within 1 to 3 hours of a change in environmental conditions. As a result, vaginal Candidiasis is more common around the time of your period.

Sugar Content of Vaginal Discharge and Candida

During the second half of your menstrual cycle (after ovulation) hormone changes increase the glycogen content of vaginal cells. Glycogen is a starchy storage compound that is broken down in the cells to provide sugar (glucose) as an energy source – it is also a favourite fuel for developing yeast cells.

With the tailing off of acidity that also occurs around the time of a period, increased cell sugar content increases the risk of developing thrush. Women with sugar diabetes (*Diabetes mellitus*) also have increased sugar levels in their vaginal secretions unless their condition is tightly controlled by diet, insulin injections or sugar-lowering drugs. This increases the risk of Candidal vulvo-vaginitis, and many new cases of diabetes are picked up each year when women with recurrent Candida are routinely screened for the presence of excess sugar in the urine or blood.

Synthetic Hormones and Vulvo-vaginal Candida

Many women who have problems with vaginal discharge and Candida are on the contraceptive Pill or taking certain types of hormone replacement therapy (HRT). Synthetic hormones alter the normal monthly changes that occur in the vaginal discharge cycle, and can change normal vaginal acidity. Your discharge may become continuously thin and watery or thick and barely there, depending on which blend of combined oral contraceptive Pill or HRT you are using.

Hormone treatments that are predominantly oestrogenic (contain more oestrogen compared with progestogen) encourage increased vaginal secretions which tend to be thin, elastic and sometimes copious. This is partly because they increase the number of mucus-secreting cells found around the cervix. Oestrogen also seems to increase the stickiness of vaginal cells, so that Candida yeasts are more likely to bind to them. It also stimulates production of a yeast-fibre network (mycelium) so that it spreads more quickly. Hormone treatments that are relatively progestogenic (contain more progestogen compared with oestrogen) produce the opposite effect – scant, thick mucus which is accompanied by vaginal dryness.

Taking synthetic hormones can also affect the glycogen/sugar content of vaginal cells, so that women taking the oral contraceptive Pill or HRT also seem to be at increased risk of developing vulvo-vaginal Candida. This is most likely if the hormone blend you are on contains relatively high doses of oestrogen. Blends containing low doses of oestrogen are less likely to cause problems with vulval or vaginal thrush.

Pregnancy and Vulvo-vaginal Candida

During pregnancy, vulvo-vaginal thrush is so common that 30–40 per cent of women develop symptoms at least once during their pregnancy.

- Pregnancy is a time when the mother's natural immunity is lowered so that the developing baby, who contains 'foreign' genes inherited from the father, is not attacked by the mother's defences.
- Very high levels of circulating hormones increase the glycogen/sugar content of vaginal cells – pregnancy is also a time when the body's ability to metabolize sugar becomes increasingly impaired, so that sugar levels throughout the body are likely to be higher than normal. This provides increased carbohydrate to fuel the growth and division of Candida cells.
- High levels of oestrogen (as found in pregnancy) seem to increase the stickiness of vaginal cells so that Candida yeasts are more likely to bind to them – oestrogen also seems to

stimulate the production of the yeast's fibre network so that it spreads more quickly.

■ During pregnancy, high levels of progesterone are produced. This hormone has a relaxant effect on smooth muscle cells throughout the body, so that the vagina may not flush its secretions through as effectively as normal.

■ Increased needs to visit the bathroom due to pressure of the growing womb on the bladder and bowel increase the risk of gut Candida being transferred from the bowel to the vagina.

Thrush is most likely to strike during the last 3 months of pregnancy, and recurrences are common. Unfortunately, it also seems that standard treatments are less effective during pregnancy – presumably because the Candida have so many positive environmental factors in their favour that they can survive a certain exposure to anti-fungal agents.

Antibiotics and Vulvo-vaginal Candida

Many women notice that their symptoms develop during or after a course of antibiotics. The most common culprits are so-called broad-spectrum antibiotics (for example tetracycline, ampicillin, amoxycillin, cephalosporins) which wipe out some of the healthy bacteria found in the vagina as well as the disease-causing bugs they are designed to treat. These healthy bacteria (especially *Lactobacillus*) keep Candida at bay by competing with it for nutrients and for binding sites to vaginal lining cells and by secreting chemicals that increase the acidity of the environment and inhibit yeast cell growth. When women on antibiotics are screened for the presence of vaginal Candida (even if they are not having any symptoms), yeast cells are found in 3 times more women than among a similar group not on antibiotics. Thrush spores are present in the air and germinate in warm, moist places. Candida thrives when natural immunity falls, as during times of stress and illness or when antibiotics destroy the normal vaginal bacteria that keep yeast infections at bay.

Lack of Iron and Vulvo-vaginal Candida

White blood cells need the mineral iron to make an array of powerful chemicals used to combat infections such as Candida. Even a mild iron deficiency can result in reduced immunity – although the deficiency may not be pronounced enough to cause anaemia. While your blood count (haemoglobin concentration) may be normal, a low reserve of iron can be detected by measuring blood levels of an iron compound called ferritin. Ferritin is the main way iron is stored in the body and one of the ways it is transported around the circulation. It is made up of a protein, apoferritin, linked to a varying number of iron atoms – one molecule of apoferritin may contain as many as 4,500 atoms of iron. When iron stores are low, less apoferritin is made, and iron in the bloodstream moves from apoferritin to another iron-transporting protein, transferrin.

Ideally, all women suffering from recurrent thrush should have their ferritin level measured. If it is low, treatment with an iron-containing vitamin and mineral supplement may be enough to solve the problem, although this remedy will need to be continued for several months until iron stores are back to normal. If you are found to have a low ferritin level, you and your doctor will also need to think about why your iron levels are low:

- Do you eat a good, nutritious diet full of iron-rich foods? (*see page 155*)
- Do you suffer from heavy or frequent periods?
- Have your iron stores been depleted through pregnancy?
- Are you losing hidden blood from your bowels?
- Does your body have a problem absorbing the iron in your diet?
- Is there a problem with production of red blood cells in your marrow?

If the iron deficiency is significant, you may well need investigations to find out its cause.

WHERE IRON IS FOUND IN THE BODY

- 70 per cent of body iron is in the red blood pigment, haemoglobin
- 3 per cent is in the red muscle pigment, myoglobin
- 27 per cent is in the form of ferritin

Tight Synthetic Clothes and Vulvo-vaginal Candida

Wearing tight or poorly ventilated underclothes – especially those fashioned from man-made fibres that are unable to 'breathe' – are strongly linked with an increased risk of developing vulvo-vaginal Candida. This is because yeast spores love to germinate in warm, moist places; tight clothes increase the humidity and temperature of vulval skin creases. If you suffer from recurrent vaginal thrush, it may be helpful to wear loose, well-ventilated clothes and cotton underwear. Avoid nylon tights, and instead wear stockings – either those with elasticated tops that stay up on their own, or with a suspender belt for support.

Low-Temperature Wash Cycles and Candida

In the old days, underwear was given a thorough, regular boil-up in a pan of water on top of the stove. Modern wash-day practices often involve the use of low-temperature wash cycles to protect delicate fashion lingerie. As a result, Candida spores may survive the process and linger in your underwear, to cause reinfection. There are several ways in which you can prevent this:

- Continue washing your lingerie as before, but iron the cotton gussets with a very hot iron to kill any residual Candida spores.
- Pre-soak underwear in concentrated detergent and scrub the crotch before putting them into the wash.
- Wear white cotton underwear, which can survive a hot wash without undue damage
- Soak pants in bleach (if the material will take it) before washing.

Don't, however, put your underpants in the microwave as was once recommended – they may go up in smoke!

These simple measures are often enough to break the misery of recurrent thrush infection.

Sun Beds and Candida

Some women seem to suffer a bout of Candida after using a sun bed. This is partly due to the increased warmth and moistness generated while under the lamps. Ultra-violet light is known to trigger recurrences of Herpes simplex infection, and it has recently been discovered that Candida can 'switch' (*see page 14*) from their smooth form to a rough one when exposed to low doses of ultraviolet light. The switched (rough) colonies produce different patterns of germ tube threads (hyphae) and seem to:

- proliferate more readily
- stick to body lining cells more easily, making it easier to invade tissues
- secrete more enzymes that break down proteins, fats and cell walls
- be more invasive
- escape from detection by immune cells more easily
- be less susceptible to anti-fungal treatments.

Using a sun bed may therefore trigger symptoms of thrush in someone who has previously lived quite happily with Candida without developing symptoms.

While washing the vulval area after using a sun bed and wearing loose cotton clothes may help to prevent an attack of thrush due to increased humidity and warmth, it is worth avoiding sun beds altogether if you suffer from recurrent Candidiasis.

Investigation

While your doctor may suspect a diagnosis of vulval or vaginal thrush just by asking you questions about your symptoms, it is important that you are examined and a swab taken to confirm the diagnosis. If the infection is advanced, the vagina may be full of thick, white cottage-cheese-like clots that are obviously due to a yeast infection. In mild or early cases, however, the mucous membranes may just look red and there may be a grey-white-yellow discharge similar to that seen in other common vaginal conditions such as:

- Gardnerella vaginalis
- Bacterial vaginosis (anaerobic bacterial imbalance)
- Herpes simplex infection
- Trichomonas vaginalis
- Chlamydia
- Early wart virus infection (itching)
- Pubic lice (itching)
- Skin problems such as eczema or psoriasis.

Don't be afraid to ask for an examination and for a swab to be sent to hospital. Similarly, if you decide to treat your symptoms of vulvo-vaginal Candida yourself with over-the-counter products, always consult your doctor if the symptoms don't start to clear up quickly (within 3–5 days).

Sending vaginal swabs to hospital for culture is not always helpful, as delays in transit may mean that Candida cells in the swab may die and go undetected. If you continue to have problems of vulvo-vaginal irritation, soreness or discharge but swabs persistently claim to be negative or normal, don't be embarrassed about attending a genito-urinary medicine (GUM, VD, STD or Special) clinic. You will be treated sympathetically and confidentially and, as fresh secretions are examined under the microscope there and then, any infection is usually picked up quickly. You will also be screened for an infection called chlamydia, which is not usually done in general practice. Chlamydia are too small to be seen under the light microscope and they are extremely difficult to culture. They can only be detected in a cervical swab by using a special immunological technique which takes several days. All genito-urinary clinics will check for this disease, while only a few GPs have the special culture bottle required.

As a bonus, treatments provided by a genito-urinary medicine clinic are free as they do not attract a prescription charge.

A genito-urinary check-up is especially important if you notice:

- any abnormality of your vaginal discharge, for example increased quantity, unusual smell or staining
- itching, soreness, tenderness or pain
- abnormal bleeding
- lumps or ulceration
- pain on urinating (dysuria, cystitis)
- low abdominal pain
- discomfort during intercourse
- genital problems in your sexual partner
- if you are at risk of having contracted a sexually transmittable disease.

Treatment

A number of orthodox treatments are available for treating vulvo-vaginal thrush. Some of these treatments (for example clotrimazole, fluconazole) are now available over the counter, while others remain prescription only. As the situation is constantly changing, with more and more drugs coming off prescription each year, it is worth asking your pharmacist for advice on which treatment will suit you best if you wish to self-medicate:

Clotrimazole:
- 1 per cent cream for use on vulva – applied 2 or 3 times a day and ideally continued for 1 week after symptoms have gone
- pessaries for insertion in the vagina at night:
- 100-mg pessaries are used for 6 nights in a row
- 200-mg pessaries are used for 3 nights in a row
- 500-mg pessary has only to be used for 1 night
- 10 per cent vaginal cream in pre-filled applicator: to be squirted into the vagina last thing at night as a single dose
- 2 per cent vaginal cream plus 6 applicators: squirted into vagina twice a day for 3 days, or used nightly for 6 nights in a row

Econazole:
- 1 per cent cream/lotion: applied 2 or 3 times a day and continued for 1 week after symptoms have gone
- 150-mg long-acting pessary: inserted into vagina at night as a single dose
- 150-mg pessaries: inserted into vagina for 3 nights in a row

Miconazole:
- 2 per cent cream with applicators: inserted into vagina twice a day for 7 days, or used on vulva twice a day
- vaginal capsules (1,200 mg) plus finger stall: inserted into vagina at night as a single dose
- 100-mg pessaries: inserted into vagina twice a day for 7 days

Fenticonazole:
- 200-mg gelatin pessaries: inserted into vagina for 3 nights in a row
- 600-mg gelatin pessary: inserted into vagina at night as a single dose
- Isoconazole: 2 300-mg vaginal tablets inserted into the vagina for a single night

Nystatin:
- cream/gel: applied to vulva 2–4 times a day for 2 weeks
- vaginal cream plus applicators: inserted into vagina for 14 nights in a row
- oral tablets (500,000 units): 4 times a day during vaginal treatment to eradicate gut infection
- Fluconazole: 150-mg capsule taken by mouth as a single dose
- Itraconazole: 2 100-mg capsules taken twice daily for 1 day (total of 4 capsules)
- Ketoconazole: tablets/suspension for oral use in chronic, recurrent vaginal thrush that does not respond to other treatments. Taken once a day with meals for 5 days.

For alternative (complementary health) treatments, see Chapter 9.

Prevention

Self-help remedies to help treat/prevent vulvo-vaginal thrush include:

- Avoid wearing tight underwear, especially nylon pantyhose or tight trousers. Stockings and cotton underwear are best as they allow air to circulate, so that warmth and humidity are reduced.
- Avoid getting hot and sweaty – use panty-liners and change them as necessary throughout the day; shower, wash or bathe immediately after exercise.
- Don't use bath additives, vaginal deodorants or douches – they can upset your natural acid and bacterial balance.
- Avoid trauma to vaginal tissues from vigorous sex or rubbing too hard with a bath towel.
- Try boiling cotton underwear or hot-ironing panty gussets. Modern low-temperature washing machine cycles don't kill Candida spores.
- Use an acid gel (0.9 per cent acetic acid in a jelly base, available over the counter) to help maintain vaginal acidity so that Candida cells remain in their simple non-invasive form.
- Smear the vulva and lower vagina with natural BIO yoghurt containing live *Lactobacillus acidophilus* – these bacteria can colonize the vagina and help to prevent Candida overgrowth. Taking Acidophilus tablets (from healthfood shops), eating BIO yoghurt and drinking Yakult (a culture of *Lactobacillus casei* Shirota) may also help to reduce bowel colonization with thrush (*see page 97*).
- Try following an anti-yeast diet or a simpler regime of cutting out alcohol, mushrooms, sugary foods, tea, coffee and chocolate. Eat a wholefood diet of salads, fruit, vegetables, pulses and wholegrain cereals instead.
- Try to avoid stress – make time for regular exercise, rest and relaxation.
- Take a good multivitamin and mineral supplement containing around 100 per cent of the recommended daily amount (RDA) of as many vitamins and minerals as possible.
- If you are being treated for Candida, make sure your partner

uses an anti-thrush cream too. Thrush spores can survive under the male foreskin without causing any symptoms. They may then be passed back to you.

■ If the problem is recurrent, have a vaginal health check at your local genito-urinary medicine clinic.

Chapter Six

CANDIDA INFECTION OF THE DIGESTIVE TRACT

NORMAL DIGESTION

The intestinal tract is one of the main sites where yeast cells are normally found colonizing the body. In order to understand the problems this may cause, it is worth having a quick look at the normal structure and function of the intestines.

The gastro-intestinal tract is a long tube which starts at the mouth and ends at the anal sphincter. It is basically a food-processing system that accepts complex food molecules at one end and breaks these down into simpler, soluble nutrients which are absorbed into the bloodstream. Waste products are disposed of – usually in neat packages – at the other end.

The Mouth

Digestion starts in the mouth. Saliva contains an enzyme, amylase, which starts breaking down starchy complex carbohydrates into simpler sugars. The teeth chew and grind food into small pieces which are moistened with saliva. Each mouthful is then rolled into a small ball (bolus) by the tongue and pushed to the back of the mouth where it is swallowed by a reflex action. Yeast cells present in your food can easily survive this process.

The Oesophagus and Stomach

The food bolus travels down your gullet (oesophagus) to the stomach, where it is mixed with powerful secretions containing hydrochloric acid and enzymes. Proteins, fats and carbohydrates are broken down into simpler units while muscular contractions

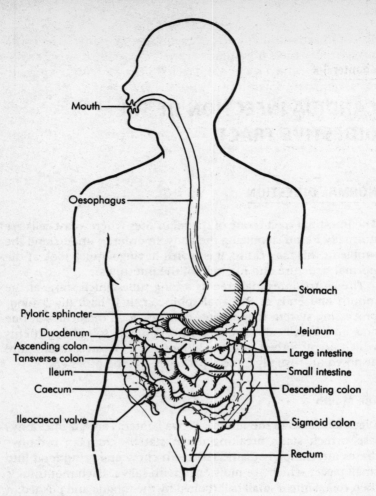

The digestive tract

churn the whole stomach contents to mix the food and digestive juices thoroughly. Food usually spends around 6 hours in your stomach while it is processed and converted into a liquid porridge-like slurry known as chyme.

Glands in your stomach produce around 3 litres of acidic fluid per day. While yeast cells can live quite happily in your mouth and oesophagus, most are usually rapidly killed once they reach your stomach, as long as it is functioning properly. A few will survive the process from time to time – especially if you are taking antacids, which reduce stomach acidity, or have a stomach ulcer – and pass down further into the gut.

Once the food in your stomach is converted into chyme, the stomach exit valve (pyloric sphincter) opens momentarily for a few seconds at a time to let stomach contents squirt through into the first part of the small intestines.

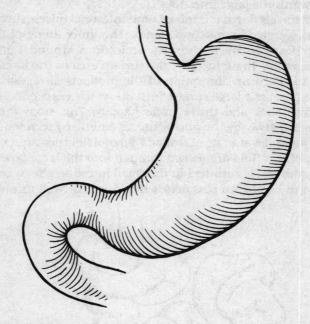

The oesophagus and stomach

The Small Intestines

The small intestines, or foregut, are highly coiled to fit into the abdominal cavity. They form a tube around 285 cm long and 3.5 cm in diameter. The first part of the small intestine after the stomach is the duodenum. The intestinal juices secreted into the duodenum are alkaline, to neutralize acidity from the stomach. Bile from the liver and powerful enzymes from the pancreas also flow into the duodenum to start the next phase of digestion.

The jejunum is the name given to the first 40 per cent of the small intestine below the duodenum, while the next 60 per cent of the small intestine is known as the ileum. As there is no distinct border between the two this division is somewhat arbitrary. Surprisingly, Candida cells can survive quite happily throughout the small intestines, becoming more and more frequent towards the large intestines.

As food travels down it is mixed with intestinal juices (succus entericus) secreted by mucosal glands. The inner lining of the small intestines is covered in tiny projections around 1 mm long, called villi. These increase the surface area of the intestinal wall to speed up absorption of the products of digestion. They also provide a large surface area on which yeast cells and bacteria can stick and thrive quite happily. This stops them being washed away by the juices (succus entericus) secreted by the small intestines at a rate of around 7 litres of fluid per day. Only 1–2 litres of this fluid are passed through into the large bowel, however, the rest is absorbed in the small intestines. Yeast cells also seem to be able to pass across the intestinal wall through

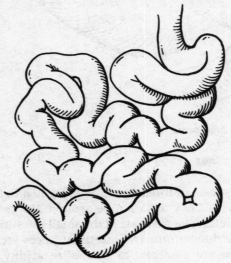

The small intestines

this large surface area of your small intestines in a process known as translocation (*see page 14*). By the time food has reached the end of the small intestines and passed into the large bowel, the process of digestion is complete.

The Large Intestines

The large intestines form a wide tube that is around 1 m long. The large bowel – made up of the colon, rectum and anal canal – is the main site where yeast cells thrive happily in the normal gut. The large intestines are where excess fluid, salts and minerals are absorbed from the gut, while waste – mainly indigestible fibre – is compacted and made ready for an orderly disposal through the anus.

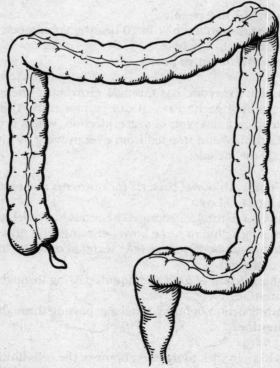

The large intestines

The large intestines are home to billions of bacteria which ferment indigestible fibre waste to produce acids and gases, as well as many useful vitamins such as biotin. Altogether, bowel micro-organisms – including yeasts – make up around 30 per cent of normal stool bulk.

CANDIDA IN THE HEALTHY GUT

The intestinal tract is one of the main sites where yeast cells are normally found colonizing the body. Organisms living in the body in this harmless way are known as *commensals*. When swabs are taken from healthy people, Candida can be grown from:

- the mouth of 1 in 2 people
- the oesophagus (gullet) of 1 in 10 healthy volunteers
- the rectum of 1 in 3 people
- the faeces of 8 out of 10 people

It is likely that everyone has Candida growing in their gut at some time during each year – if not permanently. The gut is thought to act as a reservoir of yeast infection, which is usually kept under control and stopped from overgrowing by a variety of factors. These include:

- competition with bowel bacteria for nutrients and binding sites on intestinal cells
- production of natural anti-fungal chemicals by bowel bacteria
- the sterilizing action of some bowel enzymes and juices
- the action of antibodies (type IgA) secreted onto the inner surface of the gut
- the flushing action of food and liquids passing through the small intestines
- the scouring action of bulky roughage passing through the large intestines.

Yeast cells have to stick to the membrane of the cells lining your gut if they are to survive without being flushed through your system and out the other end. They need to stick to special binding sites on your cell membranes – but these sites are also used by other bowel organisms such as the *Lactobacillus* bacteria. Many healthy bacteria also secrete substances that interfere with the growth of other organisms. Acting together, these different factors usually damp down Candida growth so that it lives quite happily inside you – and may even do you some good. Vitamins made by yeast cells – especially the B group and biotin – seep into your intestinal juices and are readily absorbed.

How Candida Gets into Your Gut

Candida yeasts mostly enter your gut through your mouth:

- in the food that you eat
- from the skin of your hands
- if you suck on anything (pens, etc.) that may have yeast cells on it
- through kissing and oral sex.

Live Candida yeasts are frequently present in food and drinks. In one study which analysed a range of common foods, live Candida cells were recovered from a number of them, of which the worst culprits were:

- fruit juices
- drinks
- ice cubes
- salads
- snacks
- cereals.

With the juices, all vegetable and fruit varieties were affected, including apple, pineapple, orange, tomato, grape, apricot and lemonade. The yeast contamination seemed to be related to the type of packaging and processing used during preparation rather than the type of fruit involved. All juices sealed with foil wraps were contaminated, while those in cans or bottles were yeast-free:

Type of Food	Number of samples tested	Number positive for live Candida yeasts	per cent
Drinks	16	4	25
Breads	8	0	0
Cereals	17	2	12
Condiments	23	0	0
Desserts	39	1	3
Fish	4	0	0
Fruits	6	0	0
Juices	61	38	62
Meats (cooked)	20	0	0
Milk and dairy products	27	1	4
Salads	8	3	38
Sauces	10	0	0
Snacks	25	3	12
Soups	16	0	0
Vegetables	44	2	5
Ready-cooked meals	21	0	0

CANDIDA INFECTION OF THE MOUTH

Candida infection of the mouth (oral thrush) is common. It can occur at any age, but is most often seen in young babies up to the age of 18 months, the middle-aged, and the elderly.

Yeast cells seem to prefer living in certain sites in the mouth more than others. In order of preference, these include:

- upper surface of your tongue
- palate
- inner surfaces of the cheeks
- on dentures, especially upper ones.

Bacteria and yeasts can often be seen on top of the tongue as a white/yellow thick coating which may smell offensive and contribute to bad breath (halitosis).

Mouth infections, including thrush, are more common if you suffer from:

- a dry mouth (zerostomia), which may be due to increasing age, poor saliva production, taking certain drugs (for example, some antihistamines) or prolonged mouth breathing
- asthma and use inhaled corticosteroids to control the underlying inflammation
- diabetes – especially if you also smoke, which seems to lower your resistance to oral thrush
- impaired immunity through illness, stress, drugs or a nutrient deficiency.

People who wear dentures are also more likely to develop oral thrush – known as denture stomatitis. Experiments show that Candida yeasts can stick to the denture material and act as a continuous source of reinfection.

Symptoms

The symptoms of oral thrush may include:

- a thick coating on the tongue
- a red, sore, shiny tongue
- sores at the corners of the lips (angular stomatitis)
- white plaques on the inside of your cheeks
- itching, for example on the roof of your mouth, beneath dentures
- soreness
- dryness (xerostomia)
- pain on eating or drinking
- ulceration inside the mouth.

When oral thrush develops as cream/white curd-like plaques in the mouth, this is known as acute (recent onset) pseudomembranous (false-membrane) Candidiasis. The plaques are easily rubbed away and contain yeast cells, hyphae (yeast cell germ tubes), inflammatory cells, bacteria, lining (epithelial) cells from the mouth, food debris and dead cells which are starting to break down. Underneath the plaque is a raw, tender area that is usually painful and red and which may bleed.

When the plaques are dislodged (for example while you are eating) they leave behind a shiny, red, glossy area that is known as acute (recent onset) atrophic (wasted) Candidiasis. These areas of the tongue usually reveal a localized loss of tastebuds. If left untreated, the lesions take on a lumpy, granular appearance as underlying cells and blood vessels multiply in an attempt to heal small areas of ulceration. This is usually diagnosed as chronic (long-term) atrophic (wasted) Candidiasis.

If still left untreated, these areas may thicken and develop tough, white membranes with a roughened surface. These tend to be larger than the false membranes seen in early thrush infections and cannot be scraped away easily or dislodged during eating. This stage of oral thrush is known as chronic (long-term) hyperplastic (thickened) Candidiasis, or Candidal leukoplakia (white patches). If this type of white patch forms in the mouth, it is important that it is biopsied and properly diagnosed. Other conditions – some of which are precancerous – can also cause white patches (leukoplakia) in the mouth; these need to be picked up early and treated to prevent mouth cancer (*see page 77*).

Investigation

Oral thrush can usually be diagnosed by looking in the mouth and seeing characteristic areas of redness and white patches. Swabs can be examined under the microscope for yeast cells, hyphae and spores, or sent to be cultured in the laboratory to confirm the diagnosis and rule out other causes.

Treatment

Oral thrush is usually easily treated with anti-fungal agents. If you are pregnant or breastfeeding, don't use any preparations before checking with a pharmacist or doctor:

- Mild infections may respond to a Hexetidine antiseptic mouthwash/gargle used 2 or 3 times a day.
- Miconazole gel is available from pharmacies and comes in a pleasant orange-flavoured base. This is used 2–4 times per

day (depending on age). The gel should be held in the mouth for as long as possible before swallowing. It can also be applied directly to lesions using a clean finger. Treatment should be continued for at least 2 days after symptoms have disappeared.

- Sugar-free pastilles containing dequalinium chloride can be bought from pharmacies: to be sucked every 4 hours. They help to treat both bacterial and fungal infections of the mouth and throat.
- Amphotericin lozenges (prescription only): to be sucked 4–8 times daily for up to 15 days. If preferred, an amphotericin suspension can also be inserted into the mouth with a dropper and used 4 times a day for 14 days. Keep both preparations in contact with lesions for as long as possible. Use for at least 2 days after symptoms have disappeared.
- Nystatin pastilles (prescription only): to be sucked 4 times daily – do not eat or drink for 5 minutes before or 1 hour after treatment. If preferred, a suspension for inserting into the mouth with a dropper is also available. Hold preparations against the lesions for as long as possible. Continue for at least 2 days after symptoms have disappeared.

  For severe infections:

  - a course of anti-fungal Fluconazole (capsules or suspension) can be prescribed: to be taken once a day for 7–14 days
  - a course of Itraconazole (capsules) can be prescribed for use once a day for 15 days (twice a day for patients with an underlying disease affecting their immunity).

If your mouth is really sore, a local anaesthetic spray (for example benzocaine) or anti-inflammatory spray/rinse (for example benzydamine) can be used to help numb the pain.

If you suffer from oral thrush and use dentures, these can be treated using a miconazole denture lacquer which comes in a pack containing 3 bottles, brushes and tissues (prescription only). The entire contents of 1 bottle is applied to the upper surface of a clean, disinfected and dried upper denture. Allow to dry for at least 1 hour before inserting into the mouth. This is repeated twice more at weekly intervals.

Prevention

A mouthwash containing chlorhexidine has some anti-Candida action and may help to keep recurrent oral thrush at bay – but check with your dentist that this will suit you first. Not all dentists recommend chlorhexidine mouthwashes, and they can cause staining of teeth with prolonged use.

If you suffer from a dry mouth, an artificial saliva solution (for example carboxymethyl-cellulose aerosol/spray or mucin xylitol spray) will help to keep your mouth moist and discourage infection. This comes in natural, lemon or peppermint flavours. A pastille containing malic acid can also be sucked to stimulate the flow of saliva.

If you wear dentures, it is important to keep these scrupulously clean and not let stains build up. They should be kept in a sterilizing solution at night and checked regularly by your dentist for signs of wear or infection, and to check their fit.

Most people with asthma need to use a corticosteroid inhaler regularly to damp down the inflammation in their lungs. Even when inhaled correctly, up to 90 per cent of the medication will be deposited in the upper airways and then swallowed – only around 10 per cent of the dose reaches the lungs. As the corticosteroid works by damping down excessive immune reactions in the tissues it touches, this makes oral thrush more likely. It's therefore a good idea to clean your teeth, use a mouthwash or gargle immediately after using your inhaler (especially if it is a dry powder inhaler) to remove remaining particles. If recurrent oral thrush is a problem, ask your doctor about using a device such as a spacer to help minimize the amount of drug that deposits in your throat.

People with gum disease are 4 times more likely to develop a thrush infection than other people. If you have redness or swelling of the gums round your teeth, or if your gums bleed when brushing, you may well have gingivitis (infected gums) which harbour bacteria and yeasts in infected pockets between your gums and teeth. If this is ignored, infection will spread to involve the jawbone round your teeth (periodontitis), and your gums will start to recede. Ignore periodontitis and you will eventually lose your teeth altogether.

Unfortunately, cleaning your teeth twice a day is not enough to solve gum disease. What you need is an expert assessment of your mouth by a dentist committed to oral hygiene, followed by a course of treatment with a dental hygienist. By having your gum pockets cleared of infected plaque and rotting food, gum disease can be beaten. You will then need to continue with a regular programme of proper brushing and flossing, to keep your mouth healthy and disease-free.

Sores at the corners of the mouth where the lips meet (angular stomatitis) are sometimes signs of iron-deficiency anaemia. If you feel tired and washed out, or if the problem is recurrent, it is important to ask your doctor if you might be suffering from anaemia. If so, the cause of this will need to be investigated.

If you smoke, try to stop – smoking damages the lining of your mouth, increases the risk of oral thrush and is also linked with mouth cancer.

Mouth Cancer

Mouth cancer is becoming increasingly common. Around 2,000 new cases are diagnosed each year and it now makes up 5 per cent of all tumours. While mouth cancer is not especially linked with Candida infection, it can be triggered by long-term infections (sepsis) of the mouth or ill-fitting infected dentures. It can be mistaken for chronic hyperplastic Candidiasis. Sadly, the outlook is often poor as mouth cancers have often grown quite large before they are picked up. Those that develop on the roof of the mouth or top of the tongue may be spotted early, but those on the floor of the mouth, under the tongue or in 'coffin corner' – an aptly nick-named crevice lurking at the back of your throat – are difficult to detect in the early stages. Two out of every three sufferers are male, and most cases occur in the over-forties.

Mouth cancer is linked with several risk factors, known as the 5 S's:

1. *Smoking* – those who smoke cigars, a pipe or cigarettes, chew tobacco or inhale snuff are at greatest risk
2. *Spirits* – drinking excessive amounts of alcoholic spirits can trigger oral cancer

3. *Spices* – long-term exposure to hot spices has been linked with this disease
4. *Syphilis* – though this infection is now relatively rare
5. *Sepsis* – chronic irritation or infection from ill-fitting dentures, a jagged tooth or infected gums.

Mouth cancers usually start as a whitish patch (leukoplakia) or a red velvety patch (erythroplakia), both of which can mimic Candida infections. These pre-cancerous changes may cause a slight burning sensation in the mouth, but most are painless. As the tumour develops it will form a small, raised lump which eventually ulcerates or forms a deep crack. This may bleed as it eats into surrounding tissues and is usually quite painful. It is important that you do not continue to treat a mouth lesion which does not respond to anti-thrush treatment for longer than a week or two without consulting a doctor or dentist.

EXAMINING YOUR MOUTH
Most mouth cancers, and many thrush infections, are detected by dentists – an excellent reason to have regular dental check-ups, even if your teeth are perfect. It is also worth inspecting the inside of your mouth yourself from time to time – especially if you're over 40. Use a dental mirror to view the floor of your mouth, underneath and along the sides of your tongue, and the gutters around your gums. The things to look for are:

■ unexplained white patches
■ unexplained red velvety patches
■ raised lumps
■ an ulcer that refuses to heal.

Any unexplained mouth ulcer lasting longer than 3 weeks needs full investigation. Similarly, don't ignore a persistent sore throat or hoarseness lasting longer than 3 weeks.

If you should find unusual changes in your mouth, try not to panic. Early diagnosis and treatment leads to a cure in 3 out of 4 cases. If a biopsy shows that abnormal cells are present, these will be removed by surgery, radiotherapy or a combination of the two. New advances in tissue grafting and repair produce an excellent cosmetic result in most cases.

CANDIDA INFECTION OF THE OESOPHAGUS

While Candida can be grown from the oesophagus of 1 in 10 healthy people, it is usually present as a normal non-harmful organism (commensal) without causing symptoms. Despite this, the oesophagus is one of the most common sites of infection in the intestinal tract. Symptoms usually occur because of an underlying problem with the immune system or with the oesophagus itself. Candida seems to prefer infecting the lower two thirds of the oesophagus – nearer the stomach – probably because this area is most likely to be damaged by acid reflux from the stomach into the gullet, which causes inflammation and heartburn. Although many people with Candidal overgrowth in the oesophagus also have oral thrush, around 1 in 3 haven't.

Candida infection of the oesophagus (gullet) is more likely if you suffer from heartburn (gastro-oesophageal reflux disease) or any condition that interferes with normal swallowing, such as:

- blockage of the oesophagus (through peptic ulceration, operative scarring, enlarged glands in the chest, thyroid goitre, tissue webs or a tumour)
- achalasia – a condition in which the oesophagus does not produce the normal muscular waves of activity during swallowing; the bottom half of the oesophagus is constricted while the upper half dilates and contains stale food
- conditions in which the soft tissues of the oesophagus become hardened (for example systemic sclerosis)
- nerve or muscle disorders in which swallowing is affected (for example myasthenia gravis, bulbar palsy, motor neurone disease)
- pouching of the oesophagus (for example diverticuli).

Sometimes, severe Candida infection of the oesophagus is caused by reduced immunity linked with a malignancy (for example leukaemia), drug treatment (such as chemotherapy, oral steroids, drugs used after transplant surgery) or AIDS. These conditions affect the way that immune cells (especially neutrophils) limit Candida infection to keep outbreaks within a limited area.

Symptoms

Candida overgrowth of the oesophagus may cause:

- difficulty swallowing
- pain on swallowing
- pain behind the breastbone (retrosternal pain)
- nausea
- vomiting
- bringing up blood (haematemesis)
- sometimes fever

In a few cases, however, it may cause no symptoms at all.

If left untreated, the raw areas may heal on their own, but this can lead to scarring and narrowing of the oesophagus, with recurrent difficulty swallowing. If you notice any symptoms that you think may be due to infection, ulceration or narrowing of the gullet, it is important to tell your doctor without delay. All symptoms should be taken seriously as, apart from anything else, other conditions such as peptic ulceration or an early cancer of the throat need to be ruled out.

Investigations

If you develop problems with swallowing, or if Candida infection is suspected, two main tests are used to investigate symptoms: a barium swallow and endoscopy.

Barium Swallow
This involves drinking a barium solution made with a flavoured liquid, or eating a biscuit or piece of bread soaked in barium. The barium drink lines the gullet so that it shows up on x-ray, while swallowing the bread/biscuit allows the swallowing pattern to be followed on a screen. By examining a series of x-rays,

a radiologist can see how well-coordinated your muscles are during swallowing, whether there is any spasm, and whether there are any obvious areas of ulceration, narrowing, dilation or abnormal blockage. While x-ray appearances may suggest a Candida infection, they cannot confirm it. Some typical appearances on x-ray include plaques separated by ulcers (which look rather like cobblestones) and severe infection of the wall of the oesophagus (giving it a shaggy, irregular outline).

Endoscopy

This involves being lightly sedated with an injection (for example with diazepam tranquillizer). Your oesophagus can then be examined with a narrow, flexible snake-like instrument (endoscope) containing a light, a camera and a tiny biopsy device. The doctor can directly view the walls of your gullet and identify any abnormal areas such as ulcers, strictures or Candida plaques. If a Candida fungal infection is found, it can be graded according to its severity:

Grade 1: scattered raised white plaques up to 2 mm in diameter
Grade 2: numerous plaques larger than 2 mm in diameter
Grade 3: plaques that merge together to form long white patches or nodules with some ulceration
Grade 4: as Grade 3, but with swelling and narrowing of the oesophagus and bleeding when the walls of the oesophagus are touched.

During endoscopy the doctor will take small biopsies for examination under the microscope. Infected areas of the oesophagus can also be brushed to provide swabs for examination and culture. This gives direct evidence of invasion of tissues by a yeast infection. Brushings seem to be more accurate than biopsies – in one study, 100 per cent of brushings taken from the oesophagus were positive for Candida, compared with only 16 per cent of biopsies performed on the same patients.

Treatment

Treatment of oesophageal Candida is usually with drugs taken by mouth. Some of these are absorbed from the gut and enter the circulation to attack the infection from the inside.

- Fluconazole (capsules or suspension): once a day for 14–30 days
- Itraconazole (capsules): once a day for 15 days (twice a day for patients with an underlying disease affecting their immunity)
- Ketoconazole: may be used where other drugs have failed; once a day for at least 1 week after symptoms have gone. Absorption of oral Ketoconazole depends on stomach acidity – treatment may fail if taken with antacids or ulcer-healing drugs.
- Amphotericin (not absorbed from the gut) is given by mouth (4 times daily) – for severe infections it may be given intravenously.

Prevention

Candida infection of the oesophagus can be minimized by avoiding heartburn and preventing acid damage to tissues in the lower oesophagus. One of the most common causes of heartburn is acid reflux, in which stomach contents reflux back up into the oesophagus. This damages and inflames the tissues lining your lower oesophagus and makes Candida infection and overgrowth more likely.

Normally, acid is stopped from coming up into the gullet by a muscle sphincter between the oesophagus and upper stomach, and by downward contractions of muscles (peristalsis) in the wall of the oesophagus. This protective mechanism may fail due to poor muscle co-ordination, weakness of the stomach sphincter, the presence of a hiatus hernia, or increased pressure on the stomach (caused, for example, by excess weight or eating too much).

Acid reflux causes hot, burning sensations in the chest that may rise up into the throat. It usually comes on within 30 minutes of eating and may be triggered by eating too much, taking exercise, bending or lying down. Meals containing fat, pastry, chocolate, acidic fruit juices, coffee or alcohol are the most common culprits. There are several self-help measures that will help to control symptoms, of which the most important are the first two in this list:

- Lose any excess weight.
- Avoid smoking cigarettes.
- Eat little and often throughout the day, rather than having 3 large meals.
- Drink fluids little and often, rather than large quantities at a time.
- Avoid hot, acid, spicy, fatty foods.
- Avoid tea, coffee and acidic fruit juices.
- Cut right back on alcohol intake – preferably avoid it altogether.
- Avoid aspirin and related drugs (for example ibuprofen).
- Avoid stooping, bending or lying down after eating.
- Avoid late-night eating.
- Elevate the head of your bed by about 15–20 cm.
- Wear loose clothing, especially around the waist.

If you suffer from recurrent indigestion or heartburn it is important to tell your doctor. A recent Gallup poll of over 1,000 people found that 48 per cent had suffered heartburn but only a quarter had sought help from their doctor or pharmacist. Seventy-five per cent of people put up with the problem or took simple remedies such as drinking milk, taking sodium bicarbonate solution or buying simple antacids over the counter. It is now known that taking antacids long term does not protect against the damage caused by acid on delicate tissues – and may also increase your risk of Candida infection. After 10–20 years, recurrent heartburn can result in scarring of the lower oesophagus with resultant difficulty in swallowing.

If symptoms of heartburn last longer than a week or two, or keep coming back, consult your doctor and tell him or her what remedies you have already tried. Your symptoms may need investigation. Research suggests that 1 in 10 people taking regular antacids – especially those over the age of 40 – could have a more serious underlying problem – including a cancer – which if picked up at an early stage is much more likely to be treated successfully.

CANDIDA INFECTION OF THE STOMACH

After the oesophagus, the stomach is the most common site of active Candida infection in the intestinal tract. Growth of Candida yeasts stop once acidity falls to a pH of 4.5, so at normal levels of acidity infection of the stomach is unusual. Candida only usually overgrows when stomach acidity drops significantly (for example when antacids are used in the treatment of peptic ulcers), when the tissues are damaged (from peptic ulcers or a tumour) or in someone with a serious illness affecting immunity (such as leukaemia, AIDS).

■ Candida can be grown from 1 in 3 biopsies taken from stomach peptic ulcers.
■ Candida can be grown from the stomach of 1 in 4 people suffering from stomach cancer.

Some doctors believe that Candida infection of peptic ulcers is so common that it should be suspected in anyone whose stomach ulcer doesn't heal with usual treatment – especially in the elderly. In one study, 5 out of 7 elderly patients with stomach ulcers did not improve with standard antacid drugs. Once they were started on an anti-fungal tablet their ulcers healed within a month.

Production of stomach acid often decreases with increasing age. This is also linked with an increased risk of Candida overgrowth in the stomach. Apart from the fact that acidity is lower, these conditions encourage production of a thicker, stickier mucus in the stomach which coats yeast cells and protects them from what little acid is present.

Symptoms

There are no typical symptoms due to active Candida infection of the stomach. Many people have no symptoms at all, while a few develop non-specific problems that can occur with any stomach disease. These symptoms include:

- loss of appetite
- weight loss
- feelings of fullness after eating very little
- burning indigestion (gastritis), triggered especially by certain foods
- nausea
- vomiting
- bringing up blood (haematemesis)
- abdominal pain
- sometimes fever.

If you develop any of these symptoms, you should tell your doctor as soon as possible.

Investigation

Stomach problems are sometimes investigated with a barium meal. You are given a barium solution to drink and then asked to lie on a table in various positions so that the solution lines your stomach. By examining a series of x-rays, a radiologist can look for areas of ulceration, growths in the stomach wall, or evidence of Candida infection such as small single or multiple ulcers, the presence of fungus balls or small cobblestone-like nodules.

If a stomach problem is suspected you are more likely to have an endoscopy these days. This is similar to the procedure described on page 81, except that the doctor will concentrate on examining your stomach and the first part of your small intestine (the upper duodenum). Biopsies will be taken from any suspicious-looking areas for examination under the microscope.

Treatment

Candida infection of the stomach can be treated with:

- Nystatin (tablets or suspension): 4–6 times daily for as long as necessary
- Fluconazole (capsules or suspension): once a day for 14–30 days
- Itraconazole (capsules): once a day for 15 days (twice a day for patients with an underlying disease affecting their immunity)
- Ketoconazole: may be used where other drugs have failed; once a day for at least 1 week after symptoms have gone. Absorption of oral Ketoconazole depends on stomach acidity – treatment may fail if taken with antacids or ulcer-healing drugs.
- Miconazole (tablets): 4 times a day for 10 days or up to 2 days after symptoms have cleared
- Amphotericin (not absorbed from the gut) is given by mouth (4 times daily) – for severe infections it may be given intravenously.

Prevention

Candida infection of the stomach can be minimized by avoiding inflammation of the stomach (gastritis or indigestion) and damage to stomach tissues.

Indigestion is a common term covering a variety of symptoms linked with eating. These include feelings of distension from swallowing air, flatulence from excessive wind in the intestines, nausea, abdominal pain and sensations of burning. Doctors refer to indigestion as dyspepsia, meaning a discomfort/burning felt centrally in the upper abdomen.

The stomach is normally protected from digesting itself by a lining of mucus that is resistant to acid attack. If this mucus lining is breached, however, acid can get through to the stomach wall and start digesting it, leading to inflammation and pain (gastritis).

Gastritis produces symptoms similar to those of a stomach ulcer, with burning or gnawing pain in the upper abdomen, nausea and vomiting. If gastritis is severe, you may even vomit and bring up blood-stained fluids (haematemesis). As the blood has usually been partly digested, it is clotted and dark, resembling dark brown tea leaves or ground coffee.

Acute gastritis can be triggered by drugs that irritate the stomach lining. These include tobacco, alcohol, and aspirin, ibuprofen and other anti-inflammatory drugs used to treat musculoskeletal problems such as arthritis or sports injuries.

Helicobacter pylori

The main cause of gastritis is now known to be infection of the stomach with a bacterium called *Helicobacter pylori*. In the UK, at least 20 per cent of 30-year-old adults and 50 per cent of those over 50 are infected. In some parts of the world up to 90 per cent of 20-year-olds are infected.

Helicobacter pylori is a mobile bacterium that can move around thanks to small whip-like propellers (flagellae). The bacteria burrows into the mucus lining of the stomach to avoid stomach acids, leaving a small breach in the wall through which acids can reach the stomach wall. *Helicobacter* then makes a special enzyme, urease, which it uses to coat itself with a small bubble of alkaline ammonia gas. This keeps the bacteria safe from acid attack and, at the same time, irritates your stomach wall leading to more inflammation. This also lets Candida yeast cells penetrate through to the gut wall so they are protected from acid attack and can start to invade your tissues if your immunity is low.

Helicobacter pylori can be diagnosed through:

- blood tests to look for antibodies to the bacteria
- breath tests – swallowing radioactive urea and breathing into a sealed bag after half an hour. If *Helicobacter* is present, its enzyme, urease, will convert urea to ammonia and radioactive ammonia will be detected in the bag.
- picking up signs of infection from saliva
- testing stomach biopsies taken during endoscopy for signs of infection.

Once diagnosed, *Helicobacter* can be eradicated by a mixture of two antibiotics plus bismuth (triple therapy) or one antibiotic plus a drug that stops the stomach from making acid (double therapy). Unfortunately, treatment (especially triple therapy) is unpleasant and can cause side-effects of sore mouth, unpleasant metallic after-taste, nausea, diarrhoea, abdominal pain and blackening of the stools and tongue. One in five patients drops out of treatment with triple therapy, although double therapy is better tolerated.

Some research from New Zealand suggests that honey made from the flower of the Manuka, or New Zealand Tea Tree, contains a unique antibiotic that can also eradicate *Helicobacter*. Taking 4 teaspoons of Manuka honey 4 times a day on an empty stomach for 8 weeks can wipe out the infection. Manuka honey is available in larger healthfood shops. If following an anti-Candida regime, however, you may wish to avoid taking honey. *NB:* If you suffer from diabetes, you should consult your doctor before using a honey treatment.

Peptic Ulcers

If erosion of the mucus lining is extensive, acid attack will lead to a raw area on the stomach wall known as a gastric ulcer. 1 in 30 adults suffers from stomach ulcers at some time in life, with men being twice as likely to develop the condition as women. It tends to come on in the age range 30–50, some 10–20 years later than duodenal ulceration. In the UK, up to a million people suffer from stomach ulcers each year, of which 9 out of 10 are a recurrence of a previous problem. Half of all patients with a stomach ulcer will have a recurrence within 2 years.

Infection with the stomach bacteria *Helicobacter pylori* is linked with 85 per cent of stomach ulcers and virtually all peptic ulcers in the duodenum (upper part of the small intestine). In addition, 1 in 3 peptic ulcers contains signs of Candida infection.

A peptic ulcer in the stomach (gastric ulcer) can produce symptoms of:

- gnawing, burning pain in the upper abdomen beneath the ribs
- pain that is usually relieved by antacids
- pain that is usually relieved by vomiting
- pain that is usually made worse by eating.

To reduce the risk of a stomach ulcer:

- Stop smoking.
- Avoid drinking alcohol, which can cause a chemical inflammation of the stomach wall (alcoholic gastritis).
- Cut right back on intakes of tea and coffee.
- Avoid aspirin and related drugs such as ibuprofen.
- Eat several small meals per day rather than 3 larger ones.
- Try to avoid stress and take regular rest and relaxation.
- Follow a relatively bland diet, avoiding foods that are excessively acidic, hot or spicy.

CANDIDA INFECTIONS OF THE SMALL INTESTINES

Normally, the contents of the jejunum (first 40 per cent of the small bowel below the duodenum) are virtually sterile. This is due to the digestive enzymes present, and the fact that the semi-solid porridge-like contents of the gut (chyme) pass through relatively quickly to flush any surviving bacteria and yeast cells through. Despite this, Candida have been isolated from the duodenal secretions of 1 in 25 healthy volunteers sampled using a naso-gastric tube, and from the jejunum of 1 in 2 apparently normal and healthy adults. As samples are taken lower and lower throughout the small intestines, the likelihood of finding Candida species increases. This implies that yeast cells can survive exposure to the strong alkaline chemicals and enzymes which join the duodenum from the bile and pancreas. The fact that Candida can survive in concentrated bile is no longer in doubt, since yeasts can be grown from up to 2 per cent of gallbladders removed at operation (cholecystectomy).

Yeasts and bacteria can survive passage through the stomach to reach the small intestines (duodenum, jejunum, ileum) if:

- your stomach empties more quickly than usual, for example if you are suffering from gastroenteritis (when food seems to go straight through you)
- a large enough quantity of yeast cells are ingested

- the yeast cells are coated and protected, for example by extra-sticky mucus
- you have a peptic ulcer that acts as a source of continual infection
- you are taking antacid preparations which reduce stomach acidity
- stomach acidity falls off (as happens with increasing age)
- you have a medical condition in which production of stomach acids is lowered (for example achlorhydria).

Candida albicans is the species most frequently grown from the small intestines, followed by *C. tropicalis*, *C. parapsilosis*, *C. stellatoidea* and *C. guillermondii* plus other closely related yeasts such as *Torulopsis glabrata*.

Symptoms

In most cases, Candida in the gut is harmless and causes no problems. If it overgrows and invades the wall of the small intestines, however, it can produce symptoms such as:

- sensitivity to certain foods
- flatulence
- bloating
- nausea
- vomiting bile-stained fluids
- abdominal pain
- diarrhoea – which is usually watery, explosive, without blood or mucus, and comes and goes over several weeks
- ulceration of the intestinal wall leading to bleeding (blood lost from this part of the bowel will usually be dark red/brown/black by the time it reaches the anus).

Most people with Candida overgrowth of the small intestines have taken broad-spectrum antibiotics or suffer from malnutrition or a serious illness that lowers their natural immunity – especially in the elderly. This is not always the case, however, and a number of apparently well people have been found to have symptoms linked with Candida overgrowth in the small intestines.

One study reported 6 cases of small bowel Candidiasis in adults, 5 of whom had no obvious underlying illness or immune problem – and only 2 of whom had recently taken antibiotics. The main symptom was diarrhoea that lasted from 4 days to 3 months. As soon as a course of anti-fungal treatment (nystatin) was started, symptoms disappeared within 3–4 days.

In another study, 50 adults with recurrent diarrhoea and a variety of gastro-intestinal symptoms were found to have a heavy growth of *Candida albicans* in their stool which was thought to be the cause of their problem.

Babies can also suffer from diarrhoea as a result of Candida infection of the small intestines. When 96 newborn babies with oral thrush were investigated, all were found to have Candida in their faeces as well. Of these, 33 babies then developed diarrhoea and, when investigated, were found to have strands of actively growing yeast colonies (hyphae and mycelium) in their bowel motions. All 33 got better with anti-fungal treatment. Six other babies developed diarrhoea but had only simple yeast cells in their stools – there were no signs of activation or overgrowth – and these did not respond to anti-fungal drugs. It is thought that diarrhoea in these 6 babies may have been linked with an allergic reaction to the yeast cells rather than to an infection itself.

Another study involving 24 babies with diarrhoea and positive stool cultures for Candida also reported that all got better within 1–8 days of starting anti-Candida treatment (nystatin).

Candida and Food Sensitivity

While overgrowth of Candida in the small intestines produces obvious inflammation which can be diagnosed and treated, the presence of non-invasive (that is, harmless) Candida in the gut is now also thought to be linked with an allergic hypersensitivity reaction. Some researchers believe this can trigger symptoms of Irritable Bowel Syndrome (IBS) – especially diarrhoea – in certain people. This may occur after taking antibiotics. Where recurrent diarrhoea is linked with hypersensitivity to yeast cells on skin testing, and where Candida are cultured from bowel motions, bowel symptoms have been shown to get worse when sufferers were given Candida extracts to eat.

Treatment to wipe out bowel Candida infection, plus a yeast-free diet (*see page 159*), have been found to help.

In many cases, however, anti-Candida treatment has not improved symptoms. Rather than dismissing Candida as a cause, researchers should instead look for another explanation in which Candida may play a role. It may be that an overgrowth of Candida has damaged the bowel wall enough to make it leaky, so that other chemicals – including partially digested food particles – which do not usually reach the bloodstream are absorbed. This may set up an immune response known as immuno-antagonism (*see page 108*). Candida overgrowth has therefore acted as a trigger for the problem even if it has not caused it directly. Once the damage is done and the bowel and immune system are sensitized to these food particles, treatment to eradicate the yeast overgrowth could not be expected to help. A diet eliminating the foods to which you are sensitive may help to solve the problem, however.

Investigation

Candida infection of the small bowel may be investigated with abdominal x-rays to look for signs of thickened and dilated loops of bowel. Endoscopic examination and small bowel biopsy will show yeast infiltration of tissues.

In severe cases, endoscopy of the duodenum and upper jejunum may reveal multiple small white patches (plaques) and ulceration in the bowel wall. This leads to swelling of the bowel lining and dilation of loops of bowel.

Occasionally, it may be necessary to take a biopsy of the lower part of the jejunum. This is achieved using a small, cylindrical device (called a Crosby capsule) that is attached to 2 metres of polyethylene tubing. The tubing is filled with saline and the capsule swallowed so that the tubing trails from the mouth as the capsule progresses through the bowel. Its position is monitored by x-ray, or positioned using an endoscopic viewing instrument. When the capsule is in the lower part of the small jejunum, a syringe is attached to the end of the tubing and suction produces a slight vacuum. This gently pulls the bowel lining up against a small hole in the capsule. A spring-loaded knife-blade within the capsule is then activated to snip off a tiny piece of the bowel lining. The capsule is then gently pulled back up through the gut to retrieve the biopsy. This test has been widely used for almost 40 years and seems to be safe. It has a few drawbacks, however:

■ It is relatively time-consuming.
■ The capsule, once withdrawn, is frequently found to be empty.
■ the capsule can become detached from its tubing during withdrawal so that the stools have to be collected and sieved for several days afterwards to retrieve the cylinder.

Treatment

Nystatin, Fluconazole, Ketoconazole, Miconazole, Amphotericin: *see page 86* for dosages.

Duodenal Ulcers

Inflammation of the duodenum (duodenitis) and duodenal ulceration increase the risk of Candida infection in the small intestines. Duodenal ulcers affect around 15 per cent of adults at some time in their life. It is most common among those aged 20–40 years. Some 60 per cent of sufferers with a duodenal ulcer will have a recurrence within 1 year.

The symptoms of duodenal ulceration include:
■ gnawing, burning pain in the upper abdomen
■ burning pain that tends to come on when hungry
■ burning pain that tends to come on at night
■ pain that is relieved by antacids
■ pain that is relieved by eating, as this triggers the release of alkaline duodenal secretions which help to neutralize excess acid in this part of the gut
■ flatulence.

Like gastric ulceration, duodenal ulcers are also linked with the bacteria *Helicobacter pylori*. Measures to help prevent duodenal ulcers are similar to those for stomach ulcers (*see page 89*).

CANDIDA INFECTIONS OF THE LARGE INTESTINES

The large intestines are made up of the colon, the rectum and the anal canal. The colon consists of 5 parts: the caecum plus appendix (counts as one), and the ascending, transverse, descending and sigmoid colon. The lining of the large bowel (mucosa) is different from that found in the small intestines – it does not contain absorption villi, only colonic glands that secrete lubricating mucus. The three muscle layers of the gut are also arranged differently in the large bowel compared with those of the stomach and small intestines. The outer layer of muscle fibres are collected together into three longitudinal bands (*taenia coli*). Because these bands are shorter than the rest of the colon, they act rather like drawstrings to pull the colonic wall into out-pouchings known as haustra. These pouches provide an ideal hiding place for bacteria and yeast cells. Mucus production is mainly stimulated by the mechanical contact of faeces with the colon wall.

Once food reaches the large bowel, most nutrients have already been absorbed. The large intestines are mainly concerned with taking up excess fluid, salts and minerals from the bowel contents. After passing through the large bowel, semi-liquid bowel contents are transformed into solidified waste matter as 90 per cent of their fluid content is absorbed – of around 2 litres of bowel contents received into the colon each day, only 200–250 ml of semi-solid waste remains for voiding.

While a few bacteria are normally found in the small intestines, it is not until the colon that masses of bacteria are seen. These bowel bacteria are usually beneficial, in that they:

- ferment and help to break down undigested fibre
- bulk up the stools to make defecation easier – over half the weight of your stools consists of bacteria
- compete for nutrients with potentially harmful bacteria and yeasts (such as Candida), which helps to stop them overgrowing
- make acids and natural antibiotics/anti-fungal substances which inhibit the growth of other organisms

- make and secrete vitamin K, B group vitamins, biotin and folic acid, which can be absorbed and used in the body
- absorb some cholesterol and fatty acids from the gut, preventing their reabsorption – when some antibiotics are given, blood cholesterol levels (especially of the more harmful LDL-cholesterol) can go up.

Candida can be grown from rectal swabs in 30 per cent of healthy people who have no symptoms of ill-health – the yeast cells are present as harmless commensals. If conditions in the large bowel change to favour Candida overgrowth (for example if normal bowel bacteria are killed by a prolonged course of antibiotics), symptoms such as bloating, loose stools and flatulence may develop. Candida can be grown from the stools of as many as 8 out of 10 people with these problems.

Symptoms

Symptoms of Candida infection of the large intestines include:

- sensitivity to certain foods
- flatulence
- bloating
- watery diarrhoea, usually without blood or excess mucus
- constipation
- uncomfortable spasm and straining when trying to pass a stool (tenesmus)
- problems similar to those of Irritable Bowel Syndrome.

Some researchers feel that diarrhoea can also be triggered in some people without an overgrowth of Candida as a result of an allergic reaction to Candida products absorbed from the bowel (*see page 91*).

Candida and Irritable Bowel Syndrome

Irritable Bowel Syndrome (IBS) is the most common condition to affect the gut. It is a problem of bowel function rather than structure, and as a result there is nothing abnormal to find during investigations and no obvious clues to help with the diagnosis. IBS is therefore referred to as a functional problem rather than an organic one. It seems to be linked with abnormal or exaggerated bowel movements and muscular spasm. To diagnose IBS, there must be *at least 3 months, continuous or recurrent symptoms of abdominal pain or discomfort which is:*

- relieved by defecation
- and/or associated with a change in frequency of passing stool
- and/or associated with a change in the consistency of stool

plus two or more of the following, on at least a quarter of occasions or days:

- altered stool frequency
- altered stool form (lumpy/hard or loose/watery)
- altered stool passage (straining, urgency, or feeling of incomplete evacuation)
- passage of mucus
- bloating or feeling of abdominal distension.

Altered stool frequency is usually taken to mean more than 3 bowel movements per day, or less than 3 bowel movements per week. Different people, however, have their own individual sense of what is normal for them, and it is this which changes in bowel habit are measured against.

Irritable Bowel Syndrome is increasingly common. At least a third of the population is affected at some time during life, even if only mildly. Overall, 15 per cent of people are affected badly enough to consult their doctor.

While overgrowth of Candida in the gut produces ulceration and inflammation which can be diagnosed and treated, the presence of non-invasive (that is, harmless) Candida in the bowel is now also thought to trigger IBS symptoms – especially diarrhoea – in certain people. This is believed to be linked with an allergic hypersensitivity reaction which may occur after a bout of gastroenteritis or taking antibiotics. Both disrupt the normal balance of bacteria found in the bowel, affect the normal process of fermentation in the colon, and change the amount and composition of bowel gases produced.

Many people with IBS develop symptoms for the first time after an attack of gastroenteritis (bowel infection). During 1994, 38 victims of an outbreak of Salmonella food poisoning were studied by researchers; over the next year, almost a third (12 out of 38–32 per cent) went on to develop recurrent bowel symptoms consistent with IBS. In most cases, they developed intermittent diarrhoea. Those with the worst symptoms of gastroenteritis (diarrhoea lasting longer than 7 days plus vomiting leading to weight loss) were more likely to develop IBS than those with milder symptoms. They were also the ones who took longer to recover their appetite, weight and energy levels.

Another study looked at 75 patients who developed gastroenteritis (from various organisms) that was bad enough for them to be admitted to hospital. Of these, 22 (29 per cent) had symptoms 3 months later that were consistent with IBS. Nine out of 10 of these were still suffering after 6 months, and three-quarters still had IBS problems 1 year later. As in the first study, those with the worst symptoms (longer-lasting diarrhoea, with abdominal pain and mucus in the stools) were more likely to develop IBS.

Researchers are unclear why bacterial bowel infections are linked with IBS, but a sensitivity to Candida products, or to a yeast overgrowth which somehow interferes with normal bowel function, have been suggested as possibilities.

While taking a course of antibiotics, it is worth eating live (unpasteurized) BIO yoghurt containing organisms such as *Lactobacillus acidophilus*, or a drink (sold as Yakult) containing *Lactobacillus casei* Shirota. There is evidence that these bacteria can survive the journey through the stomach and small intestines to reach the bowel and recolonize the large intestines with friendly bacteria. This can help to damp down Candida overgrowth. Many IBS sufferers claim that eating BIO yoghurt every day keeps their symptoms under control – whether they have recently taken antibiotics or not.

Altogether, bowel micro-organisms – including yeasts – make up around 30 per cent of normal stool bulk:

Stools contain:

water   75 per cent
solids   25 per cent

Of which:

- around 30 per cent = bacteria and some yeasts
- around 15 per cent = inorganic material (for example calcium and phosphates)
- around 5 per cent = fats
- a varying amount is undigested plant fibre (roughage) depending on diet
- a small amount of desquamated (shed) bowel lining cells, mucus and digestive enzymes.

Investigation

Investigation of large bowel symptoms may involve:

- an abdominal examination
- a digital (finger) rectal examination
- stool cultures to look for bacteria or Candida – although if yeast cells are found they may not be reported if they are in their simple cell form (no hyphae) and are assumed to be a normal part of the bowel flora
- testing for hidden blood (faecal occult blood) which may be a sign of inflammation or possibly a tumour
- ultrasound to look for abnormal masses
- proctoscopy – insertion of a speculum to examine the inner walls of the rectum to look for inflammation or ulceration
- sygmoidoscopy – insertion of a tube with a light on the end to examine the inner lining of the lower (sigmoid) colon and to biopsy any lesions seen
- colonoscopy – insertion of a longer, flexible instrument similar to a sigmoidoscope, to inspect further up the colon. You will be given a powerful laxative (or oral bowel cleansing solution) to take beforehand which acts within 10–14 hours. This helps to empty the bowel and provide a better view. You will probably be sedated during the procedure.
- a barium enema – coating the bowel lining with a substance that shows up on x-ray, such as barium sulphate. Before

having a barium enema you will be asked not to eat anything the night before, and to drink plenty of fluids instead. You will also be given a powerful laxative to empty your bowel so that faeces don't get in the way of the test.

■ a test for deficiency of the enzyme, lactase – which can also cause symptoms such as bowel distension, pain, flatulence and diarrhoea.

Where recurrent diarrhoea is linked with hypersensitivity to yeast cells on skin testing (not often performed on the NHS) and where Candida are cultured from bowel motions, bowel symptoms have been shown to get worse on being given Candida extracts to eat. Treatment to wipe out bowel Candida infection, plus a yeast-free diet (*see page 159*) may help.

Treatment

Nystatin, Fluconazole, Ketoconazole, Miconazole, Amphotericin: *see page 86* for dosages.

Prevention

Try to eat more fibre – every gram of dietary fibre increases stool weight by around 5 g. This is because fibre provides fermentable food for bacteria, allowing them to grow and divide – to compete with Candida cells. Fibre is also thought to bind Candida toxins in the gut, helping to move yeast cells downwards; this may relieve symptoms.

Drink plenty of fluids to bulk up dietary fibre.

Eat natural BIO yoghurt containing *Lactobacillus acidophilus*, or a drink containing *Lactobacillus casei* Shirota.

Stop smoking, and try to avoid passive smoking, too. Receptors in the gut react with nicotine and affect bowel function, which may make symptoms worse.

Increase the amount of exercise you take. This improves bowel function and can help to relieve symptoms of bloating and distension.

Try to avoid unnecessary stress – the intestines contain receptors which interact with stress hormones and can make symptoms worse.

Try following an anti-Candida diet (*see Chapter 10*) to see if this helps.

ANAL ITCHING

Everyone suffers from anal itching at some time in life – in the UK, around half a million people receive treatment for the condition each year. For some reason, it seems to attack men more than women. It is usually worse at night and when increased sweating occurs – as a result of central heating being set at too high a temperature, warm weather, taking part in vigorous sport, or sitting for long periods of time. There are many different causes:

- thrush (fungal infection)
- poor hygiene after opening the bowels
- wearing tight, nylon underwear
- threadworms
- an allergy to cloth dyes or washing powders
- eating spicy foods
- drinking excessive amounts of caffeine
- haemorrhoids (piles)
- anal fissures
- anal skin tags
- genital warts
- infestations such as scabies or pubic lice
- skin diseases such as eczema or psoriasis
- other medical problems such as diabetes, anaemia or vitamin deficiency.

In half of all cases, no obvious cause is found.

Even if an itchy bottom isn't originally due to a Candida infection, it will soon lead to anal thrush if constant scratching damages the surrounding skin. Candida is present in the faeces of up to 80 per cent of the population and will rapidly overgrow when skin is broken and conditions are warm and moist.

Symptoms

- intense itching
- soreness, especially on wiping the bottom
- moist discharge
- weeping sores
- discomfort on opening the bowels
- difficulty opening the bowels
- worsening of symptoms due to piles.

Investigation

In most cases, no investigations are necessary. A swab may be sent for analysis if a diagnosis of thrush is not obvious – this will also help to pick up a bacterial infection and threadworm eggs.

Treatment

Anal itching caused by Candida is treated with anti-fungal creams such as Clotrimazole. For non-infective itching, or itching due to haemorrhoids (piles), over-the-counter remedies such as Anusol, Germaloids, Hemocane or Preparation H can be used. In general, a cream formulation is less messy and uncomfortable than an ointment, although an ointment is more soothing if you are sore or have intense itching.

If symptoms persist for more than a few days, do consult your doctor. Stronger agents are available on prescription – including a new spray treatment (Perinal) containing a local anaesthetic and an anti-inflammatory agent.

Prevention

- Bathe or shower every day using unperfumed soap.
- Use wet wipes and soft toilet roll – not rough, medicated paper.
- Wipe your bottom correctly (from front to back).
- Wash the area with unperfumed soap after every bowel movement – using water alone will not remove greasy residues.

- Dry the anus thoroughly by patting it gently with a soft towel (a rough one will only make matters worse) – or use a hair-dryer set on gentle heat.
- Wear loose cotton underwear, changing it at least once per day.
- Avoid using talcum powder – although an anti-fungal powder spray can be helpful.
- Eat a mild, non-spicy diet and go easy on caffeine.
- If you keep scratching at night, try wearing cotton underwear and even cotton gloves.
- Take steps to reduce Candida colonization of your bowel (*see page 86*).

Threadworms

A threadworm infestation involves a small, parasitic worm called *Enterobius vermicularis*. Threadworms are also known as pinworms, as the mature female has a blunt head and a long, thin, pointed tail. Threadworms commonly infect the gut; as many as one in five children may carry them at any one time. The female threadworm is around 1 cm long and white. She comes out of the anus, mainly at night, to lay her eggs; she may deposit as many as 10,000 in one go. This causes a strong tickling sensation which makes you scratch, often in your sleep. Eggs are then deposited on the fingers and frequently transferred back to the mouth to set up a cycle of (faeco-oral) infection. Eggs can also be passed on to toys, blankets, etc., where they may survive for up to 3 weeks, increasing the chance of infecting others. Diagnosis is simple as the worms can usually be seen around the anus and on the surface of bowel motions.

Apart from causing itching, threadworms do not seem to cause any harm. If you can stop scratching at night, the infection will disappear spontaneously within a few weeks. Ointments can stop anal itching, or a drug treatment, piperazine, can be bought from pharmacies. The dose needs to be repeated after 2 weeks. The whole family may need to be treated.

BREAKING THE RE-INFESTATION CYCLE

- Wear pyjamas to minimize direct scratching of the anus.
- Have a bath/shower every morning to remove eggs laid overnight.
- Change sheets and nightwear frequently (nightly if possible).
- Wash sheets and nightwear at high temperatures, then press with a hot iron to kill the eggs.
- Keep fingernails short.
- Wash hands thoroughly and scrub with a nailbrush after visiting the bathroom and before each meal.
- Eating garlic, carrots and pumpkin seeds are all said to help clear the infection.
- Herbalists may prescribe Wormwood, Tansy or Male Fern, which have purgatives that can help to clear the infection.

Chapter Seven

SYSTEMIC AND CHRONIC CANDIDA INFECTION

SYSTEMIC CANDIDA

The most serious type of Candida infection is systemic Candidiasis, in which yeast cells spread throughout the body to infect two or more organs such as the liver, kidneys, lungs, heart, spleen or brain. As you can imagine, this only usually occurs where there is a major breakdown in immune defences.

Candida yeasts mainly enter the body from the intestines. This is known as translocation and was first proved by a brave doctor volunteer who drank a solution containing 1 billion Candida yeast cells. He developed signs of blood infection (fever and shakes) within 3 hours. Yeast cells were found in his bloodstream and urine within 6 hours.

Further research suggests that live yeast cells can move across the bowel lining into the bloodstream and lymphatic system from all parts of the digestive system, but mainly from the jejunum in the small intestines. Blood from the intestines contains absorbed nutrients and travels straight to the liver, so this is usually the first organ to show signs of a systemic Candida infection (for example small abscesses), closely followed by the spleen, which filters cells and infections from the blood. Candida yeast cells can also cross into the circulation from the lungs, but this is thought to account for only 3 per cent of systemic Candida infections.

Usually, Candida yeast cells only enter the circulation if:

- a very large number of organisms are present and swamp the system
- the normal bacterial content of the gut is disrupted leading

to Candida overgrowth (for example after a prolonged course of antibiotics)

- the immune system is suppressed (for example by drugs or illness)
- the lining of the gut is damaged (for example by peptic ulceration)
- blood flow to the gut wall is reduced (for example in the case of shock).

When only a small number of yeast cells are involved, these are usually quickly mopped up by macrophage scavenger cells or neutrophil pus cells, unless the immune system is under strain. As a result, systemic Candidiasis usually only develops in people who have:

- cancer – especially one involving the blood such as leukaemia or lymphoma
- poor immunity due to drug treatment (for example for organ transplants or cancer)
- had a major operation and are on intravenous antibiotics
- AIDS.

Treatment

Options include:

- Itraconazole by mouth
- Ketoconazole by mouth
- Flucytosine by intravenous injection
- Amphotericin by intravenous injection
- Fluconazole by intravenous injection.

CHRONIC CANDIDA INFECTION

For many years *Candida albicans* was thought to be a relatively harmless organism, or one that only caused nuisance problems such as recurrent vaginal thrush. More and more people are now convinced that a large number of common symptoms are linked with a chronic (long-term) sensitivity to *Candida albicans* yeasts. This is known as the Candida hypersensitivity syndrome. These recurrent symptoms may include:

- fatigue
- tiredness all the time
- irritability
- anxiety
- depression
- insomnia
- difficulty concentrating
- headache
- joint and muscle pains
- sugar and carbohydrate cravings
- recurrent cystitis where no evidence of infection is found
- Irritable Bowel Syndrome (IBS)
- alcohol intolerance
- problems after taking antibiotics.

Despite the fact that this is a controversial area, many researchers and doctors are starting to believe that Candida hypersensitivity, or some form of food intolerance, is linked with other long-term problems such as:

- pre-menstrual syndrome
- chronic fatigue syndrome (also known as ME)
- asthma
- eczema
- arthritis
- IBS
- cellulite.

These symptoms and conditions are not due to an overgrowth of Candida or invasion of tissues with yeast cells as such, and anti-fungal treatments do not seem to help.

Some researchers have suggested that the problem is due to an oversensitivity of the immune system to Candida proteins. These are absorbed from the gut into the bloodstream and interact with antibodies and immune cells to trigger symptoms.

These antibodies may persist and attack other parts of the body to continue causing problems even when the original Candida infection is long gone. Although there is no proof of this at present it is known that, in conditions in which antibodies bind to foreign proteins to form circulating soluble complexes, symptoms such as fatigue and feeling non-specifically unwell (malaise) usually occur.

It is also possible that the normal presence of Candida yeast cells living relatively harmlessly in the gut makes the intestinal lining more leaky, so that incompletely digested food particles can enter the circulation more easily. Once this leakiness has occurred, the immune system may become sensitized to these food particles to produce a variety of symptoms. This would explain why anti-fungal drugs do not seem to improve the problem.

Food Allergy and Intolerance

Food intolerance and allergy is an interesting but controversial topic. Food intolerance is defined as a reproducible, adverse reaction to a specific food or ingredient which occurs even when the food is eaten in a disguised form. It is relatively common. In contrast, a food allergy is a relatively rare form of food intolerance in which an abnormal immune response triggers a potentially devastating chain of reactions in the body, often involving the production of histamine and a type of antibody called IgE.

There are several medically accepted types of food intolerance and allergy, including:

- severe anaphylactic reaction – with life-threatening symptoms (falling blood pressure, difficulty breathing, tissue swelling) triggered by foods such as peanuts
- hypersensitivity – with widespread, itchy rash (urticaria), eczema, asthma, vomiting, abdominal pains or diarrhoea when eating foods such as strawberries, eggs or shellfish
- food sensitivity – chemicals in chocolate, cheese or red wine, for example, can trigger migraine
- lactose intolerance – due to the inability to digest lactose

sugar in milk, causing bloating, abdominal pain and diarrhoea

■ gluten intolerance – causing bloating, abdominal pain, bulky stools, malabsorption and weight loss (coeliac disease).

The type of food reaction that has been linked with Candida is different from these, and is not really an allergy at all. It is closer to a food intolerance; some researchers have labelled it an immuno-antagonism. The area is controversial, but the theory goes that when food is eaten, it is broken down in the intestines into small building-blocks (proteins are broken down into amino acids, fats into fatty acids and carbohydrates into simple sugars) before being absorbed. In some cases, however, it is thought that certain foods, to which your immune system is sensitive, make your intestinal wall porous. It is thought that this leakiness may be linked to the presence of Candida cells. This lets incompletely digested food particles enter your bloodstream. This theory is supported by research in which proteins from egg yolk and cow's milk have been found in human breastmilk. The only logical way in which they could have got there was through the bloodstream from the gut.

Once in the circulation, food particles to which you are sensitive are quickly attacked by the immune system, coated by immune proteins and destroyed by white blood cells called neutrophils (pus cells). If you eat too many of the foods to which you are sensitive, however, it is thought that your immune system becomes swamped. You run out of complement proteins, and incompletely coated food particles are free to roam around your body. This challenge to the immune system has been linked with feelings of being tired all the time. The food particles are eventually filtered out in the kidney and destroyed, but may set up immune reactions in different parts of the body linked with the chronic illnesses mentioned above.

At present this is just a theory and there is no firm evidence to confirm it, although much research continues in the area.

Researchers have found that the people most likely to have a food sensitivity and who respond best to avoiding certain foods (for example by following an anti-Candida diet) are those who suffer from chronic diarrhoea.

Elimination Diet

The diagnosis of food intolerance and allergy can only be made with any degree of reliability when symptoms disappear during an elimination diet and reappear when the suspected food is reintroduced – even in a hidden form.

There are several degrees of an exclusion diet:

- simple exclusion, with the elimination of a single food
- multiple exclusion – elimination of several foods which have been linked with a particular health problem
- restriction diet – which consists of eating very few foods, for example nothing but a single meat (for example lamb), a single source of carbohydrate (such as rice) and a single fruit (for example pears) and drinking only spring, mineral or distilled water.

After following the elimination diet until symptoms have disappeared (commonly 10–21 days), the eliminated foods are reintroduced one by one, usually at 3-day intervals, to see which triggers a recurrence. You will need to keep a careful food and symptom diary during this time. Following an elimination diet is time-consuming, can be boring, and requires a great deal of motivation.

There are many other tests that can be arranged to test for food sensitivity.

Sublingual Testing

A few drops of a solution containing the food to which you are thought to be intolerant (and which you haven't eaten recently) are placed under your tongue and your response noted. There is a possible risk of an anaphylactic reaction if you are highly sensitive to the food (for example peanuts) and swelling of the tongue and throat may occur, although this is rare. In most cases, unfortunately, this test proves inconclusive.

Food Challenge Tests

The food to which you are thought to be sensitive is given orally and your response noted. This can be helpful in establishing whether a particular food triggers symptoms but where there is a risk of a severe allergic response (anaphylaxis). It should only be carried out under close medical supervision.

Skin Contact Tests
These are sometimes used to investigate food allergies. A diluted extract is placed on the skin, and if a reaction occurs, allergy is said to be present. No one is sure how useful these tests are, as many false results occur.

Skin Prick Tests
A substance you are thought to be allergic to is applied to the skin; the substance is then pricked into your skin with a fine, sterile needle. Measuring the size of weal produced shows how severe the reaction is – for a positive result, a visible skin reaction usually covers an area at least 1 cm square around the injection site. False results (positive and negative) are common, so results should be interpreted with caution. When performed by a specialist, the area showing the skin reaction may be biopsied, stained and examined under a microscope to look for the presence of immune cells. Skin tests in which an allergic substance is pricked into the lower levels of the skin (intradermal tests) can prove dangerous, as they may trigger a severe allergic reaction.

Hair and Nail Analysis
While this may provide useful information on vitamin and mineral deficiencies, it has no proven benefit in helping to diagnose food intolerance.

Pulse Testing
Some researchers believe that, after eating a food to which you are intolerant, your pulse rate will go up. This is not reliable, however, as many factors affect the pulse rate, including anxiety, exercise, certain drugs and smoking cigarettes.

Antibody Screening
This can detect true allergy by looking for special allergy antibodies known as IgE. The technique, known as RAST (radio-allergosorbent test), measures specific IgE antibody levels in

response to the suspected allergen. Unfortunately the test is not that sensitive – false positives and negatives occur, so results must be interpreted with caution. Some patients with little specific IgE may have severe allergic symptoms, while someone with lots of specific IgE can have few symptoms.

The LEAP Test

A sample of blood is split and incubated with 50 or 100 food extracts for $1^1/2$ hours. All the white cells in the sample are then analysed to see if they have changed in size. If the white cells (neutrophils) in a sample have changed in size by more than 9 per cent, or if they have disintegrated, it suggests you are sensitive to that food. You can also be tested for sensitivity to 20 natural and man-made chemicals and fungi, including Candida.

This testing is controversial. For more information about the LEAP programme, contact Oxford Nutritional Services on 01703 222007.

NuTron Test

This takes food intolerance testing even further. A sample of blood is split and incubated with 92 food extracts (including yeasts) for 1 hour. The neutrophils in the sample are then analysed. As well as determining whether they become larger, smaller or disintegrate, radio-frequency waves and direct current testing detects other changes inside the cells (such as the formation of vacuoles, granulation) which would be missed by simply measuring cell volume. If any changes are found, you are said to be sensitive to that food.

This testing is controversial. For more information, phone NuTron Laboratories on 01483 203555.

Food Allergen Cellular Test (FACT)

Immune cells (including neutrophils, basophils, eosinophils) are incubated with food samples and the chemicals released by the cells are analysed to determine which foods you are sensitive to.

This testing is controversial. For more information about FACT, contact the Institute of Individual Well-Being, 0171–495 7040.

Other recurrent problems linked with food intolerance include:

- migraine
- eczema and psoriasis
- rheumatoid arthritis
- depression
- tinnitus
- fluid retention and weight gain
- palpitations and breathlessness
- nasal congestion (rhinitis)
- myalgic encephalomyelitis (ME)

Chronic Mucocutaneous Candida

Some people with chronic recurrent Candida infections do suffer from an obvious Candida overgrowth which can be confirmed by finding activated yeast cells in the hyphae form. This is known as Chronic Mucocutaneous Candidiasis. It can affect any one of any age, but sufferers commonly fall into the following groups:

- infants under the age of 3 – with persistent or recurrent nappy rash and/or oral thrush with widespread skin involvement
- teenagers – possibly linked with taking long-term antibiotics for acne, which allows the growth of Candida in the intestinal tract or vagina
- young adults – possibly linked with use of inhaled steroids for asthma, with an abnormality of the thymus (a gland in the chest where immune T-cells are programmed) or with HIV
- women of reproductive age with recurrent vaginal thrush – may be linked with iron deficiency
- women of reproductive age with chronic mouth Candidiasis but no skin or nail problems – linked with iron deficiency
- older people with chronic mouth problems – linked to wearing dentures (denture stomatitis).

These chronic Candida infections involve the skin, nails and mucous membranes and may be hereditary in some families.

Infections respond to taking oral anti-fungal treatments – mouth thrush clears in 5–7 days and skin lesions improve within 2 weeks as normal, but signs of infection usually recur soon after treatment is stopped.

Research suggests that most people with chronic Candidiasis have defects in their immunity which make them more susceptible to infection of yeast cells. These defects are thought to involve the T lymphocytes, neutrophils (pus cells) or macrophages (scavenger cells), although some people have abnormalities with their B lymphocytes and antibody production.

Some sufferers have been found to have one or more poorly functioning endocrine (hormone) glands such as the thymus, adrenals, parathyroids, thyroid or ovaries.

A few people with chronic Candida infection develop patchy loss of skin pigmentation (vitiligo) or loss of hair (alopecia). This may affect a small area (alopecia areata) or be widespread (for example alopecia totalis).

One in five people with chronic recurrent Candidiasis also has recurrent problems with other types of fungal infections such as dermatophytes (*see page 27*). Others have repeated and often severe viral or bacterial chest infections.

Although sufferers develop recurrent Candida infections of the skin, nails and mucous membranes – including those in the gut – they do not seem to develop serious Candida invasion of the blood or organs (systemic Candidiasis).

Treatment

A variety of treatments has been tried to help overcome Chronic Mucocutaneous Candidiasis. These include long-term, daily use of anti-fungal mouth treatments such as lozenges, pastilles or gel for recurrent oral thrush, weekly use of pessaries for recurrent vaginal thrush and regular use of anti-fungal creams if only a small area of skin is affected. For more widespread problems, long-term treatment with anti-fungal tablets or capsules is needed, although there is a risk of side-effects (*see Chapter 8*) or the development of resistance to treatment. Symptoms will unfortunately return if treatment is stopped.

Various experimental treatments are being tried to correct the immune deficiency that causes an increased susceptibility to Candida. These include immunoglobulin, transplantation of bone marrow or thymus tissues, immune transfer factors and gene therapy.

An anti-Candida diet (*see Chapter 10*) will often help to improve symptoms by reducing the number of Candida cells present in the gut.

Chapter Eight

ANTI-CANDIDA DRUGS

Anti-Candida treatments mainly work by making fungal cell walls leaky, so yeasts swell with water, lose some of their contents, and quickly die.

Candida infections are usually treated with either a topical skin cream/gel/ointment, a pessary or concentrated cream for insertion into the vagina, or a tablet/suspension/capsule taken by mouth. In serious infections (for example systemic Candidiasis), an intravenous drug may be needed.

This chapter looks at some anti-fungal drugs, giving information on possible side-effects, those for whom the drugs may not be suitable, and which medications the drugs interact with. If you develop any side-effects that you think may be linked with your medication – even if not listed here – always tell your doctor. Do not take any drugs if you are pregnant or breastfeeding, except under medical advice.

TOPICAL PREPARATIONS

With topical preparations, the risk of side-effects is small and usually only involves mild burning – especially when applied to raw, inflamed skin or mucous membranes – and sometimes irritation. Hypersensitivity reactions such as itching, redness, swelling and an allergic-type rash may occasionally occur, but this is rare. Some creams (for example nystatin) may cause weakening or destruction of rubber contraceptive diaphragms or condoms.

ORAL DRUGS

If you need to take an oral anti-fungal agent and are already taking other medications – including those bought over the counter – always check with a pharmacist or doctor that the drugs will not interact.

Amphotericin

Amphotericin is not absorbed from the gut and, when given orally to treat intestinal yeast infections, is usually tolerated quite well. It can also be given into the veins to treat systemic Candidiasis, but does not penetrate body tissues very well and commonly causes side-effects by this route – a small test dose to check for sensitivity reactions is important. One preparation, in which amphotericin is bound to fat globules (liposomes), is much less toxic when given into the veins.

Possible side-effects of intravenous amphotericin include nausea and vomiting, diarrhoea, abdominal pain, fever, headache, muscle and joint pains, anaemia, salt imbalances, nerve problems (including hearing loss or fits), liver and kidney problems, allergic reactions, irritation at injection site.

Amphotericin should not be used during pregnancy or breastfeeding.

Fluconazole

Possible side-effects of fluconazole include gastro-intestinal symptoms (for example nausea, diarrhoea, flatulence, pain), rash and allergic reactions (rare).

Should not be taken during pregnancy or breastfeeding – nor by those with kidney problems except under medical supervision.

Oral fluconazole interacts with some drugs including anticoagulants, and with some drugs used to treat epilepsy, asthma or breathing problems, diabetes and heartburn/indigestion.

Intravenous fluconazole can be given for systemic Candidiasis.

Flucytosine

Given by intravenous injection to treat systemic Candidiasis. Tablets may also be used by certain patients.

Possible side-effects of flucytosine include gastric upsets, confusion, hallucinations, fits, headache, dizziness, sleepiness, liver or blood problems.

Should not be used in people with liver or kidney problems without monitoring blood tests. Should only be used cautiously in pregnancy or when breastfeeding.

Griseofulvin

Griseofulvin is inactive when used topically, but when taken by mouth is well absorbed from the gut and is taken up by cells containing keratin (skin, hair, nails). It must be used for several weeks or months to cure an infection, but side-effects are uncommon. Possible ones include headache, nausea, vomiting, allergic reactions, dizziness, fatigue, confusion, blood abnormalities, sensitivity to light, reduced tolerance to alcohol. Lupus erythematosus, erythema multiforme and epidermal necrolysis have rarely been reported.

Griseofulvin should not be taken by those with porphyria, liver disease or SLE, or during pregnancy.

Griseofulvin interacts with some drugs, including alcohol, anticoagulants, barbiturates and oral contraceptives.

Itraconazole

Possible side-effects with oral Itraconazole include nausea, abdominal pain, indigestion, constipation, headache, dizziness, period problems and allergic reactions. In long-term treatment, jaundice fluid retention or hair loss have been reported, albeit rarely.

Oral Itraconazole should not be used during pregnancy or breastfeeding. It is important to take proper contraceptive precautions before, during and for 1 month after taking a course of treatment. It should only be used with caution in people with liver problems.

Itraconazole can interact with some drugs, including antacids and some antihistamines.

Ketoconazole

Possible side-effects of oral ketoconazole include gastric upsets, rashes, headache, allergic reactions, altered liver function, nerve problems, low platelet count and breast enlargement plus low sperm count in males (rare). People taking ketoconazole usually have their liver function checked by blood tests at regular intervals after the first 2 weeks of treatment. Oral ketoconazole should not be used for superficial fungal infections because of the risk of liver damage during use.

Should not be taken during pregnancy or by people with liver problems.

Ketoconazole interacts with some other drugs, including antacids, some anti-epilepsy treatments and antihistamines. Absorption of oral ketoconazole depends on stomach acidity – treatment may fail if taken with antacids or ulcer-healing drugs.

Ketoconazole cream and shampoos are only available on prescription at NHS expense for people with seborrhoeic dermatitis, (for example dandruff) or pityriasis versicolor.

Miconazole

Possible side-effects of oral treatment include nausea and vomiting, itching and allergic rashes.

Oral tablets or gel should only be used under medical advice during pregnancy, and should be avoided by people with porphyria.

Miconazole interacts with some drugs, including anticoagulants, anticonvulsants, some anti-diabetes drugs, cisapride and amphotericin.

Nystatin

Nystatin is not absorbed from the gut when given by mouth. It is too toxic to be given intravenously.

Possible side-effects from oral nystatin include nausea, vomiting, diarrhoea, irritation, rash.

Oral nystatin should not be used during pregnancy or breast-feeding except under close medical supervision.

Terbinafine

Possible side-effects of oral terbinafine include stomach discomfort, loss of appetite, nausea, diarrhoea, headache, rash, joint pains, skin sensitivity, taste disturbance and jaundice (rare).

Should not be taken by people with liver or kidney problems, or during pregnancy or breastfeeding.

Terbinafine interacts with some drugs, including ulcer-healing drugs (cimetidine).

Chapter Nine

COMPLEMENTARY TREATMENTS

Many people suffering symptoms of chronic or recurrent Candida infection seek help from alternative therapists. There are many reasons for this:

■ Those with symptoms of Candida infections may feel their doctor is uninterested in the problem – in contrast, alternative practitioners take a holistic approach, which minimizes some patients' sense of abandonment.
■ Sufferers are often left feeling that their problems are due to an emotional cause which a holistic approach may be more successful in treating.
■ Orthodox medicine may be able to improve Candida symptoms for a short while, but in many cases the problems recur – it is then only natural to seek relief from the many complementary therapies available.
■ Alternative treatments are often helpful in relieving Candida symptoms without the side-effects associated with some drugs.

Before trying alternative treatments for your symptoms, make sure you have been fully investigated and the diagnosis of Candida has been confirmed by your doctor – sometimes other conditions can mimic recurrent thrush (for example anaerobic vaginosis, oral leukoplakia, Irritable Bowel Syndrome, skin diseases) and it is important that the correct diagnosis is made.

When choosing an alternative practitioner, bear in mind that standards of training and experience vary widely. Where possible:

- Select a therapist on the basis of personal recommendation from a satisfied client whom you know and whose opinion you trust.
- Check what qualifications the therapist has, and check his or her standing with the relevant umbrella organization for that therapy. This organization will be able to tell you what training their members have undertaken and their code of ethics, and can refer you to qualified practitioners in your area.
- Find out how long your course of treatment will last and how much it is likely to cost.
- Ask how much experience the practitioner has had in treating Candida, and about his or her success rate.

The following complementary therapies have helped many people with recurrent or chronic Candida but, just as with orthodox medicine, not every treatment will suit every individual.

ACUPUNCTURE

Acupuncture is based on the belief that life energy (*chi* or *qi*) flows through the body along 12 different channels called meridians. When this energy flow becomes blocked, symptoms of illness are triggered. By inserting fine needles into specific acupuncture points overlying these meridians, blockages are overcome and the flow of *qi* corrected or altered to relieve symptoms. Altogether, there are 365 acupoints in the body; your therapist will select which points to use depending on your individual symptoms. Fine, disposable needles are used, which cause little if any discomfort. You may notice a slight pricking sensation, or an odd tingling buzz as the needle is inserted a few millimetres into the skin. The needles are usually left in place for up to 20 minutes, and may be twiddled periodically. Sometimes a small cone of dried herbs is ignited and burned near the active acupoint to warm the skin. This is known as moxibustion. The best known effect of *qi* manipulation is pain relief (local anaesthesia). Research suggests that acupuncture causes the release of heroin-like chemicals (endorphins) in the body which act as natural painkillers. Acupuncture can be effective in treating the symptoms of Candida.

Acupressure is similar to acupuncture, but instead of inserting needles at selected points along the meridians, these points are stimulated using firm thumb pressure or fingertip massage. The best-known example of acupressure is Shiatsu massage.

AROMATHERAPY

The following oils have anti-fungal properties and can be diluted to massage into affected areas, or added to water to bathe lesions or help to prevent recurrences:

- Bergamot
- Cajeput
- German Chamomile (do not use during first 3 months of pregnancy)
- Eucalyptus oil
- Geranium (do not use during pregnancy)
- Lavender (not during first 3 months of pregnancy)
- Lemon
- Marjoram (not during pregnancy)
- Myrrh (not during pregnancy)
- Niaouli
- Palmarosa
- Patchouli
- Rosemary (do not use if you suffer from epilepsy or are pregnant)
- Tea Tree
- Thyme (not during pregnancy)
- Yarrow.

Always use aromatherapy oils in a diluted form (for example by adding to a carrier oil) as some neat oils can irritate tissues, especially ones that are already inflamed by a Candida infection. There are a few exceptions – small amounts of Rosemary or Lavender oils can be used neat on the skin as long as they don't irritate.

For Oral Thrush

- Rinse your mouth with a home-made mouthwash made by adding 3 drops Tea Tree and 1 drop Myrrh essential oils to a small glass of water. Stir the solution vigorously before using 3 times a day. Alternatively, use tincture of Myrrh.

For Vulvo-vaginal Thrush

- Add 5 drops each Tea Tree, Myrrh and Lavender to 30 ml carrier oil and add to your bath water. Lie in the water and soak for 20 minutes.

For Vulvo-vaginal Itching

- Add 2 drops of Tea Tree, Myrrh or Lavender to a little vitamin E cream, live Bio yoghurt or KY jelly and apply to the vulval area. Use as often as necessary to relieve symptoms.

For Itching around the Anus

- Add 5 drops each of Bergamot, Lavender and Geranium to 30 ml carrier oil. Add to your bath and soak for 20 minutes, or add a few drops to warm water and use to bathe the affected area as often as necessary.

For Balanitis

- Add 4 drops Tea Tree oil and 4 drops Lavender or Patchouli oil to a bowl of warm water and use to wash under the foreskin twice a day. Add the same oils to 30 ml carrier oil (preferably Jojoba) and apply to the end of the penis at night.

For Fungal Infections of Skin Folds

- Add 10 drops Eucalyptus and 5 drops Lavender to 30 ml carrier oil and add to bath water. Lie back and soak the affected area (groin, under the breasts) for 20 minutes. Add the same oils to a bowl of warm water and bathe the affected area twice a day.
- Use an aromatherapy dusting powder (*see below*) to keep skin folds fresh and dry after bathing.

For Fungal Infections of the Groin
- Dissolve 2 drops of Lavender, Cypress, Tea Tree or Patchouli oil in 30 ml carrier oil and apply to the area twice a day.
- Also add one or more of these oils to your bath water.

For Athlete's Foot
- Clean out debris from under and around the toenails (where infection often lurks), then bathe the cleaned foot in water to which you have added a few drops of Lavender, Myrrh, Palmarosa or Tea Tree essential oils.
- Add 1 drop of Lavender, Myrrh, Palmarosa or Tea Tree to 1 tablespoon of Calendula or Chamomile cream. Mix well and rub into the affected area.
- If the area is very moist, dissolve one or more of the above oils in surgical spirits and apply for a few days until the skin dries out.
- Use an aromatherapy dusting powder (*see below*) to keep feet fresh and dry after bathing – dust the inside of your shoes and socks with this powder, too.

For Ringworm on the Body
- Add 1 drop each of Myrrh, Lavender and Tea Tree essential oils to 1 tablespoon of Calendula or Chamomile cream and mix. Apply to skin lesions 3 times a day.
- 1 drop of neat Rosemary oil can be rubbed into small areas of skin if preferred.

For Ringworm on the Scalp
- Rub the scalp with a solution of Rosemary oil in water if scalp is dry. If lesions are moist, or scalp is greasy, add the Rosemary oil to a little surgical spirits and rub into the affected area once or twice a day.

Anti-fungal Dusting Powder

- 150 g pharmaceutical grade talc (from a chemist)
- 15 drops Tea Tree oil
- 10 drops Lavender
- 10 drops Rosemary
- 5 drops Bergamot

Mix in a blender and apply to skin folds and feet after washing to help prevent fungal infection.

HERBALISM

Phytotherapy – the use of plant extracts for healing – is one of the most exciting areas of medical research. Traditional herbs have provided orthodox medicine with many powerful drugs including aspirin (from the willow tree), digoxin (from the foxglove) and even potent new cancer treatments such as paclitaxel (from the Pacific Yew tree). World-wide, specialists known as ethnobiologists are continually seeking new products from among the traditional herbs used by native healers. The Amazon has proved to be one of the richest sources, providing a wide range of traditional remedies.

Different parts of different plants are used – roots, stems, flowers, leaves, bark, sap, fruit or seeds – depending on which has the highest concentration of active ingredient. In most cases these materials are dried and ground to produce a powder which is made into a tea, or packed into capsules for easy swallowing.

Aloe Vera

Aloe vera looks similar to a cactus but belongs to the lily family. There are many species of Aloe, or which four have medical uses. *Aloe barbadensis* (Aloe vera) is reputed to have the most useful medicinal properties.

Aloe gel is squeezed from the succulent leaves, which can grow to over 60 cm long. This gel contains a unique mix of vitamins, amino acids, enzymes and minerals which have been valued for their healing properties for over 6,000 years. When diluted to form a juice, the extract is said to increase energy and is widely used to help a wide range of illnesses. It contains substances that have several healing effects:

■ anti-inflammatory (anthraquinones and natural plant steroids)
■ hastens wound healing (fibroblast growth factor)
■ powerful antioxidants (vitamins C, E, betacarotene)
■ antiseptic (saponins and anthraquinones) against bacteria, viruses and fungi.

Aloe vera is helpful in the treatment of:
■ oral thrush
■ intestinal Candidiasis
■ heartburn
■ gastritis (inflammation of the stomach)
■ peptic ulcers
■ constipation
■ Irritable Bowel Syndrome (IBS)
■ Crohn's disease
■ colitis (inflammation of the colon)
■ diverticulitis
■ haemorrhoids (piles)
■ threadworms.

It is also widely used to help treat several skin conditions, arthritis, and ME.

Aloe vera juice can be made from fresh liquid extract (gel) or from powdered Aloe. The fresh gel has to be stabilized within hours of harvesting to prevent oxidation and deactivation. When selecting a product, aim for one made from 100 per cent pure Aloe vera. Its strength needs to be at least 40 per cent by volume (ideally approaching 95 per cent) to be effective. Also choose one that is made from Aloe liquid rather than powder. You may find it more palatable to choose a product containing a little natural fruit juice (for example grape, apple) to improve the flavour, although some people with Candida find that fruit juice makes their symptoms worse.

Some women using Aloe vera notice that it increases their menstrual flow. Aloe vera stimulates uterine contractions; for this reason it should not be used during pregnancy. Similarly, it should be avoided when breastfeeding as its active ingredients are excreted in breastmilk and can produce diarrhoea in the infant.

Dose

15–50 ml Aloe gel/juice per day. Start with a small dose (for example 1 teaspoon) and work up to around 1–2 tablespoons per day to find the dose that suits you best. Aloe has a powerful cathartic effect and taking too much will produce a brisk laxative response. Swill Aloe juice in the mouth to help oral thrush. Aloe gel can also be rubbed into skin ringworm lesions 3 times a day.

Echinacea (Purple Coneflower)

Echinacea, or Purple Coneflower, is known to boost the immune system and increase resistance to viral, fungal and bacterial infections. It is a traditional remedy used by Sioux Native Americans to treat blood poisoning, infections such as boils, and snake bite. It is used by herbalists to help prevent recurrent upper respiratory tract infections such as the common cold, laryngitis, tonsillitis or sinusitis, and to treat skin complaints. A tincture of Echinacea can be used as a mouthwash to treat and help to prevent recurrent oral thrush.

Dose

Capsules containing the powdered root (500 mg) or an infusion made from boiling 2 teaspoons Echinacea root in 200 ml water can be taken twice a day with meals, to complement the treatment of Candida infections. A tincture of Echinacea can be taken by mouth (4 ml) or applied undiluted to ringworm lesions 3 times a day.

Garlic (*Allium sativa*)

Garlic is a member of the Lily family. Its bulbs are divided into segments known as cloves. World-wide, each person eats an average of 1 clove garlic per day. The cloves contain a variety of volatile oils which have powerful antimicrobial actions. Garlic is effective against disease-causing bacteria, viruses and intestinal infections – including Candida – yet does not seem to harm beneficial intestinal bacteria such as *Lactobacillus*. Garlic can also be used externally to treat skin ringworm infections and warts, although some people develop a severe skin reaction – it is wise to protect surrounding skin with petroleum jelly and to wash the garlic juice off if the area becomes uncomfortable. The most common use of garlic is as a medication to lower blood pressure and reduce the risk of coronary heart disease.

Dose
Powdered garlic (in tablet form), 600–900 mg per day.

Ginseng

Siberian ginseng (*Eleutherococcus senticosus*) is used extensively to improve stamina and strength, particularly during or after illness. It seems to help the body adapt when under physical or emotional stress and can also boost immunity. When given to 13,000 workers at a Russian car factory, the number of days off work due to health problems dropped by a third. Siberian ginseng – and related roots such as Korean ginseng (*Panax ginseng*) and American ginseng (*Panax quinquefolium*) – are useful herbal supplements to take when you are feeling under the weather, or suffering from a relapse of symptoms that is dragging you down.

Dose
0.2 g–1 g, 3 times a day

Golden Seal

Golden Seal (*Hydrastis canadensis*) is an astringent anti-fungal herb whose roots are used to treat several skin conditions, including ringworm, eczema and itching (pruritis). It can stimulate immunity by increasing the activity of white blood cells. As Golden Seal also stimulates uterine contractions, it should be avoided during pregnancy.

Dose

An infusion of 1 teaspoon powdered root steeped in boiling water for 15 minutes can be cooled and used to soak ringworm lesions or Athlete's foot. Alternatively, the infusion can be applied directly to lesions 3 times a day. A tincture of Golden Seal can be taken by mouth (4 ml) or applied undiluted to ringworm lesions 3 times a day.

Guarana

Guarana comes from the Brazilian rain forest where it is known as the Food of the Gods. Sun-dried extracts from its seeds are used to make a sweet, cola-like, stimulating tonic containing a complex of natural stimulants similar to caffeine. It lifts the mood and stimulates the immune system but without the side-effects associated with drinking too much caffeine. The active ingredients, including guaranine, are buffered by special oils (saponins) to produce a natural time-release effect. A single dose of Guarana will provide a natural energy boost that lasts for up to 6 hours. Although it acts as a stimulant, it also has a calming effect and will not interfere with sleep or make stress-related symptoms worse. Research in Denmark found that after taking Guarana extracts for 3 months, volunteers had a significant increase in energy levels and reacted better to stress. As well as boosting the immune system, Guarana can thin the blood, reduce fluid retention and raise the metabolic rate.

Guarana is used to:

- relieve exhaustion and chronic fatigue
- increase mental alertness and concentration
- improve physical performance
- relieve stress
- help nervous insomnia
- relieve mild depression

- relieve tension headache and migraine
- relieve pre-menstrual syndrome and period pains
- hasten convalescence.

Dose

Guarana is available in capsules, a wine-based elixir, energy bars, as a chewing gum and in an energy drink. The recommended dose is 1 gram per day.

Lapacho

Lapacho is an unusual Brazilian tree with carnivorous flowers. These feed on insects, keeping it free from parasites and infections. Research in the US and Japan has found that extracts from Lapacho bark can stimulate the human immune system to increase resistance to infection, aid healing and reduce inflammatory reactions and pain. Its extracts are active against fungi including Candida, certain bacteria and malaria. Lapacho is used to treat a number of conditions, including:

- Candida (thrush)
- skin infections, including poorly healing wounds
- colds and other viral illnesses such as influenza
- boils
- urinary tract infections
- rheumatism and arthritis
- multiple sclerosis
- diabetes
- snake bite.

In Japan, a substance known as lapachol has been isolated from Lapacho and is currently being evaluated in trials to treat certain cancers.

Dose

A cup of Lapacho tea or 4 ml tincture can be taken daily to help prevent Candida infections. When treating an acute problem, doses can be increased by as much as 6 times. The infusion can also be used to bathe areas of infection such as ringworm, balanitis or vulvitis. Alternatively, take 1–2 g powdered bark by mouth in capsule form. (May cause nausea or diarrhoea if taken in very high doses.)

Marigold

Marigold petals have excellent anti-fungal properties. As well as being used internally and externally to treat infections such as Candida, Marigold is also used to help treat indigestion, peptic ulcers and gallbladder problems.

Dose

Pour 200 ml boiling water onto 2 teaspoons petals and infuse for 15 minutes. Drink 3 times a day. A tincture of Marigold (4 ml) can be taken by mouth or applied undiluted to ringworm lesions 3 times a day. Marigold can be combined with Golden Seal and Myrrh to make an anti-fungal wash.

Myrrh

Myrrh is a gum resin secreted by an East African bush. It stimulates the immune system by increasing the production of white blood cells and also has an antimicrobial effect. It is used as a mouthwash to treat mouth infections, including oral thrush, and is drunk to help combat infections such as boils, viral illnesses and Candida.

Dose

2 teaspoons powdered myrrh should be added to 200 ml boiling water and allowed to steep for 15 minutes. Cool and drink 3 times a day. A tincture of myrrh (4 ml) can be used as a mouthwash, applied undiluted to ringworm lesions or drunk 3 times a day.

Pfaffia

The golden root of *Pfaffia paniculata* is often referred to as the Brazilian ginseng, although it is unrelated to the Oriental varieties. Like the ginsengs, however, Pfaffia is a powerful 'adaptogen', which means it helps the body's immune system to adapt to various stresses including overwork, illness and fatigue. It is regarded as a panacea for all ills, as well as a sustaining food by local Brazilian Indians, who call it *para todo* – 'for everything'. It is a rich source of vitamins, minerals, amino acids and plant hormones (which act as building-blocks for the female hormone, oestrogen). It is therefore useful for treating gynaecological problems linked with hormonal imbalances such as pre-menstrual syndrome and menopausal symptoms. Because of its hormone content, Pfaffia should not be taken by pregnant women. Pfaffia is used to:

- boost energy levels
- improve physical and mental stamina
- increase concentration
- speed convalescence
- improve cellulite
- relieve pre-menstrual syndrome
- relieve menopausal symptoms
- help symptoms related to the oral contraceptive Pill
- relieve impotence
- relieve arthritis
- help maintain normal blood sugar levels in people with diabetes (use with medical supervision only).

Dose
1 gram per day.

Thuja

Thuja – the Tree of Life – is a member of the Cypress family. Its young twigs contain a volatile oil that tones muscles and is used in the treatment of cystitis, rheumatism and skin conditions such as psoriasis, ringworm or warts. As Thuja also causes uterine contractions, it should not be taken during pregnancy.

Dose
Pour 200 ml boiling water onto 1 teaspoon dried leaves and infuse for 15 minutes. Drink 3 times a day. A tincture of Thuja

(2 ml) can be taken by mouth or applied undiluted to ringworm lesions 3 times a day.

HOMOEOPATHY

Homoeopathic medicine is based on the belief that natural substances can boost the body's own healing powers to relieve the symptoms and signs of illness. Natural substances are selected which, if used full-strength in a healthy person, would produce symptoms of the illness they are designed to treat. This is the first principle of homoeopathy: 'Like cures Like.'

The second major principle of homoeopathy is that increasing the dilution of a solution has the opposite effect, that is, increases its potency ('Less Cures More'). By diluting noxious and even poisonous substances many millions of times, their healing properties are enhanced while their undesirable side-effects are lost.

On the centesimal scale, dilutions of 100^{-6} (1 drop tincture mixed with 99 drops alcohol or water and shaken; this is then done a further 6 times, each time 1 drop of the dilution being added to 99 drops of alcohol or water) are described as potencies of 6C, dilutions of 100^{-30} are written as a potency of 30C, etc. To illustrate just how diluted these substances are, a dilution of 12C (100^{-12}) is comparable to a pinch of salt dissolved in the same amount of water as is found in the Atlantic Ocean!

Homoeopathy is thought to work in a dynamic way, boosting your body's own healing powers. The principles behind homoeopathy may be difficult to accept, yet convincing trials have shown that homoeopathic therapy is significantly better than placebos in treating many chronic (long-term) conditions including hayfever, asthma and rheumatoid arthritis.

Homoeopathic remedies should ideally be taken on their own, at least 30 minutes either before or after eating or drinking. Tablets should not be handled – tip them into the lid of the container, or onto a teaspoon to transfer them into your mouth. Then suck or chew them, don't swallow them whole.

Homoeopathic treatments are prescribed according to your symptoms rather than any particular disease, so two people with the same label of 'Candidiasis' who have different symptoms will need different homoeopathic treatments. Two homoeopathic remedies in particular – Borax and Candida – have been shown in studies to be significantly more effective in treating symptoms of Candidiasis than placebo (inactive) substances. It is best to obtain individual professional advice before using these, however, as they are not indicated in every case.

Homoeopathic remedies may be prescribed by a medically-trained homoeopathic doctor on a normal NHS prescription form and dispensed by homoeopathic pharmacists for the usual prescription charge (or exemption, where applicable). Alternatively, you can consult a private homoeopathic practitioner or buy remedies direct from the pharmacist.

Although it is best to see a trained homoeopath who can assess your constitutional type, personality, lifestyle, family background, likes and dislikes as well as your symptoms before deciding which treatment is right for you, you may find the remedies listed below helpful. After taking the remedies for the time stated, if there is no obvious improvement consult a practitioner. Don't be surprised if your symptoms initially get worse before they get better – persevere through this common reaction to treatment – it is a good sign which shows the remedy is working.

- *Calc. carb 6C*: for vaginal Candida with a milky, itchy discharge, especially if linked with pre-menstrual symptoms, headache, stress, overwork or pregnancy. (6 times a day for up to 5 days)
- *Sepia 6C*: for vaginal Candida with an offensive discharge that is worse after making love, especially if linked with menstruation or the menopause. (6 times a day for up to 5 days)
- *Sulphur 6C*: for vaginal Candida with burning pains, especially if linked with stress or another illness (for example, one for which antibiotics were taken); for intestinal Candida linked with symptoms of alternating constipation and diarrhoea plus flatulence; for intestinal Candida linked with symptoms of anal itching or irritation around the anus. (6 times a day for up to 5 days)

Bach Rescue Remedy

This homoeopathic preparation is designed to help you cope with life's ups and downs and reduce the physical and emotional symptoms of stress and chronic illness such as recurrent Candida. It contains 5 flower essences: Cherry Plum, Clematis, Impatiens, Rock Rose and Star of Bethlehem, preserved in brandy. Add 4 drops of Rescue Remedy to a glass of water and sip slowly, every 3 to 5 minutes, holding the liquid in your mouth for a while before you swallow. Alternatively, place 4 drops directly under your tongue. Useful for acute recurrences of symptoms that leave you feeling unable to cope.

After completing a course of homoeopathy, you will usually feel much better in yourself with a greatly improved sense of well-being that helps you to cope with any remaining symptoms in a much more positive way.

Well-known naturopath Jan de Vries has also designed his own Emergency Essence, up-dated for modern times. This contains essences of Chamomile, Lavender, Red Clover, Purple Coneflower, Self-heal and Yarrow.

PROBIOTICS

Many patients have found that live yoghurt eaten every day relieves their symptoms. The Lactobacilli bacteria in live (Bio) yoghurt can happily line your bowel and keep it healthy and regular – they seem to survive the passage through stomach acids in enough numbers to recolonize the bowel. Use Bio yoghurt containing *Lactobacillus acidophilus*, eating at least 1 carton (150 ml) low-fat yoghurt per day. In addition, you may also benefit from a yoghurt-like liquid supplement (Yakult) containing a culture of *Lactobacillus casei* Shirota. This was developed by a team of scientists in Europe to replenish the bowel with a healthy, human strain of *Lactobacillus*.

Supplements are also available in health food shops containing *Lactobacillus acidophilus*, *Lactobacillus bulgaricus* and related species of beneficial bacteria such as *Bifidobacterium bifidum* and *Bifidobacterium longum*. These can be taken in powder/capsule form or used to make your own yoghurt cultures.

REFLEXOLOGY

This technique was used in China over 5,000 years ago and was also popular with the ancient Egyptians. Reflexology is based on the principle that points in the feet – known as reflexes – are directly related to other parts of the body. Massage over these reflexes can detect areas of tenderness and subtle textural changes which help to pinpoint problems in various organs, including the gut. By working on these tender spots with tiny pressure movements, nerves are thought to be stimulated that pass messages to distant organs, to relieve symptoms. Some people with Candida have found reflexology helpful.

SILICIC ACID

Silicon is one of the most common elements on Earth, coming second only to oxygen. It makes up 40 per cent of the Earth's crust and is found in a variety of substances including brick, cement, glass, quartz, emeralds, silicon chips and even non-stick frying pans. The foods with the richest content of silicon include wholegrain wheat, potatoes and unprocessed barley, oats, and rye.

Although silicon in its pure form is biologically inactive, it is now recognized as an essential trace element. In its soluble (colloidal) state, silicic acid, it is essential for normal growth and development. Silicic acid occurs naturally in low concentrations in most food and water. More and more people are now using colloidal silicic acid as a health supplement.

Colloidal silicic acid can be helpful in treating the symptoms of oral and intestinal Candida. It comes in the form of a gel which, when taken internally, reduces symptoms of bloating, flatulence and irregular bowel habit, especially diarrhoea. It has also proved helpful for more serious bowel problems such as ulcerative colitis and Crohn's disease.

As well as protecting the intestinal tract, silicic acid can soothe mouth ulcers and inflamed gums (gingivitis). It lines the stomach, absorbs toxins and irritants, and protects an inflamed stomach lining from self-digestion with stomach acid. It is therefore effective in the treatment of acid indigestion (gastritis) and heartburn due to acid reflux up into the gullet (reflux oesophagitís). It is safe to use during pregnancy.

Silicic acid should be taken in a dose of 1 tablespoon (30 ml) daily, diluted with fruit juice if preferred. Silicic acid gel can also be held and swirled in the mouth before swallowing to help relieve mouth soreness.

VISUALIZATION

When you feel symptoms of Candida getting on top of you, try visualization to aid relaxation and relieve your distress.

Stop what you are doing and sit down somewhere private and quiet. Close your eyes and, instead of focusing on your symptoms, imagine yourself:

- walking through a sunlit forest glade, with the sound of gently running water and bird song surrounding you, while a cool breeze ruffles your hair
- swimming in a warm tropical ocean next to a white-sand, deserted beach
- sitting in the sun on the veranda of a log chalet high up on a snow-crested mountain – breathe in the cool air and hear the soft drip of snow melting from the surrounding fir trees.

Visualization has been shown to help bowel problems including inflammatory bowel disease and Irritable Bowel Syndrome, as well as aiding relaxation.

Chapter Ten

CANDIDA AND YOUR DIET

CANDIDA AND DIETARY DEFICIENCIES

It is estimated that only 1 in 10 people gets all the necessary essential fatty acids, vitamins and minerals from diet alone. As chronic (long-term) or recurrent Candida is linked with a faulty immune system, many researchers believe that lack of dietary nutrients is linked with an increased risk of developing symptoms.

Vitamins, minerals and essential fatty acids in your food are all needed for:

- healthy cell membranes and skin
- making the enzymes used in fighting infections
- as co-factors to help enzyme function
- making the chemicals that enable immune cells to communicate with one another
- making substances involved in inflammation
- proper healing.

Even if only one nutrient is in short supply (for example iron) it may be enough to tip the balance in favour of yeast overgrowth. At the same time, Candida yeasts cells also need nutrients to grow and put out germ tubes (hyphae) as they start to invade tissues. It is therefore important that your diet and intake of nutrients are balanced. If taking a vitamin and mineral supplement, for example, it is best to take one that supplies around 100 per cent of the recommended daily amount (RDA) of as many vitamins and minerals as possible.

---

138 Candida Albicans

Evening Primrose Oil

The beautiful Evening Primrose flower only blooms for a single day, but a valuable oil can be extracted from its seeds to provide one of the most popular and useful food supplements available. It can help a wide range of problems, from dry itchy skin, eczema, psoriasis and acne to pre-menstrual syndrome, menopausal problems and cyclical breast pain. It has also proved useful in the treatment of Irritable Bowel Syndrome (IBS), rheumatoid arthritis, high cholesterol levels and high blood pressure. It is also an immune stimulant and improves resistance to infections, as well as being under investigation for its anti-cancer properties.

Evening Primrose Oil is a rich source of an essential fatty acid (EFA) called GLA (gamma linolenic acid – sometimes shortened to gamolenic acid). These essential fatty acids cannot be made in the body in sufficient amounts to meet your needs and must therefore come from your diet. There are three essential fatty acids:

1. linolenic acid (of which one type is gamma-linolenic acid)
2. linoleic acid
3. arachidonic acid (can be synthesized from linolenic or linoleic acids).

THE EFA PATHWAY

Linoleic acid → Gamma-linolenic acid (GLA) (Evening Primrose Oil) → dihomo-gamma linolenic acid → arachidonic acid → prostaglandins

Essential fatty acids, including GLA, are metabolized in the body to form hormone-like substances known as prostaglandins. Prostaglandins are found in all body tissues and play a major role in regulating inflammation, blood clotting and hormone balance, and are involved in the immune responses concerned with infections, chronic inflammatory diseases and even cancer. Nutritional deficiency of EFAs is common. While the body can make do with other fatty acids in their place (for example saturated animal fatty acids) this results in prostaglandin imbalances, as those made from other sorts of fat cannot be converted into prostaglandins. This imbalance is thought to increase the risk of developing:

- cell membranes that are stiffer than normal
- dry, itchy, flaky skin, which increases the risk of Candida infections taking hold
- inflammatory diseases
- blood clots
- lowered immunity against infections such as Candida
- hormone imbalances.

If your diet is lacking in GLA, gamma-linolenic acid can be synthesized from dietary linoleic acid, but this reaction relies on a particular enzyme (delta-6-desaturase) that is easily blocked by a number of factors, including:

- eating too much saturated (animal) fat
- eating too many trans-fatty acids (for example those found in margarines)
- eating too much sugar
- drinking too much alcohol
- deficiency of vitamins and minerals, especially vitamin B_6, zinc and magnesium
- increasing age
- crash dieting
- smoking cigarettes
- exposure to pollution.

Taking Evening Primrose Oil supplements provides dietary GLA and feeds into the EFA pathway, bypassing any enzyme blocks and helping to correct any prostaglandin or hormone imbalances. It is so effective that doctors can prescribe Evening Primrose Oil to treat eczema and mastalgia (cyclical breast pain).

Many people find that taking an Evening Primrose Oil supplement helps to break their recurrent Candida cycle as it provides important building-blocks for immune cells and protective immune reactions.

When choosing an Evening Primrose Oil (EPO) supplement:

- Select one containing 100 per cent pure EPO.
- Choose one containing at least 500 mg EPO per capsule plus some vitamin E, which helps to protect the GLA content from oxidation and boosts its function.
- Certain vitamins and minerals are needed during the metabolism of essential fatty acids. These are vitamin C, vitamin B_6, vitamin B_3 (niacin), zinc and magnesium. If you are taking EPO, make sure your intake of these is also adequate.

For general preventive health, take 500–1,000 mg EPO per day.

For treating a specific condition, you may need to take 3,000–4,000 mg per day for at least 3 months to correct a long-term imbalance, before you can tell if it is producing a beneficial effect.

Taking too much EPO may cause mild diarrhoea. Some women taking high-dose supplements have noticed breast enlargement or a change in their normal period pattern, but these side-effects are not usually too troublesome.

If you suffer from temporal lobe epilepsy (an uncommon nervous disorder), only take EPO under medical supervision.

Some evidence suggests that EPO supplement are best taken late in the afternoon (between 4 and 6 p.m.).

DIETARY SOURCES OF ESSENTIAL FATTY ACIDS

- Linoleic acid is found in sunflower seeds, almonds, corn, sesame seeds, safflower oil and extra virgin olive oil.
- Linolenic acid is found in Evening Primrose Oil, starflower (borage) seed oil and blackcurrant seed oil.
- Both linoleic and linolenic acids are found in rich quantities in walnuts, pumpkin seeds, soybeans, linseed oil, rapeseed oil and flax oil.
- Arachidonic acid is found in many foods (for example seafood, meat, dairy products) and can also be made from linoleic or linolenic acids.

Vitamin and Mineral Deficiencies

Vitamins are naturally occurring organic substances which, although they are only needed in minute amounts, are essential for life. They cannot be synthesized in the body, or if they can (for example vitamin D, niacin) are made in amounts too small to meet your needs. They must therefore come from your food. Most vitamins act as essential intermediaries or catalysts to keep metabolic reactions running smoothly and efficiently. These reactions include:

- converting fats and carbohydrates into energy
- digestion of foods
- cell division and growth
- repair of damaged tissues
- healthy blood
- fighting infection
- mental alertness
- healthy reproduction
- mopping up harmful by-products of metabolism such as free radicals.

Minerals are inorganic elements, some of which are metals, which are essential for metabolic reactions. Those needed in amounts of less than 100 mg are often referred to as trace elements. Minerals and trace elements can only come from your diet and depend on the quality of soil on which produce is grown or grazed. Minerals have a number of functions:

- structural – for example, calcium, magnesium and phosphate strengthen bones and teeth
- maintenance – for example, sodium, potassium, calcium support normal cell function
- as co-factors for important enzymes – for example, copper, iron, magnesium, manganese, molybdenum, selenium, zinc
- involvement in oxygen transport – for example, iron
- regulation of hormone function – for example, chromium, iodine
- antioxidant – for example, selenium, manganese.

Some trace elements such as nickel, tin and vanadium are known to be essential for normal growth in only tiny amounts, although their exact roles are not yet fully understood.

Minor vitamin and mineral deficiencies are common. Lack of nutrients is rarely severe enough to cause the sort of deficiency diseases seen in the third world (for example scurvy, beri-beri) but they can be enough to impair your immunity and increase your risk of a number of diseases, including Candida. For example:

- 60 per cent of the population does not obtain the new EC recommended daily amounts (RDA) of 60 mg vitamin C on a regular basis
- 90 per cent of the population does not obtain the recommended 10 mg vitamin E.
- 99 per cent of people obtain less than 2 mg betacarotene per day from their food – the National Cancer Institute in the US suggests a minimum intake of 6 mg betacarotene per day (equivalent to 100 ml carrot juice) to protect against cancer.
- Average intakes of vitamin B_1 and B_2 are below recommended levels.
- 50 per cent of adults obtain less vitamin B_6 than ideal.

The situation with minerals is even worse. The 1993 UK Government Food Survey shows that a large proportion of the population is at risk of gross deficiency in 8 out of 13 vitamins and minerals. Compared with the new EC RDAs, the average adult only obtains:

- 53 per cent of the RDA for zinc
- 56 per cent of the RDA for vitamin D
- 68 per cent of the RDA for iron
- 78 per cent of the RDA for magnesium

and 40 per cent of people obtained less dietary calcium than recommended.

Another Government report confirms that the average intake of the mineral selenium has fallen dramatically, from 60 mcg in 1978 to just 34 mcg in 1995. The ideal intakes are 75 mcg for men and 60 mcg for women.

Even when the lowest possible intake of a mineral – the amount necessary to prevent deficiency disease – is measured, one UK Government survey found:

PROPORTION OF WOMEN WITH INTAKES BELOW THE LOWER REFERENCE NUTRIENT INTAKE (LRNI)

Nutrient	16–18 years LRNI/ %	19–50 years LRNI/ %	51—64 years LRNI/ %
Calcium (mg)	480/27 %	400/10 %	400/5 %
Iron (mg)	8/33 %	8/26 %	8/1 %
Magnesium (mg)	190/39 %	150/13 %	150/9 %
Potassium (mg)	2000/30 %	2000/27 %	2000/23 %

Dietary and Nutritional Survey of British Adults – Further Analysis MAFF. HMSO

And that's just for the lower reference nutrient intake. When you consider that optimum intakes of calcium are at least 800 mg per day, and that menstruating women ideally need at least 14 mg iron per day the number of women obtaining less than optimal levels of minerals is frightening. The recommended intakes that will supply the needs of at least 96 per cent of the population are:

VITAMIN	RDA
Vitamin A (retinol)	800 mcg
Vitamin B_1 (thiamin)	1.4 mg
Vitamin B_2 (riboflavin)	1.6 mg
Vitamin B_3 (niacin)	18 mg
Vitamin B_5 (pantothenic acid)	6 mg
Vitamin B_6 (pyridoxine)	2 mg
Vitamin B_{12} (cyanocobalamin)	1 mcg
Biotin	0.15 mg
Folic Acid	200 mcg
Vitamin C	60 mg
Vitamin D	5 mcg
Vitamin E	10 mg

MINERAL

Calcium	800 mg
Iodine	150 mcg
Iron	14 mg
Magnesium	300 mg
Phosphorus	800 mg
Zinc	15 mg

Lack of vitamins and minerals can cause a number of common symptoms, including:

- lowered immunity
- recurrent infections
- poor wound healing
- feeling tired all the time
- mouth ulcers
- sore tongue
- cracked lips
- inflamed gums
- scaly skin
- brittle nails and hair
- pre-menstrual syndrome
- constipation
- nerve conduction problems
- muscle weakness.

Why Your Diet may be Poor in Vitamins and Minerals

Many people feel they are already following a healthy diet and are unlikely to be lacking in vitamins and minerals – but you are totally reliant upon the quality and age of your food, as well as the way it has been stored and processed. Even if crops leave the soil with a good nutrient content, processing can strip much of this out:

- Food staples are grown in artificially fertilized soils boosted with nitrogen, phosphorus and potassium. Other minerals and trace elements are frequently depleted. This may not interfere with plant growth, but seriously reduces the nutritional benefit to you.

- Fruit and vegetables are bred for uniformity of colour and shape rather than for flavour and nutrient content.
- Pesticides and other pollutants interfere with the nutrient content of plants.
- Foods are heavily processed or pre-packaged for convenience.
- Foods are shipped from abroad and may be picked before they are ripe – nutrient content falls as a result.
- Food additives interfere with the nutrient content of prepared foods.
- Stored foods rapidly lose their vitamin content.
- Cooking foods rather than eating them raw decreases their nutrient content – either by destroying it or leaching it into the cooking water.
- Wholefoods are eaten less frequently – we prefer to eat more animal and dairy foods, which are full of saturated fats.
- We now eat more trans-fatty acids – chemicals which interfere with the way our body metabolizes micronutrients and essential fatty acids.
- Mechanical and chemical food processing is the biggest cause of poor nutrient intakes.

Mechanical and chemical food processing is perhaps one of the biggest causes of our nutritionally poor Western diet. Processing strips formerly nutritious foods of their vitamin and mineral content.

Vitamin A
- Boiling or frying reduces the vitamin A content of food by 40 per cent after 1 hour – and by 70 per cent after 2 hours (for example in the slow cooking of stews).
- Canning vegetables depletes them of 20–35 per cent of their vitamin A.
- Drying fruit and vegetables results in the loss of up to 20 per cent – open-air drying in the loss of all vitamin A activity.

Vitamin B_1 (thiamin)
- A common preservative in minced meat (sulphur dioxide) destroys 90 per cent of a food's thiamin content within 2 days.

- Up to 70 per cent of a food's thiamin content is lost into cooking juices if food is finely chopped or minced.
- Cooking meat at 200°C causes a further 20 per cent destruction of thiamin content.
- Baking (for example in bread) reduces thiamin content by up to 30 per cent.
- Adding baking powder increases losses to 50 per cent.
- Toasting bread reduces thiamin by a further 10–30 per cent.
- Additives used to keep processed potatoes white (sulphite) reduce their thiamin content by over 50 per cent.
- Freezing meats reduces their thiamin content by up to 50 per cent.

Vitamins B$_2$ (riboflavin) and B$_3$ (niacin)

- Light is the most usual destroyer of B$_2$ – 90 per cent is lost from milk after only 2 hours' sun exposure.
- Boiling milk reduces its riboflavin content by up to 25 per cent.
- Curing meats reduces vitamin B$_3$ content by up to 40 per cent
- Freezing meats reduces riboflavin by up to 50 per cent.
- Riboflavin is also readily lost into cooking water.

Vitamin B$_5$ (pantothenic acid)

- Processing wheat can reduce its content of vitamin B$_5$ by 60 per cent.
- 30 per cent of the vitamin B$_5$ in meat is lost into cooking juices.
- Freezing causes a slow destruction of this vitamin.

Vitamin B$_6$ (pyridoxine)

- 20 per cent of the vitamin B$_6$ in milk is destroyed by sterilization.
- 20 per cent in vegetables is lost by canning.
- 40 per cent is lost into water when frozen vegetables are thawed and cooked.
- Up to 70 per cent of vitamin B$_6$ in meat is lost during processing.

Vitamin B$_{12}$
- Around 20 per cent is leached into water during cooking.

Folate
- Up to 90 per cent of the folate content of grain is lost during milling.
- 10 per cent of the folate in vegetables is lost by steaming, 20 per cent by pressure-cooking and up to 50 per cent by boiling.
- Foods originally rich in folate may have less than one-third of their folate content left by the time they are eaten.

Vitamin C
- Processing soft fruits (for example berries) results in the loss of over two-thirds of their vitamin C content.
- Once fruit juices are opened, their vitamin C content rapidly deteriorates, even if chilled – virtually all is lost within 14 days.
- Boiling vegetables leaves behind up to 50 per cent of vitamin C into the cooking water.
- Storage of root vegetables (for example potatoes) robs them of around 10 per cent of their vitamin C content per month.
- Storage of some vegetables (for example asparagus) reduces their vitamin C content by up to 90 per cent after just 1 week.

Vitamin E
- This vitamin is rapidly depleted by exposure to air.
- Even when frozen, foods can lose up to 70 per cent of their vitamin E content within 14 days.
- Processing cereals and grains removes over 90 per cent of their vitamin E content (for example in the production of white flour).
- Cooking foods in fat (for example frying or roasting) will destroy virtually all their vitamin E content, especially if the oils are rancid (for example if you re-use fat in a chip fryer for too long).
- Boiling exhausts a third of the vitamin E content of vegetables.
- Canning methods increase losses by up to 80 per cent.

Magnesium
- 80 per cent of the magnesium in wholegrains is lost during milling.

Obtaining Maximum Goodness from Your Food

- Eat food as fresh as possible – preferably home or locally grown.
- Eat foods grown using organic farming methods where possible – these are usually significantly more expensive weight for weight, but not when measured in nutrients per pound.
- Avoid processed, pre-packaged convenience foods.
- Eat as many raw fruits and vegetables as possible.
- Eat more wholegrains, nuts and seeds.
- Cook fruit and vegetables as little as possible. Steam vegetables lightly or use only a small amount of water when boiling.
- Re-use juices from cooking vegetables, for example in sauces, soups or gravy.

Increasing numbers of experts now believe that taking a food supplement is essential for optimal health. Although there is no guarantee that this will improve your Candida symptoms, it will certainly guard against the common nutrient deficiencies and help to optimize your overall health. It may also prevent some of the common, niggling health problems linked with mild vitamin and mineral deficiency.

Important Vitamins and Minerals for Candida Sufferers

The vitamins and minerals thought to be most beneficial in overcoming Candida infections are the B group vitamins, antioxidants (vitamins C, E and betacarotene) and the minerals iron, selenium and zinc. Make sure any supplement you take includes these in sensible amounts, and ensure that you eat plenty of foods that are rich sources of them.

Betacarotene
Betacarotene is made up of 2 molecules of vitamin A joined together. It is converted into vitamin A in the body when needed

(6 mcg betacarotene = around 1 mcg of vitamin A [retinol]). Zinc is essential for this conversion. On average, around half of the betacarotene in your diet is converted into vitamin A in the cells lining the small intestine and in your liver. It is needed to:

- regulate the way genes are 'read' to produce enzymes and other proteins
- control normal growth and development, sexual health and reproduction
- maintain healthy skin, teeth, bones and mucous membranes such as those found lining the nose, throat and gums
- produce the pigment known as visual purple (rhodopsin), which is involved in sight and night vision.

Lack of betacarotene/vitamin A can cause:
- increased susceptibility to infections such as Candida
- scaly skin with raised, pimply hair follicles that encourage fungal skin infections
- flaking scalp
- brittle, dull hair
- poor eyesight and night vision
- loss of appetite
- loss of sensitivity to green light and difficulty adapting to dim light
- dry, burning, itchy eyes – and in the extreme, eye ulceration
- inflamed gums and mucous membranes.

Daily intakes of betacarotene above 15 mg per day may turn skin a yellow-orange colour – this looks like an artificial tan but is not harmful. High intakes in smokers have been linked with an increased risk of lung cancer. Betacarotene is best taken along with other antioxidants such as vitamin E and vitamins C.

Good food sources of betacarotene:
Dark green leafy vegetables and yellow-orange fruits, for example:

- carrots
- sweet potatoes

- spinach
- broccoli
- parsley
- spinach
- watercress
- spring greens
- cantaloupe melons
- apricots
- peaches
- mango
- red-yellow peppers
- tomatoes
- sweet corn.

Vitamin A is easily destroyed by exposure to light. Betacarotene is destroyed by heat and overcooking.

Vitamin B Group
- Vitamin B_1 (thiamin)
- Vitamin B_2 (riboflavin)
- Vitamin B_3 (niacin)
- Vitamin B_5 (pantothenic acid)
- Vitamin B_6 (pyridoxine)
- Vitamin B_{12} (cobalamin)
- Folic acid
- Biotin

The B group vitamins have a number of important functions in the body. Some are made by intestinal micro-organisms such as bacteria and yeasts – when there is a dietary deficiency, they may compete for your supplies. Bowel bacteria usually make lots of biotin, which you can absorb so that deficiency is rare unless you eat lots of raw egg white (for example sportsmen when training). Raw egg white contains a protein, avidin, that binds to biotin in the gut and prevents it from being absorbed. Cooked egg white does not have this effect. Interestingly, research suggests that biotin inhibits Candida growth and prevents it converting from a simple colonizing cell to the invasive mycelia form with germ tubes. It may be that people who are prone to intestinal Candida have bowel bacteria which do not produce as much biotin as usual.

B group vitamins are needed to:
- co-ordinate nerve and muscle cell functions
- produce energy from blood sugar (glucose) and fatty acids
- produce healthy red blood cells – lack of folate or vitamin B_{12} leads to anaemia
- for the healthy growth and division of cells – including in a developing fetus, where lack of folate and vitamin B_{12} are linked with congenital abnormalities such as Spina Bifida
- for the synthesis of amino acids.

Lack of B group vitamins can cause:
- tiredness
- pallor (anaemia)
- headache
- bloodshot, red eyes
- sores and cracks at the corner of the mouth
- red, inflamed tongue and lips
- mouth ulcers
- a scaly eczema-like skin rash, especially on the face and nose
- loss of appetite
- nausea
- constipation
- irritability
- loss of concentration
- poor memory
- difficulty sleeping
- difficulty coping with stress
- depression
- muscle weakness and stiffness
- nerve tingling, burning and numbness.

Large doses of niacin (B_3) may cause flushing and can lead to nausea, headache, muscle cramps, diarrhoea, low blood pressure. Very high doses are toxic and can cause liver damage. Excess B_6 (over 100 mg per day) may lead to reversible nerve damage (tingling, burning, shooting pains, pins and needles) and even partial paralysis.

Folic acid supplements can interfere with anti-epilepsy medication.

Good food sources of the B group vitamins include:
- brewer's yeast and yeast extracts (you may want to avoid these if you have Candida problems, however)
- brown rice
- wheat germ and wheat bran
- wholegrain bread and cereals
- oatmeal and oatflakes
- soya flour
- pasta
- meat and offal
- milk and dairy products
- seafood
- green leafy vegetables
- beans
- nuts.

Vitamin C

Vitamin C is a powerful antioxidant that helps to mop up harmful by-products of metabolism known as free radicals. By doing this, antioxidants help to damp down inflammatory reactions which are linked with long-term chronic illnesses such as Candida, rheumatism and colitis. It is also a natural antihistamine and helps to damp down allergic reactions. It has been shown to boost immunity, enhance the activity of white blood cells and reduce your risk of developing symptoms if you are exposed to the common cold virus and Candida. Vitamin C is also needed for:

- the synthesis of collagen, a major structural protein in the body
- the growth, repair and health of skin, bones, teeth and reproduction
- the metabolism of stress hormones.

Lack of vitamin C can cause:
- dry, rough, scaly skin
- scalp dryness
- hair loss
- broken thread veins in the skin
- poor wound healing
- misshapen, tangled, brittle hair
- dry, fissured lips
- easy bruising
- loose teeth
- inflamed, bleeding gums
- bleeding skin, eyes and nose
- weakness
- muscle and joint pain
- irritability
- depression.

Good food sources of vitamin C include:
- blackcurrants
- guavas
- kiwi fruit
- citrus fruit
- mangoes
- green peppers
- strawberries
- green sprouting vegetables such as broccoli, sprouts, watercress, parsley
- potatoes.

Vitamin E

Vitamin E is another powerful antioxidant which works mainly in the fatty tissues of your body where it is difficult for vitamin C to penetrate. It helps to:

- protect your cell membranes and body fat stores
- prevent dietary fats from going rancid
- strengthen muscle fibres
- improve skin suppleness and healing
- boost immunity.

Vitamin E is important for healing and works closely with the mineral, selenium, to boost immunity. Vitamins E and C should be taken together in supplement form, as once vitamin E has acted as an antioxidant, it needs vitamin C to reactivate it again.

Lack of vitamin E can cause:
- tiredness
- lethargy
- poor concentration
- irritability
- lowered sex drive
- muscle weakness.

Good food sources of vitamin E include:
- wheatgerm oil
- avocados
- margarine
- eggs
- butter
- wholemeal cereals
- seeds
- nuts
- bread
- oily fish
- broccoli.

Iron

Lack of iron is common, especially in women with a tendency towards heavy periods. This is because a large portion of the body's iron stores are in the form of the red blood pigment, haemoglobin, which transports oxygen and the waste gas, carbon dioxide, around the body. While long-term lack of iron can lead to anaemia, a mild shortage can increase your risk of infections. This is because blood stores of other iron-containing proteins (such as ferritin) are lowered. These proteins are needed by white blood cells to make the powerful chemicals used to kill invading micro-organisms. Lack of iron has been linked with an increased risk of recurrent Candidiasis and Herpes simplex virus infections. Iron is also:

- found in a protein, myoglobin, which binds oxygen in muscle cells
- a co-factor in many reactions involving energy production and immunity.

Lack of iron can cause:
- tiredness
- sore tongue
- cracking at the corners of the mouth
- decreased appetite
- increased susceptibility to infection
- generalized skin itching
- concave, brittle nails
- brittle hair and hair loss
- pallor (anaemia)
- muscle fatigue
- dizziness
- headache
- insomnia.

Good food sources of iron include:
- shellfish
- brewer's yeast
- offal (liver, kidney, heart)
- red meat
- fish, especially sardines
- wheatgerm
- wholemeal bread
- cocoa powder
- egg yolk
- green vegetables
- parsley
- prunes and other dried fruit

Selenium

Selenium is a mineral with a powerful antioxidant action. As well as damping down inflammatory reactions, it is needed for the synthesis of hormone-like prostaglandins and for the production of antibodies. Research suggests that antibody synthesis increases up to 30-fold if supplements of selenium and vitamin E – which work together – are taken. Selenium is also essential for healthy cell growth and division. People with the lowest intakes of selenium seem to have the highest risk of developing leukaemia or cancers of the colon, rectum, breast, ovary, pancreas, prostate gland, bladder, skin and lungs. These risks are even higher if intakes of vitamin E and vitamin A are also low.

Lack of selenium can cause:
- poor growth
- increased risk of infection
- hair, nail and skin problems
- premature wrinkling of skin
- subfertility
- arthritis
- high blood pressure
- cataracts
- muscle weakness
- Keshan disease (a form of heart failure).

Good food sources of selenium include:
- broccoli
- mushrooms
- cabbage
- radishes
- onions
- garlic
- celery
- wholegrains
- nuts
- brewer's yeast
- seafood
- offal
- butter.

Zinc
Zinc is essential for the proper function of over a hundred different enzymes, including many involved in immunity and fighting off infections such as Candida. It works by regulating

the activation of genes as and when they are needed to make specific proteins such as antibodies. It is vital for growth, sexual maturity, wound healing and immune function.

One of the earliest symptoms of zinc deficiency is loss of your sense of taste. This can be tested for by obtaining a solution of zinc sulphate (5 mg/5 ml) from a chemist. Swirl a teaspoonful in your mouth. If the solution seems tasteless, zinc deficiency is likely. If the solution tastes furry, of minerals or slightly sweet, your zinc levels are borderline. If it tastes strongly unpleasant, your zinc levels are normal.

Lack of zinc may cause:
■ impaired immunity and increased risk of infection
■ poor wound healing
■ poor hair growth and hair loss
■ poor nail growth
■ white spots on nails
■ skin problems such as eczema, psoriasis, acne
■ loss of your senses of taste and smell
■ poor growth and delayed puberty
■ underdeveloped male sex organs and low sperm count
■ poor appetite
■ cravings for odd foods
■ diarrhoea
■ visual disturbances
■ mental sluggishness
■ sleep disturbances.

If taken in doses larger than 15 mg, zinc may cause stomach upsets and nausea.

Good food sources of zinc include:
■ red meat
■ seafood, especially oysters
■ offal
■ brewer's yeast
■ whole grains
■ pulses

- eggs
- cheese.

Boosting Your Immune System

To boost your immune system without sticking to a strict anti-Candida regime:

- Follow a wholefood diet containing plenty of fresh fruit, vegetables and wholegrains with as few processed foods and additives as possible.
- Cut back on your intake of omega-6 polyunsaturated vegetable fats (found in margarine, cakes, biscuits, etc.) and eat more omega-3 essential fatty acids (such as those found in oily fish).
- Take a good vitamin and mineral supplement providing as many vitamins and minerals as possible at around 100 per cent of their recommended daily amount (RDA).
- Consider taking higher doses of the antioxidant vitamins C and E.
- Consider taking pure Evening Primrose Oil supplements.
- If you are zinc deficient, take 10 mg zinc twice a day for 2 weeks, then test yourself using a zinc sulphate solution (*see above*).
- If you smoke, stop.
- Limit your alcohol intake to no more than 1–2 units per day.
- Take regular exercise.
- Obtain adequate rest and sleep.

THE ANTI-CANDIDA DIET

Although some people view the anti-Candida diet with suspicion, it has undoubtedly helped many people with symptoms thought to be due to Candidiasis. There is little to lose by following an anti-Candida regime for a few weeks to see if it helps you. Trial and error are needed before you can isolate which foods bring your symptoms on, and the type of diet that keeps problems at bay. (For information on the types of food known to contain Candida cells, *see Chapter 6, page 72.*)

The basic anti-Candida diet involves avoiding products containing brewer's or baker's yeast, and products that stimulate yeast growth, including:

- white or brown sugar and food or drinks containing them (for example honey, jam, desserts, treacle, syrups, cakes, biscuits, sauces, ice-cream, soft drinks, dried fruits, chocolates, malt, etc.)
- refined (processed) carbohydrates (for example white flour, white rice) and products made from them (for example biscuits, cakes, buns, white bread)
- yeast extracts, cheese, bread made with yeast, alcoholic drinks, vinegar and pickled foods, smoked foods, soy sauce, tofu, grapes and grape juice, unpeeled fruits, dried fruits, frozen or concentrated fruit juices, old potentially mouldy foods and vegetables, mushrooms, and B vitamin supplements that are not labelled as 'yeast-free'
- some sugar substitutes such as sorbitol, mannitol, xylitol, aspartame and saccharin, which are metabolized like alcohol to produce substances that can stimulate Candida growth
- alcohol, tea, coffee, cocoa products, malted night-time drinks, fizzy drinks, fruit squashes.

It may take a few days for a change in diet to affect your symptoms. If you feel there is a definite link with a particular food, keep re-introducing it after avoiding it for several days to confirm that the effect is consistent. If you are fairly confident there is a problem, discuss this with your doctor or a dietitian to ensure that avoiding that particular food is not going to cause lack of any important nutrients – this is especially important if you are not overweight and find you start losing more than 1 or 2 pounds by following an anti-Candida programme.

If your symptoms are not significantly improved by following a restricted diet, it is important to return to eating a normal diet and as wide a range of foods as possible, to guard against any nutrient deficiencies. If you are able to identify a small number of foods which undoubtedly provoke your symptoms, however, these can usually be avoided without affecting your overall nutrition.

Other dietary measures to take include eating more:

- foods that tend to contain natural anti-fungal agents (for example garlic, herbs and spices, fresh green leafy vegetables)
- fibre-rich foods such as pulses (for example peas, beans, lentils, chick-peas) and wholegrain cereals (such as oats, brown rice, wholewheat pasta, whole rye, buckwheat, millet, bulgar wheat, couscous, unsweetened wholegrain breakfast cereals – but avoid those containing processed grains). In an ultra-strict anti-Candida diet, intakes of unrefined complex carbohydrates such as brown rice, wholegrain cereals and wholewheat pasta are also restricted (for example to the equivalent of just 2–3 slices wholegrain bread per day). As unrefined complex carbohydrates are an important part of a normal healthy diet, it is best not to follow a diet restricting these for more than 1 or 2 weeks without first taking expert dietary advice.
- more nuts and seeds for essential fatty acids (*see page 141*)
- fish
- raw or lightly steamed vegetables
- well-washed, peeled fruit
- extra virgin olive oil
- dairy products (an ultra-strict anti-Candida regime may ban these)
- natural BIO yoghurt and yoghurt-like drinks (for example Yakult) containing beneficial bacteria.

You should also drink plenty of mineral water and consider taking supplements containing:

- multivitamins and minerals – preferably providing around 100 per cent of the recommended daily amount (RDA) for as many vitamins and minerals as possible (check it does not contain yeast products)
- Evening Primrose Oil
- perhaps a supplement containing caprylic acid (*see below*).

Fibre

For every gram of fibre in your diet, your bowel motions increase by around 5 grams in weight. This is because dietary fibre provides nutrients for bacterial growth; much of the increased bowel motion bulk provided by a high-fibre diet is due to increased bacterial multiplication in the gut. This helps to keep intestinal Candida in check. Fibre also absorbs water and toxins (including yeast chemicals) from the gut, and helps to scour yeast cells from the intestinal wall, hastening their expulsion.

Fibre is an essential component of all plant cell structures. There are two main types of fibre: soluble and insoluble.

Soluble fibre is important in the stomach and upper intestines, where it slows down the processes of digestion and absorption. Blood sugar and fat levels only rise slowly, rather than rapidly, so the body can handle nutrient fluctuations more easily and there is less sugar available to encourage Candida growth.

Insoluble fibre is most important in the large bowel. It bulks up the faeces, absorbs water and hastens stool excretion.

All plant foods contain both soluble and insoluble fibre, though some sources are richer in one type than another. The following table gives some common examples of foods rich in dietary fibre:

SOURCES OF SOLUBLE AND INSOLUBLE FIBRE

Classification	Plant Source	A Few Examples
SOLUBLE		
	Oats	porridge, muesli
	Barley	pearl barley
	Rye	rye bread, crispbread
	Fruit	figs, apricots, tomatoes, apples
	Vegetables	carrots, potatoes, courgettes
	Pulses	cannellini beans, kidney beans

INSOLUBLE

Wheat	wholemeal bread, cereals
Maize	sweetcorn, corn bread
Rice	brown rice
Pasta	wholemeal pasta, spinach pasta
Fruit	rhubarb, blackberries, strawberries
Vegetables	cabbage, spinach, lettuce
Pulses	peas, lentils, chick peas

Ideally, you need to eat around 30 g fibre per day. Although this roughage provides little in the way of energy or nutrients, it is essential for helping the digestion and absorption of other foods. Fibre encourages the muscular, wave-like bowel contractions (peristalsis) that propel digested food through the intestines. This regulates bowel function and also acts like a sponge to absorb water, toxins, yeast cells and bacteria.

Research also suggests that dietary fibre absorbs fats and sugars in the bowel and helps to lower blood glucose and cholesterol levels by increasing the amount of fat that is excreted rather than absorbed.

A high-fibre diet helps to prevent constipation, diverticular disease, IBS and some bowel tumours – and may help reduce the symptoms associated with Candida. The easiest way to increase the amount of fibre in your diet is to eat more unrefined complex carbohydrates, as found in foods such as wholemeal bread, cereals, nuts, grains, root vegetables and fruits (unless following a strict anti-Candida regime, *see page 159*).

GRAMS OF FIBRE PER 100 G

- bran: 40 g fibre
- dried apricots: 18 g
- peas: 5 g
- prunes: 13 g
- cooked brown rice: 4 g
- cooked wholemeal spaghetti: 4 g
- brown bread: 6 g
- walnuts: 6 g

Breakfast Cereals Rich in Fibre

Bran-containing breakfast cereals provide the highest concentration of dietary fibre. There are many varieties available, including:

- muesli
- Bran Buds
- All Bran
- Bran Flakes
- Weetabix
- Puffed Wheat
- Shredded Wheat.

Caprylic Acid

Caprylic acid is a natural fatty acid found in coconut oil, palm oil and breastmilk. It has a natural anti-fungal action which has been shown to help eradicate *Candida albicans* from the gut without affecting the normal bacterial population. As caprylic acid is normally absorbed in the small intestine, you need to take a supplement formulated to allow it to reach the large bowel. As it is a dietary fat, few side-effects have been reported – but it should not be taken if you suffer from gastritis (inflammation of the stomach) or peptic ulcers.

USEFUL ADDRESSES

Please send a stamped, self-addressed envelope if writing to an organization for information.

ALLERGY SUPPORT GROUP
Little Porters
64A Marchalls Drive
St Albans
Herts
0172 758 705
Support for sufferers of any allergy.

THRUSH ADVICE BUREAU
Pre-recorded Thrush Helpline: 0171 285 5520.
For a free 16-page booklet, send a stamped, addressed A5 size envelope to: The Thrush Advice Bureau, PO Box 8762, London SW7 4ZD.

Complementary Medicine

BRITISH ACUPUNCTURE ASSOCIATION AND REGISTER
34 Alderney Street
London SW1V 4EU
0171 834 1012
Information leaflets, booklets, register of qualified practitioners.

BRITISH HERBAL MEDICINE ASSOCIATION
Sun House
Church Street
Stroud GL5 1JL
01453 751389
Information leaflets, booklets, compendium, telephone advice

BRITISH HOMEOPATHIC ASSOCIATION
27A Devonshire Street
London W1N 1RJ
0171 935 2163
Leaflets, referral to qualified homeopathic doctors.

COUNCIL FOR COMPLEMENTARY AND ALTERNATIVE MEDICINE
Suite 1
19A Cavendish Square
London W1M 9AD
0171 724 9103
Details on a variety of techniques and practices. Leaflets, booklets, newsletter.

INTERNATIONAL STRESS MANAGEMENT ASSOCIATION
The Priory Hospital
Priory Lane
London SW15 5JJ
0181 876 8261
Information on stress management and control. Leaflets, booklets, counselling.

Lapacho, Pfaffia and Guarana
For further information on these herbs from the Amazonian rainforest, contact: Rio Trading Company, 2 Centenary Estate, Brighton, East Sussex BN2 4AW; 01273 570987.

FURTHER READING

DIET AND LIFESTYLE

Leon Chaitow, *Stress* (Thorsons)
Leonard Mervyn, *Thorsons Complete Guide to Vitamins and Minerals* (Thorsons)
Stephen Terrass, *Allergies* (Thorsons)
—, *Stress* (Thorsons)

ALTERNATIVE MEDICINE

David Hoffman, *The Complete Illustrated Holistic Herbal* (Element Books)
Dr Andrew Lockie and Dr Nicola Geddes, *The Complete Guide to Homeopathy* (Dorling Kindersley)
Penelope Ody, *The Herb Society's Complete Medicinal Herbal* (Dorling Kindersley)
The Reader's Digest Family Guide to Alternative Medicine
Norman Shealy (ed.), *The Complete Family Guide to Alternative Medicine* (Element Books)
Dr Melvyn Werbach, *Healing through Nutrition* (Thorsons)
Valerie Ann Worwood, *The Fragrant Pharmacy* (Bantam Books)

INDEX

Of further interest...

RECIPES FOR HEALTH: CANDIDA ALBICANS

Featuring over 100 sugar-free and yeast-free recipes

SHIRLEY TRICKETT

Thrush, sinusitis, allergies, throat infections, depression, bloating, food cravings, weight problems, chronic muscle pain – these are just some of the conditions associated with an over-production of the yeast candida albicans in the body.

This practical self-help guide explains:

- what causes candida growth and how to prevent it
- which foods to eat and which foods to avoid

Shirley Trickett includes over 100 easy-to-prepare recipes which are low in refined carbohydrates, virtually yeast free and full of flavour, and features everyday ingredients which are readily available and economical to use.

It is a cookbook guaranteed to improve your health and well-being.

CANDIDA ALBICANS

LEON CHAITOW

Candida albicans is a yeast which exists inside all of us and normally presents no problems, but today's widespread use of broad spectrum antibiotics, contraceptive pills and steroids, as well as a sugar-rich diet, can cause a proliferation of this parasite yeast.

Its spread can often be the root cause of a wide variety of problems – ME/chronic fatigue syndrome; depression; anxiety; irritability; diarrhoea; bloatedness; heartburn; tiredness; allergies; acne; migraine; cystitis; menstrual problems, etc. Leon Chaitow shows how to detect whether yeast is your problem, and provides a comprehensive and non-drug programme for its control.

Leon Chaitow, osteopath, naturopath and acupuncturist, is a leading international practitioner and successful author of a wide range of health books.

CANDIDA ALBICANS

How your diet can help

STEPHEN TERRASS

The foods you eat and the nutritional supplements you can take may have a profound influence on your well-being. This clearly written, practical guide – based on stringent medical and scientific research – reveals how you can help yourself by explaining:

- the facts about candida albicans
- which foods to eat
- which foods to avoid
- the benefits of vitamins, minerals, herbal and other nutritional supplements

Stephen Terrass, a nutritionist and technical director for a leading vitamin company, has spent 15 years studying and researching the effects of nutritional supplementation, herbs and diet on health. He has written and narrated an award-winning series of cassette tapes which complement this Nutritional Health Series.

DIETS TO HELP: CANDIDA

The natural way to treat yeast problems

LEON CHAITOW

Thrush, chronic fatigue, allergies, anxiety, depression, bloatedness, food cravings, weight problems, chronic muscle pain – these are just some of the conditions associated with an overgrowth of the yeast candida in the body.

This book offers a full nutritional approach to managing candida albicans. Leon Chaitow clearly explains:

- what causes candida overgrowth and how to prevent it
- which foods to eat and which to avoid
- why you may need to eliminate yeast and sugary foods from your diet
- what supplements and herbs are beneficial

He includes a helpful dietary plan with delicious and easy recipes.

Leon Chaitow is a leading practitioner of osteopathy, naturopathy and acupuncture. He is the well-established author of an extensive range of health guides.

RECIPES FOR HEALTH:
CANDIDA ALBICANS   0 7225 2967 8   £5.99   ☐
CANDIDA ALBICANS   0 7225 3343 8   £3.99   ☐
DIETS TO HELP: CANDIDA ALBICANS 0 7225 3423 X   £3.99   ☐
CANDIDA ALBICANS   0 7225 3150 8   £4.99   ☐

All these books are available from your local bookseller or can be ordered direct from the publishers.

To order direct just tick the titles you want and fill in the form below:

Name: _____
Address: _____
_____
_____ Postcode: _____

Send to Thorsons Mail Order, Dept 3, HarperCollins*Publishers*, Westerhill Road, Bishopbriggs, Glasgow G64 2QT.

Please enclose a cheque or postal order or your authority to debit your Visa/Access account —

Credit card no: _____
Expiry date: _____
Signature: _____

— up to the value of the cover price plus:

UK & BFPO: Add £1.00 for the first book and 25p for each additional book ordered.
Overseas orders including Eire: Please add £2.95 service charge. Books will be sent by surface mail but quotes for air-mail dispatches will be given on request.

24-HOUR TELEPHONE ORDERING SERVICE FOR ACCESS/VISA CARDHOLDERS — TEL: 0141 772 2281.